Mathematics Revision For GCSE

Peter Kaner

**Formerly Inspector for Mathematics
Inner London Education Authority**

Unwin Hyman

Published in 1987 by Unwin Hyman Ltd.
15–17 Broadwick Street
London W1V 1FP

British Library cataloguing in publication data

Kaner, Peter
    Integrated mathematics scheme
    NR: Mathematics revision for GCSE
    1. Mathematics—1961–
    I. Title
510   QA39.2

ISBN 0 7135 2531 2

Typeset by Polyglot Pte Ltd, Singapore
Printed in Great Britain at
The Alden Press Ltd., Oxford

Mathematics Revision
For GCSE

Introduction

How to use this book

This is your revision book. It is intended to help you to get the best possible grades in your mathematics examination.

The book is organised so that you can make the best use of your revision time and keep a careful check on your progress. It is also designed so that students can help each other and get enjoyment from their revision work.

The very first step is to make up your mind to succeed. I have written assuming that you have now grown up enough to take responsibility for your own learning. After all, you are the one who will benefit from passing the examination.

Areas of study

Mathematics is one complete subject but I have divided it into eight areas of study to help you plan your revision. These are: Topic A, Number; Topic B, Measurement; Topic C, The world of money; Topic D, Geometry; Topic E, Sets, statistics and probability; Topic F, Algebra and graphs; Topic G, Trigonometry; Topic H, Vectors and matrices. Each subject area or topic is treated in the same way.

Self assessment

At the beginning of each topic there is a section of self-assessment questions. Work through these questions and mark them yourself from the answers at the end of the book. Make a chart like this, to enter up your marks.

Question	Score	Question	Score
1		11	
2		12	
3		13	
4		14	
.		.	
.		.	
.		.	
		.	
10		.	
Sub-total:		Sub-total:	
Total score:		Total possible score:	
Percentage:			

The flow chart illustrates your task.

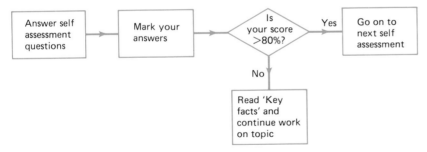

If you are good enough to score top grade in an examination you can move onto the next topic.

'Key facts'

If you find, after assessment, that you need revision you should read the 'Key facts' section for that topic. Ask the teacher to explain anything you do not understand. This will make the best use of your teacher's attention.

After each main paragraph in the 'Key facts' there are graded questions to give you practice in applying your knowledge. (The letter after each question is a guide to the level of difficulty.)

Examination questions

After working through the 'Key facts' section you should be ready to tackle the practice examination questions. These are similar to questions from examination papers and will give you a good idea of what to expect. Complete answers and a discussion of each problem are given later, but it is important that you should work through the questions first without looking at the answer pages.

After you have checked your answers, read through the discussions carefully and rewrite any answers which you got wrong. This will help you to present your work in a way that is approved by examiners. You should soon get into the habit of answering questions neatly and clearly and this will earn better grades.

Activities and investigations

Each section concludes with competitions, puzzles and activities, which are all designed to improve your knowledge of the subject area. Remember that this can be a very efficient way of learning. You are encouraged to work with other people but if you are studying on your own you can still use these sections. You will also find investigations and problem-solving projects which will be needed in the GCSE examination from 1991 onwards.

Easy or harder?

Everyone should be able to tackle most of the work in this book. But sometimes you will find ◆ in the margin. All the work marked with a ◆ is a challenge for you if you enjoy your mathematics and get on quickly. You are likely to get good grades if you can do these sections!

Summary of your progress

Each time you tackle a self-assessment task, make a table in your book to record your score (see opposite page). If you need to work through the rest of the topic, make a chart of the contents and tick off when you have done each item.

When you come to the activities and investigations section pick only one or two, and note down what you have chosen. Tick off when you have finished.

By charting your progress like this your teacher will be able to see how you are getting on, and whether or not you need help on some topics. It will also help you to be methodical about how you revise.

Examination technique

When taking an examination, it is very important to be careful and methodical. However thoroughly you have revised the topics you could lose marks purely through carelessness or bad presentation.

So, before you take your examination make sure you have read the section on examination technique (page 410). This tells you how to present your workings and answers clearly, how to make the best use of the time allowed, and how to check your work.

What mathematics is all about

Uses of mathematics

Mathematics is useful in many human activities. Everyone uses the mathematics of money. Engineers and scientists use mathematics as their language. Navigators, surveyors and astronomers use mathematics in their work and so do economists and business people.

Thinking mathematically

Mathematics involves a special way of thinking. We do not use only our experiences to understand the world of mathematics but work with symbols, drawings and graphs either on paper or on a computer screen. When an activity or problem makes us reflect about relationships or makes us try to prove things which cannot be measured we are doing mathematics and thinking mathematically.

Nevertheless the results of mathematical thinking must agree with results in the real world or they are not worth very much.

Solving problems using mathematical 'models'

Mathematical 'modelling' is used to consider a problem in the real world (for example, how to reduce the number of traffic accidents) and uses mathematical thinking in an attempt to solve the problem. The first part of the activity is to make a model of the problem. For example, we might be considering accidents which happen when roads are used by cars travelling in opposite directions. The effective approach speed on such roads is often more than 100 miles per hour. It makes overtaking very dangerous. Mathematical models could be made in which: (a) speeds were restricted to 30 mph and (b) overtaking is forbidden or (c) all roads are one way. The models would then be used to estimate the cost, loss of time, etc. which would result if (a), (b) or (c) were adopted for a real town.

This part of mathematical activity is very important. Without it mathematics would be of little use to the community at large.

Mathematical skills

Before people can use mathematics to solve real problems they need to have certain mathematical skills at their fingertips. Learning some of these skills is the main purpose of your mathematics course in school. You also need some experience of applying the skills to problems.

The first skills people learn are to do with number and, nowadays, the calculator makes an enormous difference to the level of these skills. With a calculator anyone can add, subtract, multiply, divide, square and square root any numbers from 10^{-100} to 10^{100}. This is much greater calculating power than even the most brilliant of mathematicians have had in the past.

It is very important that you learn to use a calculator efficiently, especially now that you are able to use one in your exam. If you do not own a calculator your school may provide one for you. In either case, learn how to use it!

The other skills you are learning are knowledge of measurement, graphs, money, probability, statistics, geometry, trigonometry, vectors and matrices (i.e. the main subject areas of this book). Remember, the more you know, the more you will be able to use the power of mathematics.

The next stage

Whatever job or career you hope to follow, some mathematical skill and mathematical thinking will be needed. The same is true of everyday life where the application of mathematical thinking (or planning) can make all the difference to the way you live and to the value you get from your money and opportunities. If you go on to do a training course or to take further qualifications mathematics will often be a key subject. You will certainly find it worthwhile to score a good grade in your examination so make the most of this book. It has been written to help you.

Introduction for teachers

This book is designed to help students revise for GCSE. It will be particularly suitable for students aiming for the maximum grade.

I believe that students taking responsibility for their own work is the most important factor in examination success at this stage. The book provides many opportunities for cooperative work as well as for individual investigations and project work which can be used for assessed coursework.

The examination questions and worked answers have been devised with reference to the National Criteria, the approved syllabuses, and the boards' specimen papers. Before 'past' examination papers become available they will show students the level they should be aiming at and give valuable guidance on how to present answers to earn top marks.

Throughout the book the symbol ◆ has been used to identify more difficult topics which might be skipped over the first time. The questions in the 'Key facts' section have also been graded to help you and the students to assess their performance. Questions marked C are the easiest—A the most difficult. Some of the A questions may extend the student beyond the demands of the syllabus, but this will improve the pupils' understanding. This classification is only intended as a rough guide and should not be used as an objective measure of the difficulty of the questions.

As this is the last book in IMS, I am now presenting the whole scheme to my wife Fleur in thanks for her encouragement and support.

Acknowledgements

The author and publishers acknowledge the following for permission to reproduce the photographs and illustrations which appear on the pages indicated:

Lesley Arrandale, 332
Stewart Arrandale, 239
Bruno Balestrini, 314, 364
British Architectural Library, RIBA, London, 256
BMW (GB) Ltd, 109
Mel Calman, 214
Colorsport, 154, 215, 236
Jane Cope, 43
Alan Drew, 106
'Education' Magazine, 415
Mary Evans Picture Library, 24
Forestry Commission, Edinburgh, 70
Ben Gibson/The Observer, 200
Sally and Richard Greenhill, 51, 63, 67, 115, 234
Halifax Building Society, 116
Angela Johnston, 11, 152
'Junior Education' Magazine, 237
Lyons Maid, 230
National Council of Teachers of Mathematics (America), 45
Photo Source, 1, 55, 280
Science Museum Library, 296
Scottish Tourist Board, 241
Survival Anglia, 143
Turkish Embassy, 123
Trustees of the Victoria and Albert Museum, 64, 378, 408
Wim Swaan, xiv, 38, 126
F R Yerbury, Architectural Association, 90

Topic A   Number

Contents

The number system; identities; negatives; rationals; powers; roots and irrationals; factors, multiples and primes; order.

Self assessment

The purpose of this task is to find out whether or not you need revision on Topic A. The assessment is in two sections. You should expect to score 100% in the first section. Your score in the second section will tell you whether or not you are good enough on this topic to leave revision till later.

- Make a table in your book, like the one on page vi. You need space for 36 questions.
- Write down your choice of answer for all the following questions.
- When you have finished calculate your score from the answers on page 416
- If your score is more than 80% in section 2 go on to Topic B self assessment (pp. 39–42).

Section 1

100% right in this section please.

1 What is the next number in the sequence 1, 4, 9, 16, ... ?

2 Find an odd number which is a multiple of 7, and lies between 110 and 120.

3 Two calculators are used to calculate $1·3 + 5 × 1·4$. The first calculator gives 8·82 as the result, the second gives 8·3. The sequence

$1·3 \boxed{+} 5 \boxed{×} 1·4 \boxed{=}$

is used in both cases. Which answer is right? Why are two different answers obtained?

4 $a + b = a$ and $a \neq 0$. What is the value of b?

5 What is the value of $5 - {}^-3$?

6 Write the 6th line of the table

$4 × {}^-3 = {}^-12$
$3 × {}^-3 = {}^-9$
$2 × {}^-3 = {}^-6$
$1 × {}^-3 = {}^-3$
$0 × {}^-3 = 0$

7 The temperature last night fell 8° from ${}^-5°C$ to ... ?

8 4·7 × 52 is not the same as
   A 47 × 5·2   B 0·47 × 520
   C 244·4   D 47 × 52 ÷ 10
   E 47 ÷ 52 × 10.

9 Find a fraction equivalent to $\frac{35}{57}$ in which the top and bottom have no common factors.

10 Find the fraction which has exactly the same value as 0·363636. . . .

11 Which of the numbers 35, 67, 77, 81, 91 is prime?

12 Find the smallest number which has 3, 4 and 5 as factors.

Section 2

No time limit.

1 Find the next three numbers in these sequences

   (i) 0, 7, 26, 63, 124, ...
   (ii) $\frac{1}{3}, \frac{3}{4}, \frac{4}{7}, \frac{7}{11}$, ...
   (iii) 1, 11, 121, 1331, 14641, ...

2 Which is larger:
   1^2 or 2^1?
   2^3 or 3^2?
   3^4 or 4^3?
   Can you make any predictions about n^{n+1} and $(n + 1)^n$?

3 Complete these addition and multiplication tables for odd and even numbers.

+	o	e		×	o	e
o	e	o		o	...	...
e	...	...		e	...	...

What difficulties do you find in making up similar tables for subtraction and division?

4 (i) The sequence 4 ÷ 0 produces error (E) on your calculator. Explain.
   (ii) Find the 'trick' in the following proof that 2 = 1.
   1Ø   Assume $a = b$
   2Ø $a^2 = ab$ . . . . from 1Ø, multiplying both sides by a
   3Ø $a^2 - b^2 = ab - b^2$ . . . . from 2Ø, subtracting b^2 from both sides
   4Ø $(a - b)(a + b) = b(a - b)$ from 3Ø, factorising
   5Ø $a + b = b$ . . . . from 4Ø, dividing both sides by $a - b$
   6Ø   put $a = 1$ and $b = 1$ . . . .   2 = 1

5 Which of the following definitions is satisfactory for zero (i.e. gives the properties of zero as you understand them)?

   (i) $n + z = n$ . . . where n is any number you like.
   (ii) $nz = z$ . . . where n is any number you like.
   (iii) z is the only number you cannot divide by. [Is there any number besides zero with this property?]

6 The term infinity (∞) has special rules. As listed here, they are incomplete. Fill in the missing part of each rule.
   $a + \infty =$ $a \div \infty =$
   $a \times \infty =$ $a - \infty =$

7 (i) Calculate the value of $m^2 + n$ given that $m = {}^-3$ and $n = {}^-2$.
   (ii) Given that m and n are both integers, find the range of values of m and n for which $m^2 + n < 0$.

8 Complete this proof that $^-3 \times {}^-4 = {}^+12$.
   1Ø   Start with $^-3(4 + {}^-4)$
   2Ø $^-3(4 + {}^-4) = {}^-3 \times 0 = 0$
   3Ø $^-3(4 + {}^-4) = ({}^-3 \times 4) + ({}^-3 \times {}^-4)$
   4Ø $({}^-3 \times 4) + ({}^-3 \times {}^-4) = 0$ . . . . from 2Ø, 3Ø
   5Ø $^-3 \times 4 = {}^-3 + {}^-3 + {}^-3 + {}^-3 = {}^-12$
   6Ø   . . . .
   7Ø   . . . .
   [If you feel strong you can extend this proof to all numbers, showing that $^-a \times {}^-b = {}^+ab$]

9 It is suggested that the expression $n^2 + n + 41$ has a prime number value for all integer values of n between $^-10$ and $^+10$. Do you agree?
   A little planning will make the work of this question much simpler.

10 (i) Write the numbers 360 and 405 as products of their prime factors.
    (ii) Use your answer to (i) to find the largest number that is a factor of both 360 and 405.

11 (i) Which decimal lies half way between 0·65 and 0·655 on the number line?
    (ii) Which decimals would divide the space between 0·58 and 0·59 into four equal parts?
    (iii) What is the difference between these measurements?
    0·3 metres,   0·30 metres   and
    0·300 metres.
    There is a difference.

12 Tina calculated $5·4 \boxed{\div} 0·48$ on her calculator and obtained 25·92. How could you tell this was wrong without using a calculator? What mistakes did Tina make?

13 Find
    (a) $3\frac{1}{2} + 1\frac{3}{5}$ (b) $3\frac{1}{2} - 1\frac{3}{5}$
    (c) $3\frac{1}{2} \times 1\frac{3}{5}$ (d) $3\frac{1}{2} \div 1\frac{3}{5}$
    Which one of the above is equal to $2\frac{3}{16}$?

14 Find the simplest fractional form of these decimals.
    (a) 0·2222...   (b) 0·3125
    (c) 0·545454...

15 (i) Given that $\dfrac{n}{5} = \dfrac{7}{12}$, find n.
    (ii) Given that $\frac{4}{5}$ of a box of chocolates have been eaten and that there are now 8 chocolates left, find the number of chocolates in a full box.

16 Which one of these fractions has been calculated wrongly?
    (i) $1\frac{1}{2} + \frac{3}{4} = 2\frac{1}{4}$ (ii) $\frac{2}{5} + \frac{3}{10} = 0·7$
    (iii) $\frac{4}{5} \times \frac{5}{8} = \frac{1}{2}$ (iv) $\frac{15}{16} - \frac{1}{4} = \frac{11}{16}$
    (v) $\frac{3}{8} \div 4 = \frac{3}{2}$

◆ 17 Given that a, b and c are three whole numbers, and also that a is a factor of b and b is a factor of c, which of the following are true?
    (i) c is a factor of a.
    (ii) b is a factor of a.
    (iii) a is a factor of c.
    (iv) c is a factor of b.
    Give two different sets of values for a, b and c which illustrate the situation.

18 (i) $5^3 + 5^2 = 5^5$
    (ii) $5^3 \times 5^2 = 5^5$
    (iii) $5^3 \div 5^2 = 5$
    (iv) $5^3 - 5^2 = 5$
    Two of the statements above are correct. They are
    A (i) and (iii)   B (ii) and (iii)
    C (i) and (iv)   D (iii) and (iv)

19 Which of these statements is not true?
    A $2^{-1} = 0·5$.   B $6^0 = 1$.
    C $3^{-2} > 2^{-3}$ D $4^{-3} = \dfrac{1}{4^3}$

20 Which one of the numbers does not have the same value as $\sqrt{1\,000}$?
    A 31·622 776 6...   B $\sqrt{50} \times \sqrt{20}$
    C $\sqrt{10\,000} \div 10$ D $5 \times \sqrt{40}$

◆ 21 (i) Find the value of $3^{\frac{1}{2}} \times 2^{\frac{2}{3}}$ using your calculator.
    (ii) Which one of the four numbers listed below has a different value from the other three?

    A $\sqrt{\sqrt{3^3}}$ B $3^{\frac{3}{4}}$ C $\dfrac{1}{3^4}$

    D $\sqrt{3} \times \sqrt{\sqrt{3}}$

◆ 22 One rule of indices states that $a^m \times a^n = a^{m+n}$. Give examples to show whether the rule works
    (i) when m and n are fractions,
    (ii) when m and n are negative numbers.

◆ 23 (i) For which of these inequalities could x be $\frac{1}{4}$?
    A $\frac{1}{3} > x$ and $x > \frac{1}{5}$
    B $\frac{1}{3} < x$ and $x < \frac{2}{3}$
    C $\frac{1}{2} < x$ and $x < \frac{3}{4}$
    D $\frac{1}{5} > x$ and $x > \frac{1}{8}$
    (ii) Explain the difference between
    $a < x < b$ and $a \leqslant x \leqslant b$

24 Which of the following statements are true for all values of a, b, c and d (excluding 0)?
    A $0·375\,a > \frac{1}{3}a$ B $(0·a)^2 > 0·a$
    C $a > b \Rightarrow a^2 > b^2$ D $a > b \Rightarrow \,^-a < \,^-b$
    E $\dfrac{a}{c} < \dfrac{a+b}{c+d} < \dfrac{b}{d}$

Key facts A

A.1 The number system

The number system works by grouping in 10's. [This is basically because people count on their fingers.]
Operations with numbers should follow brackets, multiplication/division then addition/subtraction. Your calculator may take care of this for you: check up.

A.1.1 Important sets of whole numbers

1, 10, 100, 1000, . . .	the powers of 10
2, 4, 8, 16, 32, . . .	the powers of 2
2, 4, 6, 8, 10, 12, . . .	the even numbers ending in 0, 2, 4, 6 or 8

> These numbers can all be represented as $\{2n\}$ where n is an integer.

1, 3, 5, 7, 9, 11, 13, . . .   the odd numbers ending in 1, 3, 5, 7 or 9

> These numbers can all be represented as $\{2n - 1\}$ where n is an integer.

1, 4, 9, 16, 25, 36, . . .   the square numbers $1 \times 1, 2 \times 2, 3 \times 3, \ldots$ etc.

> i.e. $\{n^2\}$

1, 3, 6, 10, 15, 21, . . .   the triangle numbers $1, 1 + 2, 1 + 2 + 3,$
     $1 + 2 + 3 + 4, \ldots$ etc.

> Show that these correspond to the set $\left\{\dfrac{n(n + 1)}{2}\right\}$.

1, 2, 6, 24 . . .

> The factorial numbers $1, 1 \times 2, 1 \times 2 \times 3, 1 \times 2 \times 3 \times 4, \ldots$, also written 1!, 2!, 3! etc. [$\boxed{!}$ on calculator] or $\{n!\}$.

Some facts about these number sets

(i) Powers of ten have special names:
$10^2 = 100$ (a hundred), $10^3 = 1\,000$ (a thousand),
$10^6 = 1\,000\,000$ (a million), $10^9 = 1\,000\,000\,000$ (a billion).
(ii) Any number can be formed by adding powers of 2.

> **Examples**
> $22 = 2^4 + 2^2 + 2^1$ $103 = 2^6 + 2^5 + 2^2 + 2^1 + 2^0$

(iii) The squares of even numbers are even.

(iv) The squares of odd numbers are odd.

 (v) A string of consecutive numbers, starting with 1, add to a triangle number.

(vi) A string of consecutive odd numbers, starting with 1, add to a square number.

(vii) The sum of the first n cubes is the square of the sum of the first n numbers.

$$1^3 + 2^3 + 3^3 + \cdots + n^3 = (1 + 2 + 3 + \cdots + n)^2$$

You can check this for $n = 4, 5$ or any other value.

[IMS books A2 and B2 have this result in diagram form on the cover!]

A.1.2 Other bases

Base 10 numbers can be written in other bases. It is only a question of regrouping.

Example

25_{10} ⟶ 31_8

There are two ways of changing bases. One method uses division while the other uses powers.

Example Change 139 into its base 8 form.

Division

```
          R
8 | 139
8 |  17    3
           ↑
     2  →  1
139 → 213₈
```

Power

$$8^2 = 64$$

```
     139
   - 128   2(8²)
   ─────    ↓
      11
    -  8   1(8)
    ─────
       3          139 → 213₈
```

$139 \to 213_8$

Note: the two methods produce the base 8 number in opposite order.

Exercise A.1

1 What is the smallest square number that is a multiple of 2 and 3? C

2 What is the next number in each sequence?
   (a) 1, 4, 7, 10, ...
   (b) 2, 6, 12, 20, ...
   (c) 75, 15, 3, ... C

3 p is the largest square number less than or equal to n. Find p if
   (a) $n = 14\cdot4$ (b) $n = 144$
   (c) $n = 1440$ C

4 Write down the first five numbers of the set $\{n^2 - 1\}$. Find the 50th member of the set. B

5

5 Explain why the value of 1101101_2 is 109.

6 Amrit wrote 33 instead of 3^3 by mistake in an examination, but she did not lose any marks because 33 and 3^3 had the same value. What base was she working in? Can you find any more examples like this?

B

A

A.2 Identities

The numbers 0 (zero) and 1 are the identities for the number system.

A.2.1 Algebraic rules of zero

(i) $a + z = a$ where a is any number
(ii) $az = z$
(iii) $a + b = z \Rightarrow b = {}^-a$
(iv) $ab = z \Rightarrow a = z$ or $b = z$

Facts about zero

• Zero is the only number that is neither positive nor negative.
•• When zero is added to any number the number is unchanged:
  $243 + 0 = 243$
  But writing zero on the end of a whole number multiplies the number by 10:
  $2430 = 243 \times 10$
•• Multiplying any number by zero produces zero:
  $243 \times 0 = 0$
•• It is not possible to divide any other number by zero: think about it
  $243 \div 0 \boxed{=}$ error

Proof that zero is unique

1∅   Suppose that $\mathbb{N}$ is another number such that
     $a + \mathbb{N} = a$ for all values of a.
2∅ $z + \mathbb{N} = z$ ... from 1∅
3∅ $z + \mathbb{N} = \mathbb{N}$ (rule (i) for zero)
4∅ $z = \mathbb{N}$ after all!! ... 2∅, 3∅
Can you see it?

A.2.2 Albegraic rules of 1

(i) $a \times 1 = a$ ... for all values of a.

(ii) $a \times b = 1 \Rightarrow b = \dfrac{1}{a}$ or a^{-1}

   and $a = \dfrac{1}{b}$ or b^{-1}

(iii) $a^2 = a \Rightarrow a = 1$ or 0

   $a = \dfrac{1}{a} \Rightarrow a = 1$

Facts about 1

I When a number is multiplied by 1 the number is unchanged:
   $36 \times 1 = 36$
II Every number (except 0) has a reciprocal which is the result of dividing 1
   by the number.
   The reciprocal of 4 is $1 \div 4 \ldots = 0{\cdot}25$.
   $4 \times 0{\cdot}25 = 0{\cdot}25 \times 4 = 1$
III 1 is the only number which is its own reciprocal

Exercise A.2

1 $12 + p = 12 - p$, what is the value of p?   C
2 Explain the difference between 4·3
   metres and 4·30 metres.   C
3 What is the largest number that can be
   made with digits 4, 3, 2, 1 and three
   zeros, which is less than 2 000 000?   C
4 Two numbers, m and n, produce zero
   when $(m + 1)$ is multiplied by $n - 2$.

What can you say about m and n?   C
5 Prove 1 is the only number such that
   $a \times 1 = a$ for every value of a.
   [*Hint*: consider the similar proof for
   zero.]   B
6 Find the value of a number which is 1
   more than its reciprocal. How many
   such numbers are there?   A

A.3 Extending the number system ... Negatives

Negative numbers appear below zero on the
number line.
They can be added, subtracted, multiplied
and divided in the same way as positive
numbers.

Remember

• Any number plus its negative equals zero	$n + {}^-n = 0$
• Subtracting n is the same as adding ${}^-n$	$5 - 3 = 5 + {}^-3 = 2$
• Adding n is the same as subtracting ${}^-n$	$5 + 3 = 5 - {}^-3 = 8$
• Multiplying any number by a negative changes the sign	$2 \times {}^-3 = {}^-6$ ${}^-4 \times {}^-5 = {}^+20$
• Dividing any number by a negative changes the sign	${}^-6 \div {}^-3 = {}^+2$ $8 \div {}^-4 = {}^-2$

All these results should be checked on your calculator.
[If possible, make sure you have a $\boxed{+/-}$ button]
In practice, negative numbers can be avoided by using 'below'. For example,
${}^-4°C$ is the same as 4° below zero, but negative numbers are necessary if all
equations of the form $a + x = b$ are to have solutions.
$a + x = 0 \Rightarrow x = {}^-a$.

Once negative numbers have been defined then every equation $a + x = b$ has a solution even when b is less than a

Example
$7 + x = 4 \Rightarrow x = {}^-3$

A.3.1 Proofs about negative numbers

The proofs which follow use the definition . . . "a is the number which satisfies the equation $x + a = 0$".
The proofs also use the fact that negative numbers satisfy the same rules as positive numbers.

A.3.2 Rules of numbers

Associative laws

$(a + b) + c = a + (b + c)$ .... (only one triple sum)
$\quad (ab)c = a(bc)$ .... (only one triple product)

Commutative laws

$a + b = b + a$
$\quad ab = ba$

Distributive laws

$a(b + c) = ab + ac$
$(a + b)c = ac + bc$

A.3.3 Proofs

To prove $({}^+a)({}^-b) = {}^-ab$ and $({}^-a)({}^-b) = {}^+ab$.
[*Note:* The number $a \times b$ can be written $(a)(b)$ or ab. The brackets can be left out as long as the meaning is clear.]

1∅   Consider $(a)({}^-b) + (a)(b)$
2∅ $(a)({}^-b) + (a)(b) = a(b + {}^-b)$ .... distributive law
3∅ $(a)({}^-b) + (a)(b) = a(0)$ .... from 2∅
4∅ $(a)({}^-b) + (a)(b) = 0$ .... from 3∅, property of zero
5∅ $(a)({}^-b)$ is the negative of $(a)(b)$ .... from 4∅
6∅ $(a)({}^-b) = {}^-ab$ 1st proof .... from 5∅
7∅   Consider $({}^-a)({}^-b) + (a)({}^-b)$
8∅ $({}^-a)({}^-b) + (a)({}^-b) = ({}^-a + a)({}^-b)$ .... distributive law
9∅ $({}^-a)({}^-b) + (a)({}^-b) = 0({}^-b)$ .... from 8∅
10∅ $({}^-a)({}^-b) + (a)({}^-b) = 0$ .... from 9∅, property of zero
11∅ $({}^-a)({}^-b) + {}^-ab = 0$ .... from 6∅
12∅ $({}^-a)({}^-b) = ab$ 2nd proof .... from 11∅

The above proofs should be worked through with actual numbers instead of a and b. [For example, ${}^-5 \times {}^-9$ can be proved to be ${}^+45$.]

Exercise A.3

1 (i) What is the value of $^-6 - {}^-4$?
   (ii) What is the value of $8 - {}^-4$?
   Give a diagram or reasons which
   explain your answer.   C

2 (i) $^-7 + n = 5$ ... what is the value of
       n?
   (ii) $^-6 \div n = {}^+2$ ... what is the value of
       n?   C

3 During 24 hours, from midnight to
   midnight, the temperature starts at
   $^-4°C$, falls 11°C, rises 34°C and then falls
   17°C.
   (i) What are the maximum and
       minimum temperatures during the
       period?
   (ii) What is the temperature at the end
       of the period?
   Comment on the changes which have
   taken place. Sketch a realistic graph.   C

4 Substitute the value $x = {}^-3$ into the
   expressions.
   (i) $x^2 - 5x - 6$ (ii) $\dfrac{x^2 - 1}{x - 1}$ B

5 Complete the two 'rule of signs' tables.

×	+	−		÷	+	−
+	+	−		+	...	...
−	...	...		−	...	...

   Explain why it would be difficult to
   construct similar tables for addition and
   subtraction.   B

6 (i) Prove that $^-8 \times {}^-5 = {}^+40$.
   (ii) Prove that
       $(^-a) \div (^-b) = (^+a) \div (^+b)$.
   (iii) Starting with
       $(a)(b) + (^-a)(b) + (^-a)(^-b) =$
       $(a)(b) + (^-a)(b) + (^-a)(^-b)$, prove
       that $(^-a)(^-b) = (a)(b)$. If you prefer,
       start with numerical values for a
       and b.   A

A.4 Extending the number system ... Rationals

A.4.1 Fractions (rational numbers)

When the unit is divided into equal parts,
fractions are obtained. [Decimals are base 10
fractions]

$\dfrac{a}{b}$ $\leftarrow$ numerator

$\phantom{\dfrac{a}{b}}$ $\rightarrow$ denominator or base

Each unit is divided into 4 equal parts.
$\frac{2}{4}$ and $\frac{1}{2}$ are the same division

Each unit is divided into 5 equal parts.
You can see that $\frac{1}{2}$ does not occur in base 5

Value

The value of any fraction is found by dividing the numerator by the base.

$\frac{3}{4} \rightarrow 0{\cdot}75$ $\frac{2}{5} \rightarrow 0{\cdot}4$ $\dfrac{a}{b} \rightarrow a \div b$

A.4.2 Addition : subtraction
Multiplication : division

For these operations, use the values. The result will appear in decimal form.
Sometimes the result can be converted easily to a simple fraction (but this
is not important).

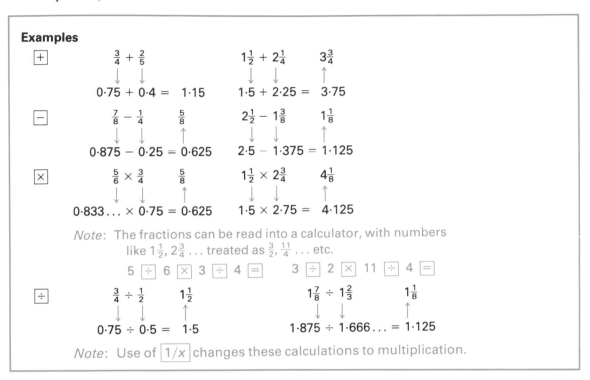

Examples

$+$ $\frac{3}{4} + \frac{2}{5}$ $1\frac{1}{2} + 2\frac{1}{4}$ $3\frac{3}{4}$

$0.75 + 0.4 = 1.15$ $1.5 + 2.25 = 3.75$

$-$ $\frac{7}{8} - \frac{1}{4}$ $\frac{5}{8}$ $2\frac{1}{2} - 1\frac{3}{8}$ $1\frac{1}{8}$

$0.875 - 0.25 = 0.625$ $2.5 - 1.375 = 1.125$

$\times$ $\frac{5}{6} \times \frac{3}{4}$ $\frac{5}{8}$ $1\frac{1}{2} \times 2\frac{3}{4}$ $4\frac{1}{8}$

$0.833\ldots \times 0.75 = 0.625$ $1.5 \times 2.75 = 4.125$

Note: The fractions can be read into a calculator, with numbers
like $1\frac{1}{2}, 2\frac{3}{4} \ldots$ treated as $\frac{3}{2}, \frac{11}{4} \ldots$ etc.

5 $\div$ 6 $\times$ 3 $\div$ 4 $=$ 3 $\div$ 2 $\times$ 11 $\div$ 4 $=$

$\div$ $\frac{3}{4} \div \frac{1}{2}$ $1\frac{1}{2}$ $1\frac{7}{8} \div 1\frac{2}{3}$ $1\frac{1}{8}$

$0.75 \div 0.5 = 1.5$ $1.875 \div 1.666\ldots = 1.125$

Note: Use of $\boxed{1/x}$ changes these calculations to multiplication.

A.4.3 Fractions worth knowing

Some fractions are always cropping up (see examples above). Make sure you
know their decimal values. These will also give you their percentage form.

Examples

1 $\frac{1}{2} \leftarrow 0.5 \rightarrow 50\%$ **2** $\frac{1}{4} \leftarrow 0.25 \rightarrow 25\%$ **3** $\frac{1}{3} \leftarrow 0.33\dot{3} \rightarrow 33\frac{1}{3}\%$

4 $\frac{1}{5} \leftarrow 0.2 \rightarrow 20\%$ **5** $\frac{3}{4} \leftarrow 0.75 \rightarrow 75\%$ **6** $\frac{2}{3} \leftarrow 0.66\dot{6} \rightarrow 66\frac{2}{3}\%$

7 $\frac{1}{8} \leftarrow 0.125 \rightarrow 12\frac{1}{2}\%$ **8** $\frac{1}{9} \leftarrow 0.111 \rightarrow 11.1\%$ **9** $\frac{1}{10} \leftarrow 0.1 \rightarrow 10\%$

A.4.4 Equivalence

Fractions with the same value are called equivalent. It is always possible to
build an equivalent fraction to $\frac{a}{b}$ by multiplying top and bottom by the same
number.

Example

$\frac{3}{4}$:   equivalent fractions are

$$\overset{\times 3}{\underset{\times 3}{\downarrow\uparrow}}\frac{9}{12}, \quad \overset{\times 5}{\underset{\times 5}{\downarrow\uparrow}}\frac{15}{20}, \quad \overset{\times 8}{\underset{\times 8}{\downarrow\uparrow}}\frac{24}{32} \quad \text{and so on.}$$

Equivalence leads to some very interesting properties of fractions which are worth remembering.

- If two fractions are equivalent, the top of the first multiplied by the bottom of the second equals the top of the second multiplied by the bottom of the first:

$$\frac{a}{b} = \frac{c}{d} \Rightarrow ad = bc.$$

- Fractions can be added, subtracted and divided using equivalence.

Example

1. $\frac{2}{3} + \frac{4}{5}$

   $$\downarrow \qquad \downarrow$$

   $$\frac{10}{15} + \frac{12}{15} = \frac{22}{15}$$

2. $\frac{3}{8} - \frac{1}{4}$

   $$\downarrow \qquad \downarrow$$

   $$\frac{3}{8} - \frac{2}{8} = \frac{1}{8}$$

3. $\frac{4}{5} \div \frac{2}{3}$

   $$\downarrow \qquad \downarrow$$

   $$\frac{12}{15} \div \frac{10}{15} = \frac{12}{10}$$

Check these results by values (using a calculator).

In the examples above, equivalence is used to convert fractions to the same denominator.

Your calculator may have a 'fractions function'. If so, find out how to use it!!!

A.4.5   Algebra of rational numbers

A rational number $\frac{p}{q}$ is really a pair of whole numbers. Rules are given in the table overleaf.

Addition, subtraction, multiplication and division of a pair of rational numbers must give the right value for sum, difference, product and quotient. Otherwise rational numbers could not be used for measurement.

Operation	Rule	Explanation	Example
Addition	$\dfrac{p}{q} + \dfrac{r}{s} = \dfrac{ps + qr}{qs}$	Only fractions with the same base can be added. $$\begin{array}{cc} \dfrac{p}{q} & + & \dfrac{r}{s} \\ \downarrow & & \downarrow \\ \dfrac{ps}{qs} & + & \dfrac{qr}{qs} = \dfrac{ps + qr}{qs} \end{array}$$	$\dfrac{2}{5} + \dfrac{3}{4} = \dfrac{8 + 15}{20}$ *Note*: Equivalence is used to convert both fractions to the same base, i.e. 20.
Subtraction	$\dfrac{p}{q} - \dfrac{r}{s} = \dfrac{ps - qr}{qs}$	see above	$\dfrac{5}{8} - \dfrac{1}{3} = \dfrac{15 - 8}{24}$
Multiplication	$\dfrac{p}{q} \times \dfrac{r}{s} = \dfrac{pr}{qs}$		$\dfrac{3}{8} \times \dfrac{5}{9} = \dfrac{15}{72}$
Division	$\dfrac{p}{q} \div \dfrac{r}{s} = \dfrac{ps}{qr}$	**1.** Dividing by $\dfrac{r}{s}$ is the same as multiplying by its reciprocal $\dfrac{s}{r}$. **2.** $$\begin{array}{cc} \dfrac{p}{q} & \div & \dfrac{r}{s} \\ \downarrow & & \downarrow \\ \dfrac{ps}{qs} & \div & \dfrac{qr}{qs} = \dfrac{ps}{qr} \end{array}$$	$\dfrac{3}{4} \div \dfrac{4}{9} = \dfrac{27}{16}$

You should check these rules using several different values for p, q, r and s and making sure the rules give the same results as your calculator.

A.4.6   Cancelling

The value of $\dfrac{p}{q}$ is not changed by multiplying top and base by the same number, an equivalent fraction is produced. $\dfrac{pn}{qn}$ is equivalent to $\dfrac{p}{q}$.

This has some simple consequences.

(i) If $\dfrac{r}{s} = \dfrac{p}{q}$ then $r = np$ where n is some number.
$\qquad\qquad\qquad\quad s = nq$

(ii) $\dfrac{r}{s}$ can be cancelled down to $\dfrac{p}{q}$ by dividing top and base by n.

Example

$\dfrac{68}{85}$ and $\dfrac{4}{5}$ are equivalent ... value 0·8

$\dfrac{68}{85}$ can be cancelled down to $\dfrac{4}{5}$ by dividing top and base by 17.

- You can now see why $\dfrac{a}{b} = \dfrac{c}{d} \Rightarrow ad = bc$ ...

$$\dfrac{a}{b} = \dfrac{c}{d} \Rightarrow \left. \begin{array}{l} a = nc \\ b = nd \end{array} \right\} \Rightarrow \begin{array}{l} ad = ncd \\ bc = ndc \end{array}$$

- The fraction $\dfrac{a + c}{b + d}$, made by adding the tops and bases of $\dfrac{a}{b}$ and $\dfrac{c}{d}$
  lies in between the two in value. (Easy to prove!)

Exercise A.4

1 Show that $1\frac{1}{2} \times 2\frac{3}{4} - 4\frac{1}{8}$.   C

2 Find the value of n so that $\dfrac{n}{12}$ is
   equivalent to $\frac{3}{4}$.   C

3 Write down the rule for adding fractions
   and use it to find the value of
   (i) $\frac{3}{8} + \frac{5}{9}$ (ii) $\frac{9}{16} + 1\frac{1}{4}$
   Check by another method.   B

4 An old rule for dividing fractions is
   "turn upside down and multiply".
   Explain this rule and demonstrate its
   use in finding the values of
   (i) $\frac{2}{3} \div \frac{3}{4}$ (ii) $\frac{4}{5} \div \frac{3}{15}$ B

5 Explain how equivalent fractions are
   used in making a pie chart from a set of
   data based on percentages.

6 Given that $\dfrac{p}{q} = \dfrac{r}{s}$ prove that

   $$\dfrac{p + q}{q} = \dfrac{r + s}{s}.$$
      A

   [*Hint*: First demonstrate using chosen
   values for $p, q, r,$ and s.]

Incomes of families (£ per week)	%
0–100	32
100–200	55
200–300	8
300–400	3
400–500	1
over 500	1

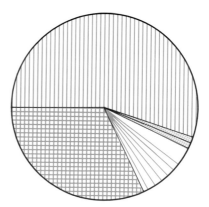

A.5   Powers

A.5.1   Value

a^2 is shorthand for $a \times a$.*

Similarly

$a^3 = a \times a \times a \qquad a^4 = a \times a \times a \times a$

While

$a^n = a \times a \times a \ldots \times a \qquad n$ of them.

It is also useful to think of a^n as "1 multiplied by a, n times".

Examples

1   $3^2 = 3 \times 3 = 9$

2   $0.4^2 = 0.4 \times 0.4 = 0.16$

3   $12.5^2 = 12.5 \times 12.5 = 156.25$

The value of a power is found on the calculator either by using $\boxed{x^y}$ or by using the constant multiplying function.

Example 1.15^{10}

1   1.15 $\boxed{x^y}$ 10 $\boxed{=}$

2   1.15 $\boxed{\times}$ $\boxed{\times}$ $\boxed{=}$ $\boxed{=}$ $\boxed{=}$ $\boxed{=}$ $\boxed{=}$ $\boxed{=}$ $\boxed{=}$ $\boxed{=}$ $\boxed{=}$
         $(\ )^2 \ (\ )^3 \ (\ )^4 \ (\ )^5 \ (\ )^6 \ (\ )^7 \ (\ )^8 \ (\ )^9 \ (\ )^{10}$

Language note: a^n is the nth power of a.
            n is the index, a is the base.

A.5.2   Rules

Powers can be multiplied and divided following simple rules.

Rule	Example	Explanation
$a^m \times a^n = a^{m+n}$	$5^3 \times 5^4 = 5^7$	$(5 \times 5 \times 5) \times (5 \times 5 \times 5 \times 5)$
$a^m \div a^n = a^{m-n}$	$7^5 \div 7^3 = 7^2$	$1 \times 7 \times 7 \times 7 \times 7 \times 7 \div 7 \div 7 \div 7$
$(a^m)^n = a^{m \times n}$	$(3^5)^3 = 3^{15}$	$3^5 \times 3^5 \times 3^5$
$a^0 = 1$	$2^0 = 1$	$2^n = 1 \times 2 \times 2 \cdots$ but $n = 0$
$a^{-n} = 1/a^n$	$4^{-1} = \frac{1}{4} = 0.25$	$4^1 \times 4^{-1} = 4^0 = 1$

- a^{-n} is 1 divided by a, n times.
- Make sure you really feel at home with the above rules before you continue.

---

* Our own Isaac Newton used xx for x^2. The x^2 was first used by Euler.

A.5.3 Standard form

Very large and very small numbers are often written in standard form (SF).

$a \times 10^n$ ... a is a number between 1 and 10.

n is a + or − whole number.

SF	Value														
$4{\cdot}75 \times 10^6$	4	7	5	0	0	0	0								
$4{\cdot}75 \times 10^5$		4	7	5	0	0	0								
$4{\cdot}75 \times 10^4$			4	7	5	0	0								
$4{\cdot}75 \times 10^3$				4	7	5	0								
$4{\cdot}75 \times 10^2$					4	7	5								
$4{\cdot}75 \times 10^1$						4	7	·	5						
$4{\cdot}75 \times 10^0$							4	·	7	5					
$4{\cdot}75 \times 10^{-1}$							0	·	4	7	5				
$4{\cdot}75 \times 10^{-2}$							0	·	0	4	7	5			
$4{\cdot}75 \times 10^{-3}$							0	·	0	0	4	7	5		
$4{\cdot}75 \times 10^{-4}$							0	·	0	0	0	4	7	5	
$4{\cdot}75 \times 10^{-5}$							0	·	0	0	0	0	4	7	5

It is clear that $4{\cdot}75 \times 10^{-5}$ corresponds to the instruction $4{\cdot}75$ divided by 10 ... 5 times.

Examples

1 The distance from earth to sun varies from $9{\cdot}3 \times 10^7$ to $9{\cdot}5 \times 10^7$ miles.

   [Do you know why? Think about the earth's orbit.]

2 The mass of the earth is $6{\cdot}586 \times 10^{21}$ tons.

3 The diameter of a cell of the human body is about 5×10^{-7} m across.

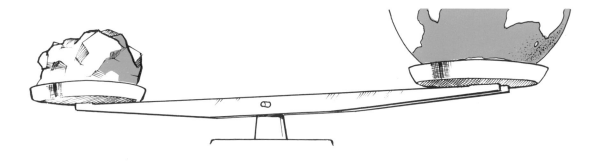

Exercise A.5

1. Calculate the values of
   (i) 4^8 (ii) $(1 \cdot 18)^{10}$ (iii) $(0 \cdot 81)^{-2}$ C
2. Given that $6^x \times 6^{x+1} = 6^{12}$, find x.   C
3. Given that $a^7 \div a^x = a^{-3}$, find x.   B
4. (i) Explain why $(x^m)^n$ and $(x^n)^m$ both have the same value.
   (ii) Find the value of m if $(2^m)^3 = 512$.   B

5. A crystal is rectangular in shape and its dimensions are $4 \cdot 2 \times 10^{-3}$ mm by $5 \cdot 1 \times 10^{-4}$ mm. What is its area in mm^2 expressed in standard form?   A
6. The mass of a protein molecule is approximately 4×10^{-9} g. How many of these proteins would make up a sample weighing 5 g?   A

A.6   Roots and irrationals

A root is the inverse function of a power.

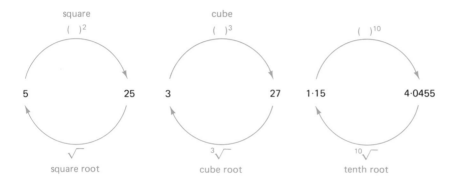

Just as fractions are more complicated than whole numbers, so roots are more complicated than powers.
  (i) The number 25 has two square roots, $^+5$ and $^-5$. In general, every positive number has two square roots.

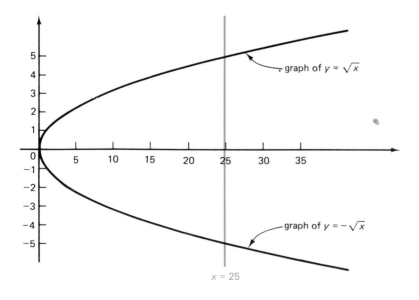

(ii) Numbers like $\sqrt{2}, \sqrt{3}, \sqrt{5}, \ldots, \sqrt[2]{2}, \sqrt[3]{5} \ldots$ cannot be expressed as fractions. They are known as irrational numbers [not 'ratios'].

A.6.1 Index form

$a^{1/n}$ is the index form of the nth root of a. Thus $a^{\frac{1}{2}} = \sqrt{a}, a^{\frac{1}{3}} = \sqrt[3]{a}$.
$a^{\frac{1}{2}} \times a^{\frac{1}{2}} = a \qquad a^{\frac{1}{3}} \times a^{\frac{1}{3}} \times a^{\frac{1}{3}} = a$

The values of roots are found using $\boxed{x^y}$ or $\boxed{x^{1/y}}$ on your scientific calculator.

Examples

1 $3^{\frac{1}{2}} = \sqrt{3}$ 3 $\boxed{x^y}$ 0·5 $\boxed{=}$ 1·73205. . . .
                    3 $\boxed{x^{1/y}}$ 2 $\boxed{=}$ 1·73205. . . .

2 $10^{\frac{1}{3}} = \sqrt[3]{10}$ 10 $\boxed{x^{1/y}}$ 3 $\boxed{=}$ 2·1544. . . . .   Check
                                           $(2·1544)^3 = 9·9995 \ldots$

Facts worth knowing about irrational numbers

1 If a ruler is made to measure the sides of a square exactly it cannot be used to measure the diagonals exactly.

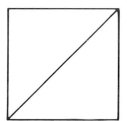

2 Program for finding $\sqrt{n}$.

   1∅   Make a guess . . . a

   2∅   Calculate $\dfrac{n}{a} = b$

   3∅   Find $\dfrac{a + b}{2}$

   4∅   Put $a = \dfrac{a + b}{2}$

   5∅   Continue until a constant value is reached for a.

      This is known as the divide and average method

3 Proof that $\sqrt{2}$ cannot be a rational number

   1∅   Suppose $\sqrt{2} = \dfrac{p}{q}$ where all common factors of p, q have been cancelled.

   2∅ $2 = \dfrac{p^2}{q^2}$ (squaring both sides)

3∅ $p^2 = 2q^2 \Rightarrow p^2$ is even
$\Rightarrow p$ is even
4∅ Write p as $2r$.
5∅ $4r^2 = 2q^2 \Rightarrow 2r^2 = q^2$
$\Rightarrow q^2$ is even
$\Rightarrow q$ is even
6∅ Since both p and q are even . . . line 1∅ leads to a contradiction.
7∅ Line 1∅ must be false.

The proof uses indirect reasoning

4   Surds (simplification)
You will find by checking on your calculator that . . .

1   $\sqrt{a}\sqrt{b} = \sqrt{ab}$

2   $\dfrac{\sqrt{a}}{\sqrt{b}} = \sqrt{\dfrac{a}{b}}$

Examples

(i) $\sqrt{72} = \sqrt{4} \times \sqrt{18}$
$= 2 \times \sqrt{18}$
$= 2 \times \sqrt{9}\sqrt{2}$
$= 2 \times 3\sqrt{2} = 6\sqrt{2}$

(ii) $\sqrt{\dfrac{9}{4}} = \dfrac{\sqrt{9}}{\sqrt{4}} = \dfrac{3}{2}$

Exercise A.6

1   What are the values of
(i) $(49)^{\frac{1}{2}}$ (ii) $(25)^{-\frac{1}{2}}$ (iii) $(36)^{\frac{1}{4}}$?   C

2   Using axes and scales as shown, sketch the graphs of $y = x^2$ and $y = \sqrt{x}$. What is the relationship between the two graphs?   C

3   Use your calculator to evaluate
(i) $(1\cdot35)^{\frac{1}{4}}$ (ii) $(3\cdot705)^{-\frac{1}{3}}$.   C

4   Given that $\sqrt{2} = 1\cdot414$, show how you could find the values of $\sqrt{50}$ and $\sqrt{98}$ without using your calculator.   B

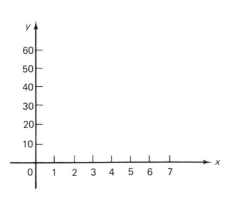

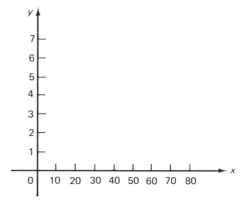

5 Use the divide and average routine to find the value of $\sqrt{15}$ correct to 4 decimal places. How many steps does it take to reach this level of accuracy? Write down your results as you go. B

6 Simplify

(i) $\sqrt{\dfrac{a^3b}{ab^3}}$ (ii) $\sqrt{x^3y^4z^6}$ B

7 Write out the proof that $\sqrt{10}$ cannot be a rational number.
[*Hint:* See the proof that $\sqrt{2}$ cannot be a rational number.] A

8 The value of $\sqrt{2}$ is 1·414213562 . . . . There does not appear to be a repeating pattern. Will a pattern appear eventually? Give reasons for your answer. A

9 The geometric mean of two numbers is found in two steps . . .

1Ø Multiply the two numbers together.

2Ø Find the square root of 1Ø.

Is it true that the geometric mean is less than the average (arithmetic mean) for any pair of numbers? Explain your answer. A

A.7 Factors, multiples and primes

The number 24 has the factors 1, 2, 3, 4, 6, 8, 12 and 24. All of these numbers will divide 24 without leaving a remainder. All the multiples of a number are to be found in its multiplication table. Thus the multiples of 4 are: 4, 8, 12, 16, . . . 40, . . . 124, . . . , etc.
A prime number has no factors (other than 1 and itself). Thus a prime number will not appear in the multiplication table of any other number. [This leads to the sieve of Eratosthenes. Ask your teacher to explain.]
Prime factors of a number are those factors which are prime.

Examples

1 2, 3, 5, 7, 11, 13, 17, 19, 23, 29 are the first 10 prime numbers; 9, 15, 21, 25 and 27 and all the even numbers have factors.

2 2 and 3 are the only prime factors of 24; 4, 6, 8 and 12 are factors but are not prime numbers.

3 The common factors of 45 and 60 are 1, 3, 5, 15. The highest of these is 15 which is known, naturally, as the highest common factor or HCF.

4 30, 60, 90, 120, . . . , are some of the common multiples of 5 and 6. The smallest or least of these is 30. This is the least common multiple or LCM.

● There is only one set of prime factors for any number, no matter how large the number may be.
For example $1234567890 = 2 \times 3 \times 3 \times 5 \times 3607 \times 3803$
and $987654321 = 3 \times 3 \times 17 \times 17 \times 379721$.
1 is not counted as a prime factor because there would be many versions of the prime factorisation if 1 were allowed.
e.g. $6 = 1 \times 2 \times 3 = 1 \times 1 \times 2 \times 3 = 1 \times 1 \times 1 \times 2 \times 3 \ldots$ etc.
This property of unique factorisation is called the fundamental theorem of arithmetic. [This has been its name for 2000 years!]

● There is no largest prime number, even though you might think that when numbers become enormous, they must break up into factors.

Proof starting from the proposition that P is the largest prime number.

1∅   Put the prime numbers in order 2, 3, 5, . . . , P, where P is the largest.
2∅   Form a new number $(2 \times 3 \times 5 \times \cdots \times P) + 1 = Q$.
3∅ Q is either a prime or it has factors.
31   If Q is prime, P is certainly not the largest.
32   If Q has factors, the factors are not 2, 3, 5, . . . , P because each of these leaves a remainder of 1 when divided into Q.
33   Thus if Q has prime factors they are larger than P.
4∅ P cannot be the largest prime.
5∅   There cannot be a largest prime number.

- There is no formula for generating prime numbers.
  Although some formulae look promising:
  e.g.   (i) $2^P - 1$, where P is prime.
        (ii) $n^2 + n + 41$, where n is odd.

No one has found a formula for constructing all the prime numbers. [You might like to find out where the above two formulae fail for the first time. Have a go!]

Exercise A.7

1   Explain why the sum of two prime numbers (other than 2) cannot be prime.   C

2   What is the smallest number that has 14, 15 and 24 as factors?   C

3   The list of rules below help to identify factors.
(a)   Give an example for each rule.

The number is a multiple of	if . . .
3	the digits add up to a multiple of 3
4	the last two digits form a multiple of 4
5	the number ends in 5 or zero
6	it is an even multiple of 3
8	the last 3 digits form a multiple of 8
9	the digits add to a multiple of 9

(b)   Use the rules to help find out if 799 is a prime number.   B

4   The fact that 'a is a factor of b' can be expressed as $b = na$.

(a)   Express the fact that a and b are both multiples of c in a similar way.

(b)   Use the $b = na$ form of factor relationship to show that
$\left.\begin{array}{l} a \text{ is a factor of } b \\ a \text{ is a factor of } c \end{array}\right\} \Rightarrow \begin{array}{l} a \text{ is a factor of } \\ b + c. \end{array}$
Give examples to illustrate the implication.   A

5   Which of the following implications are true?
(a) $\left.\begin{array}{l} a \text{ is a factor of } b \\ b \text{ is a factor of } c \end{array}\right\} \Rightarrow a \text{ is a factor of } c$
(b) $\left.\begin{array}{l} a \text{ is a multiple of } b \\ b \text{ is a multiple of } c \end{array}\right\} \Rightarrow \begin{array}{l} a \text{ is a factor} \\ \text{of } a + c. \end{array}$
(c) $\left.\begin{array}{l} a \text{ is a factor of } b \\ a \text{ is a factor of } c \end{array}\right\} \Rightarrow b \text{ is a factor of } c$
Give illustrations and/or counter examples.*   A

6   Investigate the following two formulae for generating prime numbers.
(a) $2^m m^2 - 1 = p$ where m itself is a prime.
(b) $m! - 1$ is prime for all values of m.   A

*Examples which demonstrate that the result is false.

A.8 Order

Every number has its own place on the number line. It divides the complete set of numbers into two parts.

Example

This example shows the number 8 dividing the set of all numbers into two parts.

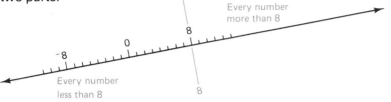

The signs $>$ and $<$ are used in this situation:

$n > 8$ ... n is a number more than 8, $n < 8$ ... n is a number less than 8.

The signs $\geq$ and $\leq$ are used to define the boundary.

$n \geq 8$ ... 8 or any number above 8.
$n \leq 8$ ... 8 or any number below 8.

These two signs put the dividing number into the upper or lower set. The number line is marked in a special way to show this.

```
-7  -6  -5  -4  -3  -2  -1   0   1   2   3
 |   |   |   |   |   ●───┴───┴───┴───┴───┘
```

The set $n \leq {}^-2$

```
-5  -4  -3  -2  -1   0   1   2   3   4
 |   |   |   |   |   ○───┴───┴───┴───┘
```

The set $n > 0$. This does not include $n = 0$.

A.8.1 Ordering fractions and decimals

- To put fractions in order find their values first.
- To put decimals in order, write them to the same number of decimal places. Check these with fractions and decimals of your own choice.
- The new fraction formed by adding tops and bases of a pair of fractions lies between the two.

Example

This demonstrates why the sum of two fractions cannot be the sum of the top over the sum of the bases.

A.8.2 Some important facts about $>$, $<$

Given three numbers a, b, c
 (i) $a > b \Rightarrow b < a$
 (ii) $a > b$ and $b > c \Rightarrow a > c$
 (iii) $a > b$ and $c > 0 \Rightarrow ac > bc$
 (iv) $a > b \Rightarrow {}^-a < {}^-b$
 (v) $a > b \Rightarrow a + c > b + c$ even if c is negative
You should check all these facts by choosing numbers (including negative numbers) for a, b and c.

. . . and some more important facts.
 * (vi) $a > b \Rightarrow a^2 > b^2$ provided both a and b are positive.
 * (vii) $n^2 > n \Rightarrow n > 1$ or $n < {}^-1$
 * (viii) $a > b \Rightarrow a^{-1} < b^{-1}$ provided a is positive.
Check these with your own choice of a, b, n.

Exercise A.8

1 Insert $>$ or $<$ to make the following into correct statements.
 (a) £4·50 . . . £5·40
 (b) $\frac{2}{3}$ . . . $\frac{3}{4}$
 (c) $^-5$ . . . $^-7$
 (d) $-\frac{2}{3}$ . . . $\frac{1}{5}$ C

2 Find all the possible values of x if $x^2 \geqslant 4$ and show the values on a number line.   B

3 Given that $a \geqslant b$ and $c \geqslant d$ which of the following are true?
 (a) $a + c \geqslant b + d$ (b) $a + c > b + d$
 (c) $a - c \geqslant b - d$ (d) $ac \geqslant bd$ A

4 Given that $a \geqslant b \Rightarrow ac \geqslant bc$, where c is positive, find the values of x for which $4x \geqslant 3\cdot6$.   A

5 Give values to a, b, c and d to show that
$$ad > bc \Leftrightarrow \frac{a}{b} > \frac{c}{d} \text{ and } ad < bc \Leftrightarrow \frac{a}{b} < \frac{c}{d}.$$
Use the above results to estimate which is the larger fraction of
 (a) $\frac{2}{3}$, $\frac{5}{7}$ (b) $\frac{40}{73}$, $\frac{100}{150}$ A

6 Use two different number lines to show the values of x which satisfy
 (a) $^-7 \leqslant 2x \leqslant 5$ (b) $\frac{1}{4} \geqslant x + 1 \geqslant \frac{-1}{4}$ A

Examination questions A

The following questions are typical of the harder questions in the top level GCSE and credit level examinations. You should work through them all as far as you can. Answers and discussions are given on page 29 so that you can check your work and style.
If you cannot understand the answer and its explanation you must ask your teacher for help.

1Ø Answer all the questions as far as you can. [Write out clear answers.]
2Ø Check your completed work against the worked answers on page 29.
3Ø Study the worked answers for those questions you could not do.
4Ø Ask your teacher (or a friend) for help where necessary.
5Ø Write out answers to all the problems you could not do in 1Ø [. . . without looking at the worked answers. Just copying will not help!]

1 Find the next 2 numbers in each sequence.
   (a) 1, 3, 7, 13, ...
   (b) 1, 1·1, 1·21, 1·331, ...
   (c) 48, ⁻24, 12, ⁻6, ...

2 The product of two numbers, which differ by 6, is 498 427. Find the numbers.

3 The calculations given below are clearly not in base 10. What is the base in each case?

   (a)   471   (b)   141   (c) 4503 ÷ 24 = 156
       +263   − 22
       ─────   ─────
        754   114

4 The argument below is supposed to prove that 2 = 1. Find the error.

   1∅   Assume $a = b$
   2∅ $a^2 = ab$ ....multiplying both sides of 1∅ by a.
   3∅ $a^2 - b^2 = ab - b^2$ ....subtracting b^2 from both sides of 2∅.
   4∅ $(a - b)(a + b) = b(a - b)$ factorising 3∅.
   5∅ $a + b = b$ ....dividing both sides of 4∅ by $(a - b)$.
   6∅ $2 = 1$ ....putting $a = b = 1$ in 5∅.

5 Prove that only one inverse is possible for any non-zero number.
   [*Hint*: b is the inverse of a if $ab = ba = 1$.]

6 The table below gives the 'products' of the rotations which correspond to R, right turn; L, left turn; and A, about turn.

·	R	L	A	S
R	A	S	L	R
L				
A				
S				

   A · B means A followed by B

   S means 'stay where you are'.

   (a) Copy and complete the table.
   (b) Which rotation corresponds to the number 1 in the multiplication of numbers?
   (c) Do the rotations obey these rules?
      (i) $a \cdot b = b \cdot a$ where a and b are any two of the rotations R L A S.
      (ii) One of the rotations is the identity such that
          $a \cdot i = i \cdot a = a$ where a is any one of the rotations.

(iii) Each of the rotations has an inverse such that
      $a \cdot a^{-1} = i$ where a^{-1} is the inverse of a and i is the identity.
   Explain your answers.

7 Find the value of
   (a) $^-3 - ^-5$ (b) $\dfrac{(^-3)(^-7)}{^-21}$
   (c) $n^2 - n$ when $n = ^-2\cdot5$

8 If the temperature falls below $^-2\cdot2°C$ the plant will die. Which of the following temperatures mean death for the plant?
   (a) 1°C   (b) ⁻4°C   (c) ⁻3°C
   (d) ⁻1·7°C   (e) ⁻2·9°C.

9 Explain why $(^-5) \times (^-7)$ must equal $^+35$.
   [*Hint*: First consider $(^-5) \times (^+7)$.]

10 (a) Find a fraction whose value is between $\frac{7}{11}$ and $\frac{12}{19}$.
   (b) Use the rule $\dfrac{a}{b} + \dfrac{c}{d} = \dfrac{ad + bc}{bd}$ to add $\frac{2}{3} + \frac{3}{5}$.
       Check the result on your calculator.

11 Find fractions whose values are
   (a) 0·7777 . . .   (b) 0·7272 . . .
   (c) 0·135135 . . .

12 (a) Show, by giving values to a, b, c and d, that
       $$\dfrac{a}{b} = \dfrac{c}{d} \Rightarrow \dfrac{a + b}{a - b} = \dfrac{c + d}{c - d}$$
   (b) Use the result to solve the equation $\dfrac{x + 1}{x - 1} = \dfrac{3}{5}$.
       [Check by a different method.]

13 Explain why $a^{\frac{1}{3}}$ is the same as $\sqrt[3]{a}$ and find the value of $(12 \cdot 8)^{\frac{1}{3}}$.

14 $1 \cdot 81 \times 10^9 \times 9 \cdot 21 \times 10^{-27} \simeq 1 \cdot 667 \times 10^n$. What is the value of n?

◆ **15** (a) Prove the rule $(a^m)^n = (a^n)^m$.
 (b) Use your calculator to evaluate $(27)^{-\frac{2}{3}}$
  in two different ways

16 Simplify
 (a) $\sqrt{\dfrac{289}{144}}$ (b) $\sqrt{(\tfrac{3}{4})^2 + (\tfrac{4}{5})^2}$

◆ **17** Show that, for any two positive numbers a, b,
 (a) $\sqrt{ab}$ lies between a and b
 (b) $\dfrac{a + b}{2} > \sqrt{ab}$

 $\left[\dfrac{a + b}{2}\right.$ is the arithmetic mean of a and b.
 $\sqrt{ab}$ is called the geometric mean. Thus part (b) asks you to prove that the arithmetic mean of two numbers is greater than the geometric mean.]

18 $\sqrt{3}$ is given as $1 \cdot 732\ 050\ 808$ on my calculator. Would it be correct to assume that the '08' pattern continues?
 [i.e. that $\sqrt{3} = 1 \cdot 732\ 050\ 808\ 080\ 808 \ldots$ to n decimal places.]
 Give reasons for your answer.

19 Find the prime factors of 2535.

20 What is the smallest number which is a multiple of 9, 24 and 27?

21 (a) a and b are two numbers. What is the smallest multiple of a^3, a^2b and a^2b^2?
 (b) Values are given to a and b. Does the choice of values make any difference to your answer to part (a) of this question? Explain your answer.

◆ **22** Find n so that $2n + 1 \leqslant 18$, where n is a whole number.

◆ **23** Illustrate the following relationships on number lines.
 (a) $^-3 \leqslant x \leqslant 5$ (b) $x^2 \geqslant 4$

◆ **24** What whole number values of n satisfy $2n - 1 > 9$ and $n^2 \leqslant 100$?

Activities and investigations A

Competition quiz A

A reads out the questions headed 'A's questions for B' and B writes down the answers: 15 minutes are allowed for this. Then B takes the book and reads out the questions headed 'B's questions for A'. Again, 15 minutes only are allowed. The two people together then use the answers on p. 418 to score their answer sheets. The winner is the person with most marks.

A's questions for B

1 What is the next number in the sequence 4, 12, 20, 28, ... ?
2 What is the next number in the sequence 2, 5, 10, 17, ... ?
3 What is the cost of 152 stamps at 17p each?
4 Calculate 118 + 282 without a calculator.
5 Calculate 1025 ÷ 25 without a calculator.
6 What is the value of 8 + ⁻5?
7 What is the value of ⁻6 × ⁻3?
8 What is n if 15 ÷ ⁻n = ⁻2·5?
9 Write down a number between ⁻100 and ⁻10.
10 Multiply 4·3 by 0·01 without a calculator.
11 Divide 0·28 by 100 without a calculator.
12 Divide 1·2 by 300 without a calculator.
13 Subtract 0·95 from 20·05.
14 Write a decimal equal to 5·6%.
15 Write a fraction equivalent to $\frac{24}{30}$.
16 Subtract $\frac{5}{8}$ from $1\frac{3}{4}$.
17 How many 5 mm slices could be cut from 9 inches of sausage (roughly)?
18 Write down all the prime factors of 128.
19 Write down all the prime numbers between 80 and 100.
20 40 is a multiple of n. What whole number could n be?
21 All the factors of an odd number are odd ... true or false?
22 Find 3 prime numbers p, q and r so that $p + q + r = 22$.
23 3^3 is a lucky number, so is 7^7. What are their values?
24 What numbers have the same value as their reciprocals $(\frac{1}{x})$?
25 What number is the cube root of 1728?
26 Write down the value of $8^{-14} \div 8^{-12}$.
27 Write 0·01805 in standard form.
28 Write down the approximation you would use to check 42·5 × 3·85.
29 Write 4·3508 correct to two decimal places.
30 Which is the largest of $\frac{1}{5}$, $\frac{1}{6}$, $\frac{2}{11}$?

B's questions for A

1 What is the next number in the sequence 2, 3, 5, 9, ... ?
2 What is the next number in the sequence 3, 9, 18, 30, ... ?
3 Calculate 7 × 999 without a calculator.
4 Calculate 444 ÷ 37 without a calculator.
5 Calculate 10 000 − 4444 without a calculator.
6 What is the value of ⁻9 + ⁻17?
7 What is the value of 6 − ⁻9?
8 What is the value of ⁻5 × ⁻9?
9 Write down a number between 12·075 and 12·076.
10 Multiply $0·045 × 10^3$ without a calculator.
11 Divide 0·6 by 25 without a calculator.
12 Add 4·2 and 0·08.
13 Write a decimal equivalent to $40\frac{1}{2}$%.
14 Write a fraction equivalent to $\frac{30}{36}$.
15 Add $\frac{1}{2} + \frac{3}{4} + \frac{5}{8}$.
16 Multiply $\frac{3}{8}$ by $1\frac{1}{2}$.
17 Write down a fraction more than $\frac{1}{5}$ but less than $\frac{1}{4}$.
18 How many multiples of 7 lie between 40 and 60?
19 Find a prime number which is the sum of two square numbers.
20 All multiples of odd numbers are odd ... true or false?
21 How could you tell that 1 357 953 is not prime?
22 Write down the value of $2^7 \div 2^{-2}$.
23 Write down the value of $(\frac{1}{4})^{-\frac{1}{2}}$.
24 Find $\sqrt{2025}$.
25 $\sqrt{3}$ = 1·732. What is $\sqrt{300}$?
26 Write $7·43 × 10^{-2}$ as a decimal.
27 What is the nearest whole number to 11·538?
28 How would you tell that 495 × 62 = 3069 was wrong at first sight?
29 Write 113·51 correct to two significant figures.
30 Which is the smallest fraction of $\frac{2}{3}$, $\frac{3}{4}$, $\frac{5}{8}$?

Treasure hunt

Two people, A and B, take part in this treasure hunt to find the two 'treasure' numbers T_1 and T_2. Each set of clues helps to find and check a number. This number may then be used to find the next number and so on until the treasure numbers T_1 and T_2 are discovered. It is important to make use of all the clues each time.

How to play

First: A looks for T_1 and B looks for T_2.
Then: B looks for T_1 and A looks for T_2.
The time taken is recorded and the results are entered into a table like the one below.

	Answer for T_1	Time	Answer for T_2	Time	Total time
A					
B					

A looks for T_1
B looks for T_2

Time recorded

↓

B looks for T_1
A looks for T_2

Time recorded

↓

Record results for T_1 and T_2 and times in table

↓

Look up values of T_1 and T_2 on page 419.

↓

Decide who is the winner

Rules to choose the winner

1: If you find T_1, score 40 marks; if you find T_2, score 60 marks.
2: The person with most marks wins.
3: If both players have the same marks the one with the best time wins.
4: If both players get wrong answers for T_1 and T_2 the result is a draw.

Treasure number T_1

The first number clue is p

Clue: $p > 36^{\frac{1}{2}}$

Clue: $p < \sqrt[3]{1000}$

Clue: p is a factor of 2023

Clue: p is a prime number

Clue: 1, 7; 2, 7; 3, 7; 4, 7; 5, 7; 5, 6; 3, 4; 3, 3; 3, 2 and 3, 1 ???

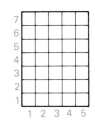

The second number clue is q

Clue: q is a symmetrical number
Clue: q is half the number of yards in a chain
Clue: $q \times (q + 1) \times (q + 2) = 1716$

Clue: $\dfrac{1}{q}$ has this fascinating multiplication table:

$\dfrac{1}{q} \times 1 = 0.090\ 909\ 09 \ldots$

$\dfrac{1}{q} \times 2 = 0.181\ 818\ 18 \ldots$

$\dfrac{1}{q} \times 3 = 0.272\ 727\ 27 \ldots$ etc.

The third number clue is r

Clue: r is prime

Clue: $\sqrt{r} = 3.605\ 55 \ldots$

Clue: $r = \dfrac{pq + 1}{p - 1}$

Clue: the length of the hypotenuse

Clue: some people think this number is unlucky

The fourth number clue is s

Clue: s is very close to 10^3
Clue: find s in the picture

Clue: $s = pqr$
Clue: s is the same forwards as backwards

$p \times q \times r \times s$ is the treasure number T_1

Treasure number T_2

The first number clue is w

Clue: w is symmetrical.
Clue: $w = (12\,321)^{\frac{1}{2}}$
Clue: If $a = 10$ then
$a^2 + a + 1 = w$.
Clue: The values of w for different bases is given in the table below.

base	2	3	4	5	6	7	8	9
value	7	13	21	31	43	57	73	91

The second number clue is x

Clue: x, written back to front is the same as $\frac{w}{3}$.
Clue: $70 < x < 80$.
Clue: the value of x is $7 \cdot 3 \times$ the sum of its digits.
Clue: $(x - 1) x (x + 1) = 388\,944$.
Clue: x is the 21 st prime number.

The third number clue is y

Clue: y is prime.
Clue: $y = \frac{w}{3} + 100$.
Clue: y is a factor of 11 234.
Clue: $\frac{1}{y} = x \div 10\,000 \ldots$ very close indeed!!
Clue: y is the square of this hypotenuse!!

The fourth number clue is z

Clue: z is symmetrical.
Clue: z could be called 10^4 but not quite.
Clue: what a lot of fuss!! about nothing.
Clue: Surprise! $z = xy$.

$w \times x \times y \times z$ is the treasure number T_2

Puzzles . . . for two

One of the best ways of revising number work is through puzzles. Working with a friend makes this even more interesting. Obviously, puzzles have to be puzzling so don't expect to get the answers straight away.

1 Consecutive sums

Most numbers can be written as a sum of consecutive numbers.
For example $7 = 3 + 4$, $12 = 3 + 4 + 5$, and so on.
One special family of numbers cannot be written this way. Can you find this family? Find out all you can about it. Explore this problem further if negative numbers are considered.

2 Pythagorean numbers

The numbers 3, 4 and 5 are famous because they fit exactly round a right-angled triangle. Find three more sets of numbers like this.
[*Hint*: $3^2 + 4^2 = 5^2$]

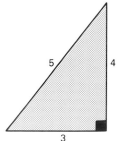

3 Factorial

The numbers 1×2, $1 \times 2 \times 3$, $1 \times 2 \times 3 \times 4$, ... etc. are called factorial numbers and written with $!$
So $4! = 1 \times 2 \times 3 \times 4 = 24$.

(a) Find the values of 5!, 6! and 7!

(b) If you have $\boxed{!}$ on your calculator, find the largest factorial number the calculator will allow.

(c) Try this 'four fours' problem. You are allowed the symbols $+$; $-$; $\times$; $-$; $\sqrt{\ }$; ( ); ! and four fours. How many of the numbers 1 to 100 can you make?

[Here is the first one: $44 \div 44 = 1$ ... easy!]

4 Decimals to fractions

It is easy to turn a fraction into a decimal. Just divide the top by the bottom! But how would you turn a decimal into a fraction? See if you can work from the easy problems below to a general method.

Turn these into simple fractions.

(a) 0·25   (b) 0·75   (c) 0·125   (d) 0·375
(e) 0·333 33...   (f) 0·666 666...   (g) 0·888 888...
(h) 0·142 857 1 ... (i) 0·090 909 ... (j) 0·363 636 36...

5 Fibonacci

The Fibonacci number 1·618 033 988 ... is connected to the Fibonacci sequence 1, 1, 2, 3, 5, 8, 13, ..., in which each number is the sum of the previous two numbers. What is the connection?

6 Repeaters

The number 142 857 has a very special property. If you multiply by 2 you get $142\,857 \times 2 = 285\,714$. Explore this further and then find another number with the same property.

[*Hint*: $\frac{1}{7} = 0.142\,857...$ $\frac{2}{7} = 0.285\,714...$ and so on.]

7 π

Which of the following is nearest to π?
Ancient Greece: $\frac{22}{7}$, $3\frac{17}{120}$.   *Ancient India*: $\frac{49}{16}$, $\sqrt{10}$.   *Ancient China*: $\frac{355}{113}$.
Kaner's approximation to π: $2.222\sqrt{2}$
The value of π to 8 decimal places is 3·141 592 65.

8 Prime numbers

The table opposite gives the start of a sieve to find the prime numbers drawn from the first 400 numbers.

How was the table constructed? Extend it to find all the prime numbers below 1000.

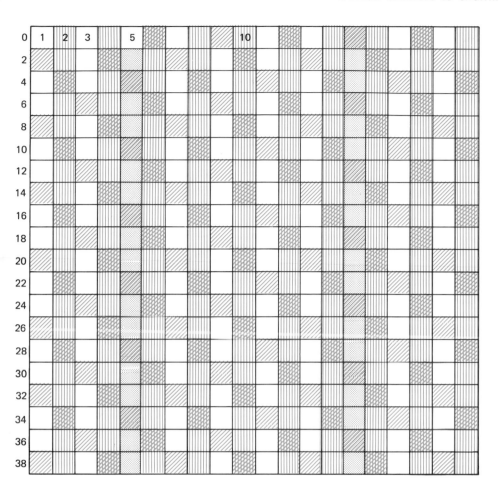

9 Finding the tail

My calculator gives these decimal values for $\frac{1}{17}$, $\frac{2}{17}$ and $\frac{4}{17}$:

$\frac{1}{17} = 0.058\ 823\ 529$, $\frac{2}{17} = 0.117\ 647\ 058$, $\frac{4}{17} = 0.235\ 294\ 117$.

(a) Use these results to find $\frac{1}{17}$ correct to 16 decimal places.

(b) Study this tail (see puzzle 6, 'Repeaters').

(c) How would you find the 'tail' for $\frac{1}{19}$, $\frac{1}{23}$, $\frac{1}{31}$?

Worked answers to examination questions A

The purpose of these answers and discussions is to show the sort of work that could get top marks in an examination. You should check that your own solutions have the same final answer and are written clearly. If you cannot understand the discussion for any question ask your teacher for help. For any questions you first get wrong, write out your answers again correctly. Show your working clearly.

1 Find the next 2 numbers in each sequence.
   (a) 1, 3, 7, 13, ...
   (b) 1, 1·1, 1·21, 1·331, ...
   (c) 48, ⁻24, 12, ⁻6, ...

   (a) 21, 31   (b) 1·4641, 1·61051   (c) 3, ⁻1·5

   (a) This problem is best solved by looking at the way the sequence grows.

$$1 \quad 3 \quad 7 \quad 13 \quad 21 \quad 31$$

   differences   2   4   6 → 8 → 10

   (b) The four numbers given are $(1·1)^0$, $(1·1)^1$, $(1·1)^2$ and $(1·1)^3$.
   The next two are therefore $(1·1)^4 = 1·4641$
   and $(1·1)^5 = 1·61051$

   (c) Each number is obtained from the previous one by dividing by 2 and changing the sign:
   48, ⁻24, ⁺12, ⁻6, ⁺3, ⁻1·5

2 The product of two numbers, which differ by 6, is 498 427. Find the numbers.

   703 and 709

   The 'heavy' way to do this question is by a quadratic equation. Let one number be n. The other is $n + 6$.
   $n(n + 6) = 498\ 427$
   $n^2 + 6n - 498\ 427 = 0$
   But even then, you still need to find factors of 498 427 before you can solve the equation.
   Common sense suggests that the numbers are near to each other and near to $\sqrt{498\ 427}$.
   $\sqrt{498\ 427} = 705·99 \simeq 706$
   This suggests trying 705 × 711   ✕ ends in 5
   704 × 710   ✕ ends in 0
   703 × 709   correct

   ● The equation can be solved by factorisation: $(n - 703)(n - 709) = 0$ (but this means you have already answered the question!) or by formula

   $$n = \frac{^-6 \pm \sqrt{36 + 4 \times 498\ 427}}{2}$$

   $$= \frac{^-6 \pm 1412}{2}$$

   This gives n as 703 or ⁻709 reminding us that ⁻703 and ⁻709 are also solutions to the problem

3 The calculations given below are clearly not in base 10. What is the base in each case?

(a)
$$\begin{array}{r} 471 \\ +263 \\ \hline 754 \end{array}$$

(b)
$$\begin{array}{r} 141 \\ - 22 \\ \hline 114 \end{array}$$

(c) $\dfrac{4503}{24} = 156$

(a) base 8   (b) base 5   (c) base 7

(a) The clue is in the second columns. $7 + 6 = 15$ only in base 8.

(b) The clue is in the units column $(b + 1) - 2 = 4$, so $b = 5$.

(c) Since $\dfrac{4503}{24} = 156, \quad 24 \times 156 = 4503$. The last digit comes from

$4 \times 6 = n \times \text{base} + 3$, where n is a natural number.

$\Rightarrow \quad n \times \text{base} = 21$

$\Rightarrow \quad\quad\quad \text{base} = \quad 7$

All these results can be checked by converting to base 10.

(a) $471_8 \rightarrow 4(64) + 7(8) + 1 = 313$

$\underline{263_8} \rightarrow 2(64) + 6(8) + 3 = \underline{179}$

$754_8 \rightarrow 7(64) + 5(8) + 4 = 492$

(b) $\quad 141_5 \rightarrow 25 + 4(5) + 1 = 46$

$\underline{- \ 22_5} \rightarrow \quad\quad\quad 2(5) + 2 = \underline{12}$

$114_5 \rightarrow 25 + \quad 5 \ + 4 = 34$

(c) $24_7 \times 156_7 \quad\quad\quad 4503_7 = 4(343) + 5(49) + 3$

$\quad\downarrow \quad\quad \downarrow \quad\quad\quad\quad\quad\quad\quad = 1620$

$\quad 18 \ \times \ 90 \ = 1620$

4 The argument below is supposed to prove that $2 = 1$. Find the error.

$1\emptyset$ Assume $a = b$

$2\emptyset$ $a^2 = ab$ .... multiplying by a.

$3\emptyset$ $a^2 - b^2 = ab - b^2$ .... subtracting b^2.

$4\emptyset$ $(a - b)(a + b) = b(a - b)$ factorising

$5\emptyset$ $a + b = b$ .... dividing by $(a - b)$

$6\emptyset$ $2 = 1$ .... putting $a = b = 1$

The error is in line $5\emptyset$ since division by $0 \ [= a - b]$ is impossible.

In line $5\emptyset$, both sides are divided by $a - b$; but line $1\emptyset$ assumes $a = b$, so $a - b = 0$. When a number is divided by zero the answer can be anything. So you cannot deduce that $a + b = b$.

$4 \times 0 = 5 \times 0 = 0$, but 4 is not equal to 5.

5 Prove that only one inverse is possible for any non-zero number.

[*Hint*: b is the inverse of a if $ab = ba = 1$.]

Proof

$1\emptyset$ Suppose the number a has two inverses x and y

$2\emptyset$ Then $ax = xa = 1$ and $ay = ya = 1$

$3\emptyset$ Consider the product xay

$4\emptyset$ $xay = (xa)y = 1 \times y = y$

$5\emptyset$ $xay = x(ay) = x \times 1 = x$

$6\emptyset$ So $x = y$, and these two inverses are not different.

6 The table below gives the 'products' of the rotations which correspond to R, right turn; L, left turn; and A, about turn. A · B means A followed by B. S means stay where you are.

·	R	L	A	S
R	A	S	L	R
L				
A				
S				

(a) Complete the table.
(b) Which rotation corresponds to 1 in the multiplication of numbers?
(c) Do the rotations obey these rules?
    (i) $a \cdot b = b \cdot a$ where a and b are any two of the rotations
               R L A S.
    (ii) $a \cdot i = i \cdot a = a$ where i is the identity and a is any one of the
               rotations.
    (iii) $a \cdot a^{-1} = i$ where a^{-1} is the inverse of a.

(a) Completed table

·	R	L	A	S
R	A	S	L	R
L	S	A	R	L
A	L	R	S	A
S	R	L	A	S

(b) S corresponds to 1 because it does not change the position.
$R \cdot S = S \cdot R = R$
$L \cdot S = S \cdot L = L$ } from the table
$A \cdot S = S \cdot A = A$

(c) (i) $a \cdot b = b \cdot a$,   this can be shown by listing all the possible products or by considering the diagonal of symmetry.
A S L R
S A R L
L R S A
R L A S

    (ii) The identity is S and every position has its inverse.
    (iii) $R \cdot L = L \cdot R = S$
        $A \cdot A = S$
        $S \cdot S = S$

7 Find the value of

(a) $^-3 - {}^-5$ (b) $\dfrac{(^-3)(^-7)}{^-21}$ (c) $n^2 - n$ where $n = {}^-2 \cdot 5$

(a) $^+2$ (b) $^-1$ (c) $8 \cdot 75$

(a) $^-3 - {}^-5 = {}^-3 + {}^+5 = {}^+2$.

(b) $\dfrac{(^-3)(^-7)}{^-21} = \dfrac{^+21}{^-21} = {}^-1$

(c) Putting $n = {}^-2 \cdot 5$

$n^2 - n \rightarrow ({}^-2 \cdot 5)^2 - ({}^-2 \cdot 5) = 6 \cdot 25 + 2 \cdot 5$
$$= 8 \cdot 75$$

8 If the temperature falls below $^-2 \cdot 2°C$ the plant will die. Which of the following temperatures mean death for the plant?
(a) 1°C   (b) $^-4°C$ (c) $^-3°C$ (d) $^-1 \cdot 7°C$ (e) $^-2 \cdot 9°C$

$^-4°$, $^-3°$ and $^-2 \cdot 9°C$.

This is best shown on a number line

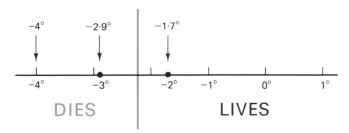

or you can draw the line vertically.

9 Explain why $^-5 \times {}^-7$ must equal $^+35$.
[*Hint*: first consider $(^-5) \times (^+7)$.]

1⌀ $7 \times {}^-5 = {}^-35$ (seven lots of $^-5$)
2⌀ $(^-7 \times {}^-5) + (7 \times {}^-5) = {}^-5(^-7 + 7) = {}^-5 \times 0 = 0$
3⌀ $(^-7 \times {}^-5) + {}^-35 = 0$
4⌀ $^-7 \times {}^-5 = 35$

Notes: (i) This answer depends on the fact that negative numbers obey the distributive law
$$a(b + c) = ab + ac.$$
(ii) A similar argument can be used to prove that
$$^-a \times {}^-b = {}^+ab.$$

10 (a) Find a fraction whose value is between $\frac{7}{11}$ and $\frac{12}{19}$.

(b) Use the rule $\dfrac{a}{b} + \dfrac{c}{d} = \dfrac{ad + bc}{bd}$ to add $\frac{2}{3} + \frac{3}{5}$.

Check the result on your calculator.

(a) The fraction obtained by adding both tops and bases is $\frac{19}{30}$.
This lies between $\frac{7}{11}$ and $\frac{12}{19}$.

Values $\frac{7}{11} = 0 \cdot 636363 \ldots$
$\frac{12}{19} = 0 \cdot 6315789$
$\frac{19}{30} = 0 \cdot 63333 \ldots$

Another way of approaching this problem is to convert the fractions to a common base.

$$\frac{7 \times 19}{11 \times 19} \rightarrow \frac{133}{209}$$

$$\frac{12 \times 11}{19 \times 11} \rightarrow \frac{132}{209}$$

So the inbetween fraction could be $\dfrac{132 \cdot 5}{209} = \dfrac{265}{418}$

(b) $\dfrac{2}{3} + \dfrac{3}{5} = \dfrac{10 + 9}{15} = \dfrac{19}{15} = 1\frac{4}{15}$

2 $\boxed{\div}$ 3 $\boxed{+}$ 3 $\boxed{\div}$ 5 $\boxed{=}$ 1·26 ... Check

11 Find fractions whose values are

(a) 0·7777 ...   (b) 0·7272 ...   (c) 0·135135 ...

(a) $\dfrac{7}{9}$ (b) $\dfrac{8}{11}$ (c) $\dfrac{15}{111}$

(a) This is obvious.

(b) $0·727272 \ldots = \dfrac{72}{99} = \dfrac{8 \times 9}{11 \times 9} = \dfrac{8}{11}$

(c) $0·135135 \ldots = \dfrac{135}{999} = \dfrac{15 \times 9}{111 \times 9} = \dfrac{15}{111} = \dfrac{5 \times 3}{37 \times 3} = \dfrac{5}{37}$

12 (a) Show, by giving values to a, b, c and d, that

$$\frac{a}{b} = \frac{c}{d} \Rightarrow \frac{a+b}{a-b} = \frac{c+d}{c-d}$$

(b) Use the result to solve the equation $\dfrac{x+1}{x-1} = \dfrac{3}{5}$

[Check by a different method.]

(a) Let $a = 1, b = 2, c = 3$ and $d = 6$.

$$\frac{a}{b} = \frac{1}{2} \quad \frac{c}{d} = \frac{3}{6} \quad \frac{a+b}{a-b} = \frac{3}{^-1} \quad \frac{c+d}{c-d} = \frac{9}{^-3}$$

Clearly $\dfrac{a+b}{a-b} = {}^-3 = \dfrac{c+d}{c-d}$

Other choices for a, b, c and d are possible, but avoid zero.

(b) $\dfrac{x+1}{x-1} = \dfrac{3}{5} \Rightarrow \dfrac{(x+1) + (x-1)}{(x+1) - (x-1)} = \dfrac{3+5}{3-5}$

$$\Rightarrow \frac{2x}{2} = \frac{8}{^-2}$$

$$\Rightarrow x = {}^-4.$$

Another method uses cross multiplication

$5(x+1) = 3(x-1)$

$\Rightarrow 5x + 5 = 3x - 3$

$\Rightarrow \quad 2x = {}^-8$

$\Rightarrow \quad x = {}^-4$

13 Explain why $a^{\frac{1}{3}}$ is the same as $\sqrt[3]{a}$ and find the value of $(12\cdot8)^{\frac{1}{3}}$.

Using rules of indices
$$a^{\frac{1}{3}} \times a^{\frac{1}{3}} \times a^{\frac{1}{3}} = a^{\frac{1}{3}+\frac{1}{3}+\frac{1}{3}} = a$$
Thus $(a^{\frac{1}{3}})^3 = a$.
So $a^{\frac{1}{3}} = \sqrt[3]{a}$ ... the number whose cube $= a$.
$(12\cdot8)^{\frac{1}{3}} = 2\cdot3392$ correct to 4 decimal places.
$12\cdot8$ $\boxed{x^{1/y}}$ 3 $\boxed{=}$

Notes: (i) Give the calculator sequence that you use. It may be different from the above.
(ii) Check by calculating $(2\cdot3392)^3$. This should give back $12\cdot8$ within 3 decimal places.

14 $1\cdot81 \times 10^9 \times 9\cdot21 \times 10^{-27} \simeq 1\cdot667 \times 10^n$. What is the value of n?

$$\begin{aligned}1\cdot81 \times 10^9 \times 9\cdot21 \times 10^{-27} &= 1\cdot81 \times 9\cdot21 \times 10^{-18}\\ &= 1\cdot667 \times 10^1 \times 10^{-18}\\ &= 1\cdot667 \times 10^{-17}\end{aligned}$$
i.e. $n = {}^-17$

Notes: (i) Both $1\cdot81 \times 10^9$ and $9\cdot21 \times 10^{-27}$ are standard form numbers.
(ii) The whole calculation can be done on a scientific calculator
$1\cdot81$ $\boxed{Exp}$ 9 $\boxed{\times}$ $9\cdot21$ $\boxed{Exp}$ 27 $\boxed{+/_-}$ $\boxed{=}$
The display should then show $\boxed{1\cdot667 \ldots {}^-17}$.

15 (a) Prove the rule $(a^m)^n = (a^n)^m$.
(b) Use your calculator to evaluate $(27)^{-\frac{2}{3}}$ in two different ways.

(a) $(a^m)^n = \underbrace{a^m \times a^m \times a^m \ldots\ldots}_{n\,times} = a^{mn}$
$(a^n)^m = \underbrace{a^n \times a^n \times a^n \ldots\ldots}_{m\,times} = a^{nm} = a^{mn}$

(b) 1st method $(27)^{-\frac{2}{3}} = (27^{-2})^{\frac{1}{3}} = \sqrt[3]{\dfrac{1}{729}} = \dfrac{1}{9}$

2nd method $(27)^{-\frac{2}{3}} = (27^{\frac{1}{3}})^{-2} = \dfrac{1}{3^2} = \dfrac{1}{9}$

16 Simplify
(a) $\sqrt{\dfrac{289}{144}}$ (b) $\sqrt{\left(\dfrac{3}{4}\right)^2 + \left(\dfrac{4}{5}\right)^2}$

(a) $1\frac{5}{12}$ (b) $\dfrac{\sqrt{481}}{20}$ $(= 1\cdot097)$

(a) $\sqrt{\dfrac{289}{144}} = \dfrac{\sqrt{289}}{\sqrt{144}} = \dfrac{17}{12} = 1\frac{5}{12}$

(b) $\sqrt{\left(\dfrac{3}{4}\right)^2 + \left(\dfrac{4}{5}\right)^2} = \sqrt{\dfrac{9}{16} + \dfrac{16}{25}} = \sqrt{\dfrac{225+256}{400}} = \dfrac{\sqrt{481}}{20}$

Notes: (i) Check by finding values on your calculator.

(a) 289 $\boxed{\div}$ 144 $\boxed{=}$ $\boxed{\sqrt{}}$ .... 1·4166 ...

      5 $\boxed{\div}$ 12 $\boxed{=}$ $\boxed{+}$ 1 $\boxed{=}$ ..... 1·4166 ...

(b) 0·75 $\boxed{(\ )^2}$ $\boxed{+}$ 0·8 $\boxed{(\ )^2}$ $\boxed{=}$ $\boxed{\sqrt{}}$ ..... 1·0965 ...

      481 $\boxed{\sqrt{}}$ $\boxed{\div}$ 20 $\boxed{=}$ .... 1·0965 ...

(ii) The question wants you to simplify not evaluate so just giving the values would not earn full marks.

17 Show that, for any two positive numbers a, b,

(a) $\sqrt{ab}$ lies between a and b (b) $\dfrac{a+b}{2} > \sqrt{ab}$

(a)   1Ø   Assume $a < b$

      2Ø $a^2 < ab$ multiplying by a

      3Ø $a < \sqrt{ab}$

      4Ø $ab < b^2$ multiplying by b in 1Ø

      5Ø $\sqrt{ab} < b$

Thus 6Ø $a < \sqrt{ab} < b$.

This argument is repeated if $b < a$ ...

      7Ø   Assume $b < a$

      8Ø $b < \sqrt{ab} < a$ from 2Ø–6Ø by analogy.

Thus $\sqrt{ab}$ lies between a and b.

(b) 1Ø $\dfrac{a+b}{2} > \sqrt{ab} \Leftrightarrow a + b > 2\sqrt{ab}$

      2Ø $\Leftrightarrow (a+b)^2 > 4ab$

      3Ø $\Leftrightarrow (a+b)^2 - 4ab > 0$

      4Ø $\Leftrightarrow a^2 + 2ab + b^2 - 4ab > 0$

      5Ø $\Leftrightarrow a^2 - 2ab + b^2 > 0$

      6Ø $\Leftrightarrow (a-b)^2 > 0$

      7Ø   Line 6Ø is true for all values of a, b.

      8Ø   Line 1Ø is true for all values of a, b.

18 $\sqrt{3}$ is given as 1·732 050 808 on my calculator. Would it be correct to assume that the '08' pattern continues?
Give reasons for your answer.

No

If the '08' pattern continued the decimal could be converted into a rational number (by multiplying by 10^5 and subtracting the original number). $\sqrt{3}$ is an irrational number so no pattern is possible.

19 Find the prime factors of 2535.

$2535 = 3 \times 5 \times 13^2$

3	2535
5	845
13	169
	13

20 What is the smallest number which is a multiple of 9, 24 and 27?

216

Expressing the numbers as products of prime factors:
$9 = 3 \times 3 \qquad 24 = 2 \times 2 \times 2 \times 3 \qquad 27 = 3 \times 3 \times 3$
The lowest multiple of all three is $3 \times 3 \times 3 \times 2 \times 2 \times 2 = 216$.

21 (a) a and b are two numbers. What is the smallest multiple of a^3, a^2b and a^2b^2?

(b) Values are given to a and b. Does the choice of values make any difference to your answer to part (a)?

(a) a^3b^2 is the smallest multiple of all three expressions.

(b) If a is a multiple of b or b is a multiple of a the answer could be different.
For example, suppose $a = 6$ and $b = 3$, then
$a^3 = 216 \qquad a^2b = 108 \qquad$ and $\qquad a^2b^2 = 324$.
The lowest common multiple is 648, but
$a^3b^2 = 6 \times 6 \times 6 \times 3 \times 3 = 1944$

22 Find n so that $2n + 1 \leqslant 18$, where n is a whole number.

$2n + 1 \leqslant 18 \Rightarrow 2n \leqslant 17$
$\rightarrow \quad n \leqslant 8 \cdot 5$

Since n is a whole number, the solution is any number up to and including 8

Note: Take care with $\leqslant$. Do not forget the 'equals' part. In this case n cannot equal $8\frac{1}{2}$ as it is given as a whole number.

23 Illustrate the following relationships on number lines.
(a) $^-3 \leqslant x \leqslant 5$ (b) $x^2 \geqslant 4$

(a) Both $^-3$ and 5 are included.

(b) Both 2 and $^-2$ are included.

Note: Don't forget the negative values in (b).

24 What whole number values of n satisfy $2n - 1 > 9$ and $n^2 \leqslant 100$?

6, 7, 8, 9, 10

$2n - 1 > 9 \Rightarrow 2n > 10$
$\Rightarrow \quad n > 5$
$n^2 \leqslant 100 \Rightarrow \quad n \leqslant 10$

The only values of n which satisfy both inequalities are $n = 6, 7, 8, 9$ and 10.
The answer should not be shown on a number line as only whole numbers are being considered.

Topic B Measurement

Contents

Units; area; volume; circular measure; relationships.

Self assessment

The purpose of this task is to find out whether or not you need revision on topic B. If not you can go straight to the next topic. There is no time limit on this task.

- Make a table in your book, like the one on page vi. You need space for 30 questions.
- Write down your answers to all the following questions.
- When you have finished calculate your score from the answers on page 419.
- If your score is more than 80% go on to Topic C self assessment (pp. 91–93).

Part A

You should obtain 100% on these questions.

1 450 mm is the same as
A 4·5 cm   B 45 cm   C 0·45 cm
D 0·45 m

2 36 ft is the same as
A 6 yards   B 10 yards   C 12 yards
D 108 yards

3 108 inches is the same as
A 3 ft   B 10 ft   C 3 yards   D 10 yards

4 1 mile is the same as
A 1000 yards   B 1000 m   C 1760 yards
D 1760 m

5 Which of these statements is not true?
A 1 ton = 20 cwt   B 1 cwt = 112 lb
C 1 stone = 16 lb   D 1 lb = 16 oz

Copy and complete the following rough conversions ['≃' means 'nearly equal to']

6 1 inch ≃ . . . cm   **7** 39 inches ≃ . . . m

8 5 miles ≃ . . . km   **9** . . . lbs ≃ 1 kg

10 100 kg ≃ . . . cwt

Part B

If you obtain 80% of the marks on this section, you can move to topic C without revising topic B.

11 Measure the distances (in mm) from the centre of this parallelogram to its vertices.

12 Estimate the diameter (*D*) and circumference (*C*) of this circle. What is the ratio *C* : *D* correct to one decimal place?

13 (i) Calculate the area of △APB.
  (ii) Deduce the area of △AQB.
  (iii) Deduce the relationship between △APR and △BRQ

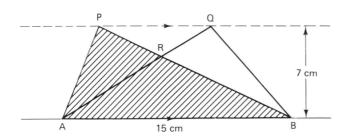

14 (i) Calculate the difference between the area of the hexagon and the area of the octagon.
  (ii) Calculate the area/perimeter ratio for each figure (cm² enclosed per cm).

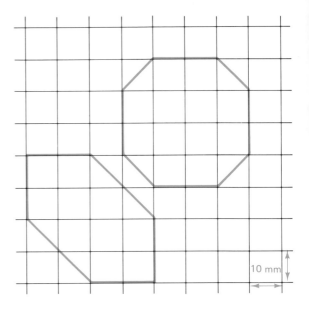

15 Calculate the area enclosed by the boundary.

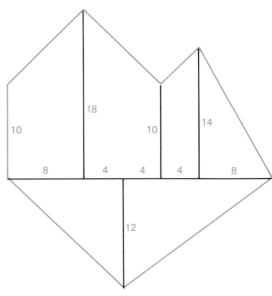

16 This block of apartments is 24 metres wide and 12 m deep. Each floor is 3 m high and the top ridge of the roof 34 metres above ground level. It is heated by warm air. Estimate the volume of air which is contained by the whole building.

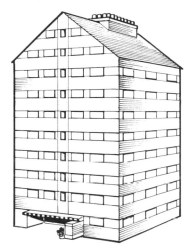

17 Find the volume of the girder in the diagram. It is 3 metres long and the cross section has two axes of symmetry.

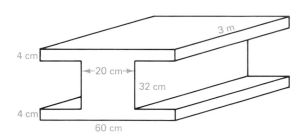

18 Complete the following using =, > or < to make correct statements.
(a) 1 gallon . . . 5 litres.
(b) 1 litre . . . 1000 cm^3.
(c) 1 m^3 of water . . . 1 ton of water.

19 Each of the formulae below is incomplete. Add the extra to complete each formula.
(a) Circumference of a circle = πr
(b) Area of a circle = πr
(c) Volume of a cylinder = $\pi r h$
◆ (d) Curved surface of a cylinder = $\pi r h$
◆ (e) Volume of a cone = $\pi r^2 h$
◆ (f) Surface area of a sphere = πr^2

20 Calculate the volume of a cylinder, diameter 4 inches, length 36 inches.

21 Copper wire, diameter 2 mm is sold in lengths of 100 metres. How much would one such length weigh [copper weighs 9 g per cm^3].

22 The pipe shown is 14 cm long. Its internal diameter is 3 cm and its external diameter is 5 cm. Calculate the volume of material in the pipe.

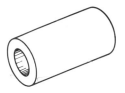

23 A small can of soup has diameter equal to its height of 4″. A large can of the same soup has height and diameter both equal to 6″. How much more soup does the large can hold (%)?

41

24 Calculate the perimeter and area of the 135° sector of a circle which is shown in the diagram.

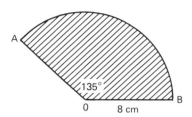

27 A circle, radius 5 cm is divided by a chord 6 cm long.
   (i) Show that the area of the small part of the circle is $\left(\dfrac{25\pi\theta}{360} - 12\right)$ cm².
   (ii) Calculate the difference between the areas of the two parts of the circle.

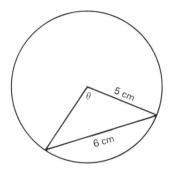

25 The sector in question **24** is rolled into a cone so that OA lies on OB. Calculate
   (i) The circumference of the base of the cone.
   (ii) The base area of the cone.
   (iii) The vertical height of the cone.
   (iv) The volume of air under the cone when it is standing on a table.

28 A cone 15 cm high has base diameter equal to 6 cm. A cone, base diameter 2 cm is cut from the top of the first cone. Calculate the volume of the remaining piece. (The frustrum).

29 A pile of paper forms a cuboid 18 cm × 20 cm × 10 cm high. Discuss how the shape of this pile could be changed (for example by pushing the pile out of the vertical). What changes would be made in the volume and surface area of the pile?

26 The size of the rectangle ABCD is such that, when the 10 cm square XBCY is removed, the sides of the remaining shape are in the same ratio as the sides of the original rectangle. Calculate the length of AB.

30 An unsharpened pencil is 12 cm long. Its section is an octagon, with diameter 1 cm. The diameter of the 'lead' is 2 mm. Calculate the volume of wood and lead in a batch of 1 million of these pencils. Make some estimate of the weight of the whole batch [density of wood = 0·7 g/cm³, density of graphite = 1·4 g/cm³].

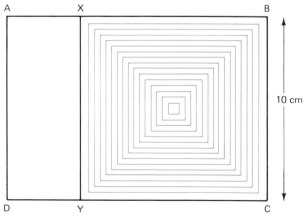

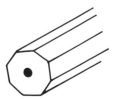

Key facts B

B.1 Units

Measuring systems are designed to save having to use
very large numbers, very small numbers, fractions or
decimals. All measurements can be expressed as a whole
number of appropriate units.

B.1.1 Length

Metric
1000 millimetres = 1 metre (m)
1000 metres = 1 kilometre (km)
Also
1 centimetre = 10 millimetres (mm)
1 metre = 100 centimetres (cm)

Useful **rough** metric/imperial conversions
1 inch $\simeq$ 25·4 mm (or 25 mm)
1 metre $\simeq$ 39 inches $\simeq$ 1·1 yards
8 km $\simeq$ 5 miles
1 foot $\simeq$ 30 cm

Imperial
12 inches = 1 foot
3 feet = 1 yard
1760 yards = 1 mile

B.1.2 Mass

Metric
1000 grams = 1 kilogram
1000 kilograms = 1 tonne

Useful **rough** metric/imperial conversions
450 g $\simeq$ 1 lb
1 kg $\simeq$ 2·2 lb
50 kg $\simeq$ 1 cwt
1 tonne $\simeq$ 1 ton

Imperial
16 ounces = 1 pound (lb)
14 pounds = 1 stone
8 stone = 1 hundredweight (cwt)
20 cwt = 1 ton
Also
1 ton = 2240 lb

B.1.3 Time

		Days in each month*			
60 seconds = 1 minute		January	31	July	31
60 minutes = 1 hour		February	28/9	August	31
24 hours = 1 day		March	31	September	30
7 days = 1 week		April	30	October	31
52 weeks = 1 year		May	31	November	30
		June	30	December	31

* Units of time are complicated by the fact that the earth takes $365\frac{1}{4}$ days to complete an orbit round the sun. This is why February is given an extra day every fourth year.

Exercise B.1

1 (a) Which would be the correct units to use in measuring a practice ground for athletics (metric and British)?
   (b) How many ounces in $1\frac{1}{4}$ lb?
   (c) How many millimetres in 14·2 cm?
   (d) How many minutes in $2\frac{1}{2}$ hours?
   (e) It will be 17·45 in 50 minutes. What is the time now?
   (f) A 'big' packet of soap powder contains 5 kg. How many pounds of powder is this?
   (g) A lift will work only when the load is less than 500 kg. How many people (average weight 45 kg) can use the lift without overloading it?
   (h) A wine lorry from the EEC carries 16 500 kg of wine. How many bottles can be filled from the lorry? (Each bottle holds 0·7 litres. Wine weighs approx. 1 kg per litre.)

   (i) Convert 2·3 kg into pounds and ounces (1 kg = 35·28 oz).   C

2 A petrol station sells petrol at £1·76 per gallon or 39p per litre. Are these two prices exactly the same? A tanker delivers 5000 gallons of petrol. What is the sale value of the petrol?   C

3 A 500 gallon water tank is built in the attic of a house. The tank weighs 40 kg. What will be the total load of the water tank when it is filled up?
   [1 gallon ≈ 4·6 litres. 1 litre of water weighs 1 kg]   C

4 An old fashioned timber business supplies wood in imperial measurements (because the customers ask for it).
   (a) Make up a conversion table which would give the dimensions in mm of wood with section . . .
   (i) 2″ × 1″   (ii) 2″ × $1\frac{1}{2}$″
   (iii) 3″ × 2″   (iv) 4″ × 2″
   (v) $2\frac{1}{2}$″ × $2\frac{1}{2}$″
   (b) The wholesaler only supplies wood in metric units (to the shop) as listed below.
       20 mm × 50 mm
       30 mm × 50 mm
       40 mm × 50 mm
       50 mm × 50 mm
       40 mm × 80 mm
       40 mm × 100 mm
       60 mm × 100 mm
       64 mm × 64 mm
       What could the shop assistant recommend to a customer who asked for
       (i) 25 feet of 4″ × 2″
       (ii) 60 ft of $2\frac{1}{2}$″ × $2\frac{1}{2}$″   B

5 The speed of light is known to be 186 000 miles per second.

  (i) Change this to km/hour, written in standard form.

 (ii) Find how far the light travels in a year. [This distance is known as one light-year and is used as a measure of distance in astronomy.]

(iii) Find the distance in km from the nearest star (4·5 light-years).

(iv) A space ship travels at 100 000 km/hour. How long would it take to get to the nearest star?

                                              B

6 It has been decided to "go metric time" from the year 2000 AD. Design a system of new metric-time units and present a table of conversions.

                                              A

B.2 Area

Area is a measure of the space enclosed by a boundary line. The boundary line is called the perimeter of the figure.

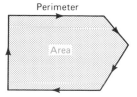

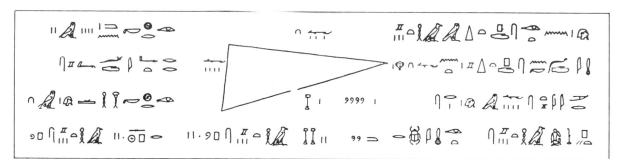

Calculating the area of a triangle in Egyptian hieroglyphics, circa 1590 BC

The areas of simple shapes can be calculated from measurements of base (b) and height (h).

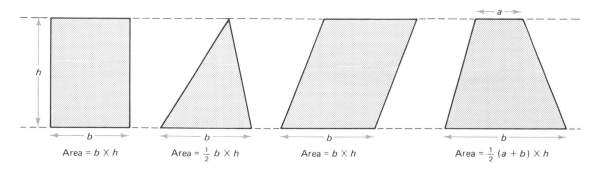

Area = $b \times h$ Area = $\frac{1}{2} b \times h$ Area = $b \times h$ Area = $\frac{1}{2}(a + b) \times h$

B.2.1 Units

Small areas are measured in 'square units'.

Metric	
Square millimetre	mm^2
Square centimetre	cm^2
Square metre	m^2

Imperial	
Square inch	in^2
Square foot	ft^2
Square yard	yd^2

Areas of land are measured in special units.

Metric
1 hectare $= 10\ 000$ m^2
100 hectares $= 1$ km^2

Imperial
1 acre $= 4840$ sq. yards
640 acres $= 1$ square mile

B.2.2 Conversions

1 inch^2 $= 6 \cdot 1$ cm^2 $= 610$ mm^2
1 m^2 $= 1 \cdot 2$ yd^2
1 hectare $= 2 \cdot 47$ acres
1 sq mile $\simeq 2 \cdot 6$ km^2

Note: The acre is an old, historical measure. In medieval times land was measured with chains, 22 yards long. The acre was a piece of land 10 chains wide and 1 chain deep. The acre is not a true square measure.

1 square chain

1 acre

B.2.3 Methods

Areas are often found by subtraction.

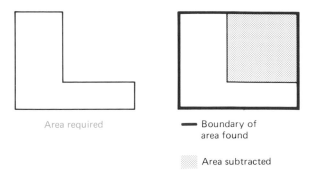

Area required

— Boundary of
area found

Area subtracted

A grid will help in many cases.
Area $= 12$ cm$^2 - (3 + 4 + 1)$ cm^2
$\quad\quad = 4$ cm^2

Area required

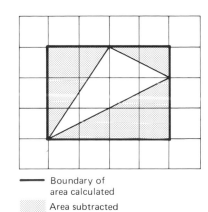

— Boundary of
area calculated

Area subtracted

If the area of an irregular shape is required, the area is divided into triangles
or trapezia. The sum of all the smaller areas is then found.

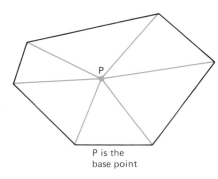

P is the
base point

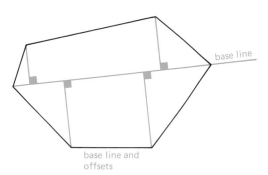

base line

base line and
offsets

These methods are used in surveying. (See projects B.)

● Especially useful if no equipment for measuring angles is available.

B.2.4 Formulae for triangles

Two useful formulae for finding the areas of triangles are given below (although they really belong to trigonometry).

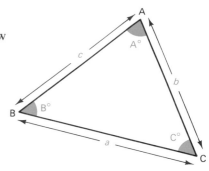

Sine formula

Area of $\triangle ABC = \frac{1}{2}ab \sin C$
$\qquad\qquad = \frac{1}{2}bc \sin A$
$\qquad\qquad = \frac{1}{2}ca \sin B$

These formulae follow from Area $= \frac{1}{2} \times$ base $\times$ height.

Example
Area of $\triangle ABC = \frac{1}{2} \times 4 \times 3 \times \sin 29° = 2\cdot9088$ cm²
0·5 ☒ 4 ☒ 3 ☒ 29 ☐sin ☐=

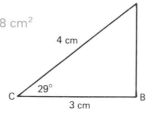

Semiperimeter formula (used when angles are not known)

1∅ $\quad s = \dfrac{a + b + c}{2}$ is calculated.

2∅ $\quad$ Area $= \sqrt{s(s - a)(s - b)(s - c)}$
3∅ $\quad s - a$, $s - b$ and $s - c$ are calculated.
4∅ $\quad$ Area is calculated.

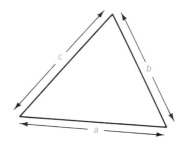

Example
1∅ $\quad s = (4 + 5 + 6) \div 2 = 7\cdot5$
2∅ $\quad A = \sqrt{s(s - a)(s - b)(s - c)}$
3∅ $\quad s - a = 3\cdot5$, $s - b = 2\cdot5$, $s - c = 1\cdot5$
4∅ $\quad A = \sqrt{7\cdot5 \times 3\cdot5 \times 2\cdot5 \times 1\cdot5} = 9\cdot92$ cm²

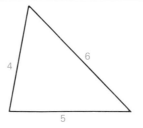

- This formula is ideal when using a programmable calculator or a computer to find the areas of a whole set of triangles where the three sides are known. The computer is programmed to ask for the values a, b and c, and when these are entered the area is calculated.

Exercise B.2

1 Calculate the area of △ABC which is drawn on a 1 cm square grid.

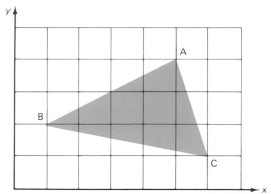

2 (a) Use the coordinates of A, B and C in question 1 to find the exact lengths of the sides of △ABC.
(b) Use your results to calculate the area of the triangle and compare the value with that found in question 1.
(c) Calculate the perpendicular distances from each side to the opposite vertex.   B

3 Investigate the perimeter/area relationship for regular plane figures with 3, 4, 5, 6, 8 and 10 sides. Make a graph of the results.   B/A

4 The diagram demonstrates that the area of the parallelogram is base × height.

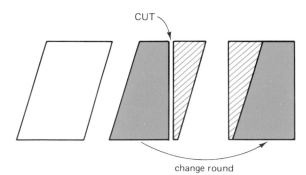

(a) Construct similar diagrams to show that . . .
area of a triangle $= \frac{1}{2}bh$
area of a trapezium $= \frac{1}{2}(a + b)h$.

(b) Show that the formulae for triangle and parallelogram can be deduced from the area formula for a trapezium.   B/A

5 A new 6th form block is to be built according to the plan shown. The building costs are estimated as £720/m².
Calculate the total cost for the building. Do you think the design would be satisfactory? Give reasons for your answer.   A

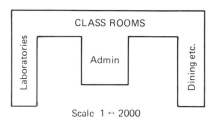

6 (a) Calculate the area of the quadrilateral by the five different methods below. You will have to measure it first!

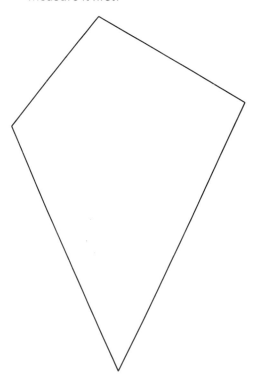

49

(i) Draw a diagonal and draw perpendicular lines from the other vertices to the diagonal.

(ii) Divide the quadrilateral into two triangles and use $\frac{1}{2}ab\sin C$, etc.

(iii) Divide the quadrilateral into two other triangles and use $\sqrt{s(s-a)(s-b)(s-c)}$.

(iv) Choose a point P inside the quadrilateral and join P to the four vertices. Use $\frac{1}{2}ab\sin C$ to calculate the areas of these four triangles.

(v) Draw a rectangle around the quadrilateral and calculate its area by subtraction.

(b) Which of the methods gives the best approximation to the exact area of the quadrilateral?*

*Whatever you think that is!

(c) Explain why it is not possible to express the area of a quadrilateral in terms of the lengths of its four sides, a, b, c and d.

A

B.3 Volume

The volume of an object is the amount of space it occupies. In the same way as an area is bounded by a perimeter, a volume is bounded by a surface area.

B.3.1 Regular cross section

The volume of any solid with regular cross section is found by multiplying
Area of cross section × length
Solids of this type are called prisms.

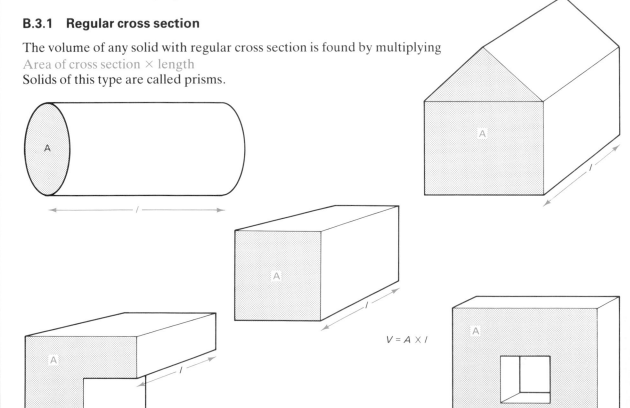

$V = A \times l$

B.3.2 Irregular cross section

If the cross section changes, the volume is found using the calculus However
all pyramids have a volume equal to $\frac{1}{3}$ × area of base × height

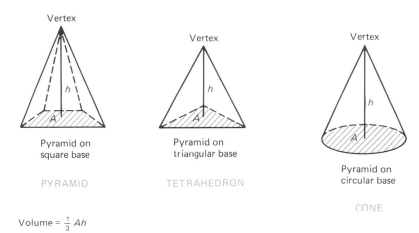

Vertex

Vertex

Vertex

h

h

h

A

A

A

Pyramid on
square base

Pyramid on
triangular base

Pyramid on
circular base

PYRAMID

TETRAHEDRON

CONE

Volume = $\frac{1}{3}$ *Ah*

B.3.3 Units

Solids

Volume is measured in cubic units

Metric*		Imperial	
Cubic centimetre	cm^3	Cubic inch	in^3
Cubic metre	m^3	Cubic foot	ft^3
		Cubic yard	yd^3

* 1 mm^3 is too small a volume to be practical

Liquids

Metric
1 litre   = 1000 cm³
1000 litres = 1 m³
1 litre of **pure water** weighs 1 kg
1 m³ of **pure water** weighs 1 tonne

1 gallon $\simeq$ 4·6 litres
1 litre $\simeq$ 1·8 pints

1 pint   1 litre   1 gallon   5 litres

Imperial
8 pints = 1 gallon
1 gallon of **pure water** weighs 10 lb
1 cubic foot of water weighs 62·5 lb
(i.e. 16 ft³ of water weighs 1000 lb)

Exercise B.3

1 Find the volume of a piece of wood 2 m long whose cross section is shown in the diagram.   C

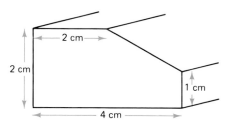

2 Calculate the height of a pyramid, standing on a base 4 cm × 4 cm whose volume is 28 cm³.   C

3 The stone spire of the church in the diagram is built on a hexagonal base, with sides 4 m long. Calculate the external volume of the spire, given that its height is 30 metres.   B/A

4 A swimming pool is 10 yards long and 5 yards across. At the deep end the depth is 12 ft, while at the shallow end the depth is 5 ft. Calculate the volume of water in the pool (in gallons!)   B

5 The spire in question 3 is built with blocks of stone which are 30 cm thick. Estimate the internal volume of the spire (space contained) and deduce an estimate for the volume of stone used to build it.   A

6 A wholesaler buys cooking oil by the lorry load. Each load is 12 m^3 in volume. He then puts the oil into 1 gallon cans for the American market. (They have not gone metric.) How many gallons could be expect from one load, allowing for 5% wastage.   A

B.4   Circular measure

All measurements of circular shapes involve the number π. The value of π is 3·141 59 . . . correct to 5 decimal places. If accuracy is not required, use $\pi \simeq 3$ or 3·14 or $3\frac{1}{7}$.

B.4.1   Circumference and area

The circumference is another word for perimeter (used for circles only).
Circumference $= \pi \times$ diameter
$\qquad\qquad = 2\pi r$.
Area $= \frac{1}{2}$ circumference $\times$ radius
$\qquad = \frac{1}{2} \times 2\pi r \times r$
$\qquad = \pi r^2$.

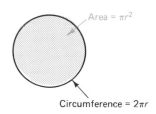

Area $= \pi r^2$

Circumference $= 2\pi r$

B.4.2   Sectors

The arc length and area of a sector depend on the angle at the centre $\theta°$

● The area is $\frac{1}{2} \times$ arc $\times$ radius for any sized sector

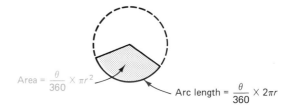

Area $= \frac{\theta}{360} \times \pi r^2$

Arc length $= \frac{\theta}{360} \times 2\pi r$

◆B.4.3   Segment

The area of a segment is found by subtraction for the smaller segment (or addition for the larger).

Example Find the area of the minor segment in the diagram.

1∅ Area of whole circle $(\pi r^2) = 36\pi$ cm²

2∅ Area of minor 140° sector $= \dfrac{140}{360} \times 36\pi$

$= 14\pi$ cm²

3∅ Area of major sector $= 22\pi$ cm² ... from 1∅, 2∅

4∅ Area of radial triangle $(\frac{1}{2}r^2 \sin\theta) = 18\sin 140°$ cm²

5∅ Area of segment = sector − triangle

$= (14\pi - 18\sin 140°)$ cm²

6∅ Area of larger segment = major sector + triangle

$= (22\pi + 18\sin 140°)$ cm²

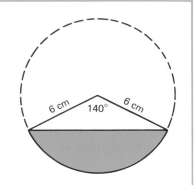

Values

Minor segment	32·4 cm²	14	☒	π	☐−	18	☒	140	sin	=
Major segment	80·7 cm²	22	☒	π	☐+	18	☒	140	sin	=
Whole circle (check)	113·1 cm²	36	☒	π	=					

◆ **B.4.4 Cylinder**

The cylinder is a prism with circular cross section.
Volume $= \pi r^2 l$.
Its curved surface can be unrolled to a rectangle whose area is $2\pi r \times l$.
Total area (including ends) $= 2\pi rl + 2\pi r^2$
$= 2\pi r(r + l)$

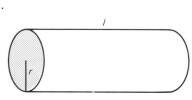

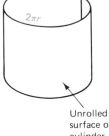

Unrolled surface of cylinder

◆ **B.4.5 Cone**

The volume of a cone is $\frac{1}{3}\pi r^2 h$, where h is the height of the vertex above the base. This follows the ordinary rule for pyramids.

The curved surface area of a cone is the area of the sector from which it was made.

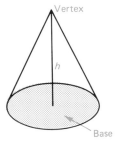

Vertex

Base

Curved surface

Area $= \frac{1}{2} \times 2\pi r \times l$
$= \pi rl$

● See area of a sector

$2\pi r$

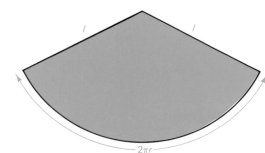

$2\pi r$

◆ B.4.6 Sphere

Volume $= \frac{4}{3}\pi r^3$
Surface area $= 4\pi r^2$

The geometry and measurement of the sphere have many applications in navigation and science.

● A hemisphere's curved area is double its base area so you could estimate the surface area of the great dome of St Paul's Cathedral by walking round the whispering gallery!

3 A metal cone is to be made from sheet metal. The height of the cone is to be 80 cm and the base radius is to be 30 cm. Calculate
  (i) the distance from the vertex to a point on the circumference of the base
  (ii) the angle of the sector from which the cone will be formed.   B

4 A flared skirt is made from a 120° sector of a circle. Calculate the area of material used.   A

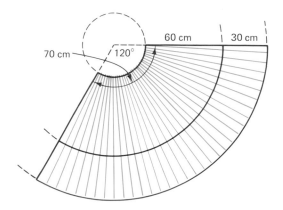

Exercise B.4

1 Calculate the volume and curved surface area of a cylinder whose length is 45 cm and radius 8 cm.   C

2 A cylindrical tin contains 600 cm³ of soup. The radius of the tin is 5 cm. Calculate the height of the tin and the area of metal sheet used to make it.   C

5 A solid gold ring is made from cylindrical wire. The diameter of the wire is 2 mm and the internal diameter of the ring is 18 mm. Estimate the volume of gold in the ring.   A

6 The tunnel shown is 150 m long. Its
section is a segment of a circle radius
5 m. The floor of the tunnel is 8 m wide.
(a) Calculate the height of the tunnel
(b) Calculate the volume of earth
removed when the tunnel was built.
Discuss some of the problems you
would expect to be associated with
digging a similar tunnel under the
channel (approx. 30 miles long).

A

◆B.5 Relationships. Similar figures

If similar figures have sides or diagonals in the
ratio $k:1$, their areas will be in the ratio $k^2:1$ and
their volumes will be in the ratio $k^3:1$.
This is clearly seen on the enlarged cube.

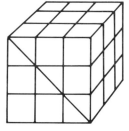

Side and diagonal ratio   3:1
Area of side ratio   9:1
Volume ratio   27:1

This has important consequences in nature (for example, in the weight of
young and mature animals).
The volume: surface area ratio also changes with change in size. This has
many applications from cooking to looking after children. [For example, we
cut up vegetables to help them cook through, and we wrap up babies in cold
weather because they lose their heat more rapidly than adults.]

BUTTER 1kg

BUTTER 8kg

Eskimo baby

Eskimo mother

The baby elephant is already half as high
as its mother but only
⅛ the weight.

Mum

Parsnip
cut for cooking

Parsnip

Exercise B.5

1   The letter 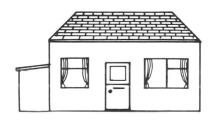 is to be enlarged for a memorial. The letter will be 40 cm high.
    (a) How long will the other two lines of the K be?
    (b) What will be the area of the enlarged letter?   C

2   This drawing of an old person's bungalow is exactly to scale. The door is 2 m high.

    (a) Estimate the width of the bungalow and the height to the top of the roof.
    (b) Make a ground plan of the bungalow allowing for a living room, bedroom, kitchen and bathroom. Would a total floor area of 60 m² be adequate?   C

3   This picture is to be enlarged to make a calendar.

    In the calendar, the diameter of the flower will be roughly 5 cm. What will be the area of the enlarged picture? What is *n* if .... area of original : area of enlargement equals 1 : *n*?   C

4   A model car is an exact replica of the real thing scaled down to one fiftieth, i.e. each measurement of the car is 50 times the same measurement on the toy. The toy is made of the same metal as the car and weighs 16 g. Make an estimate of the weight of the real car.   C

5   A 1 litre packet of fruit juice is cuboid in shape. Its base area being 9 cm × 6 cm.
    (a) Calculate the height of the packet.
    (b) Calculate the dimensions of a 2 litre packet of the same proportions.   B

6   A cylindrical tin, which contains exactly 1 litre of soup, has a base radius equal to 5 cm.
    (a) Calculate the height of the tin.
    (b) The larger size of this soup contains 1·8 litres and is in a tin of the same proportions. Calculate the base radius and height of the larger tin.   A

Examination questions B

You should do these questions before looking at the worked answers on pages 73–88. It may be convenient to take the questions in two sections, questions 1 to 12 and questions 13 to 24.
When you check your answers against the worked answers you must make sure that you understand where you have made mistakes. If you do not understand the worked answer then ask your teacher for help. Remember to rewrite any problems you got wrong first time. Show your working clearly.

1 The volume of a cube is 28 cm³. Calculate its surface area and the length of each edge.

2 (a) Calculate the area of this shape.

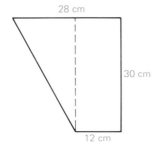

(b) A concrete beam of length 3 metres is made with the above shape as cross section. Calculate in cubic metres, the volume of concrete in the beam.

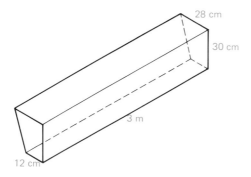

(c) The concrete has a density of 4·5 g/cm³. What is the mass of the beam?

3 A gardener has a lawn 20 m long by 8 m wide. He wants to put fertilizer on his lawn and his gardening book advises 50 g/m².
(a) What weight of fertilizer should he buy?

(b) When he goes to the shop he can only get a packet weighing 5 kg and he spreads this. What is the average weight of fertilizer on each m²?

4 (a) Show that the area between two concentric circles, radius r and R is $\pi(R + r)(R - r)$.

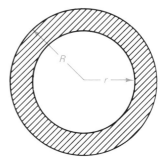

(b) Calculate the volume of material in a cylindrical pipe, 1 metre long whose thickness is 2·5 cm and whose external diameter is 18 cm.

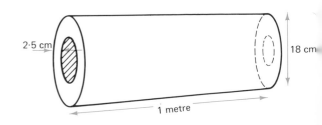

5 A rhombus is cut from a regular hexagon, side 3 cm, leaving a shape as shown (a concave regular hexagon).

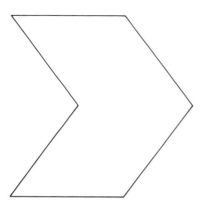

(a) Find the area of the shape.
(b) If the shape is cut out and folded it can be made into a square pyramid (without a base). What is the height of this pyramid?

6 A closed cardboard box is made from a single piece of card by cutting out the shaded pieces in the diagram on the left. It is then folded to make the box on the right.

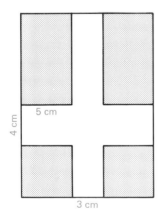

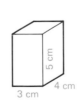

(a) What was the area of the original sheet of cardboard?
(b) What is the surface area of the box?
(c) What is the volume of the box?

7 (a) Calculate the perimeter and area of a rhombus with diagonals 20 cm and 21 cm.
(b) What is the difference between this area and that of a square with both diagonals equal to 20·5 cm?

8 This diagram shows a lawn in the shape of a rectangle from which two semicircles have been removed. The diameters of the semicircles are 11 m and 7 m. Take π as $\frac{22}{7}$ to calculate the perimeter and area of the lawn.

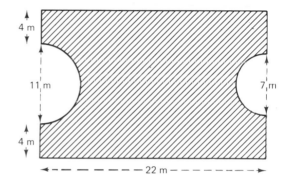

9 A woman builds a concrete ramp to get her car over the pavement. The ramp is a triangular prism as shown.

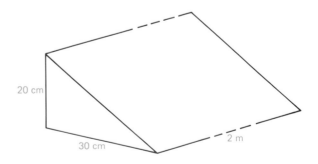

(a) Calculate the volume of concrete required to make the ramp. Give your answer in m³.
(b) The concrete is made from cement and sand in the ratio 1 : 3·5 by volume. How much cement is needed?

10 A circular pack of cheese is 1·4 cm thick. It contains six cheeses and the radius of the pack is 6·5 cm.

(a) The top of each portion is completely covered by a label. Calculate the area of one label (correct to 1 decimal place).
(b) Calculate the total volume of cheese in the pack.
(c) Calculate the cost/100 g given that the density of cheese is 0·9 gm/cm³ and the cost of the whole pack is £1.20.

♦ 11 A tree trunk has a circular core of average radius 30 cm. Each year its diameter increases by 7%.
(a) Calculate the diameter of the tree two years after the core is formed.
(b) What is the volume of wood in the first 4 metres of its trunk at this time?

12 A swimming pool is 10 m wide and 25 m long. The depth of the water increases uniformly from the shallow end, where the water is 1·5 metres deep, to the deep end where the depth is 2·5 metres.
(a) Calculate the volume of water in the pool.
(b) When the pool is emptied for cleaning, water passes through a pipe 8 cm in diameter at 1 metre/second. How long does it take to empty the pool?

13 P, Q, R and S are the mid points of the sides of a quadrilateral ABCD.
Find the relationship between the area of PQRS and the area of ABCD.

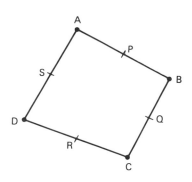

♦ 14 The cuboid in the diagram has edges of length 3 cm, 4 cm and 5 cm.
(a) Calculate the distance from one corner to the opposite one (eg E to C or D to F)
(b) Find the shortest distance from E to C, keeping to the surface of the cuboid

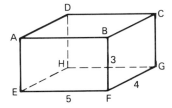

15 Two oranges are bought and compared. The first has an external diameter of 7 cm, 2 mm thick peel and costs 8p, while the second has external diameter of 9 cm, 4 mm thick peel and costs 12p. Which orange is the better value for money, given that only the fruit is used?

16 The metal used in making the walls of a spherical diving bell is 8 cm thick. The internal radius of the bell is 1·02 m.

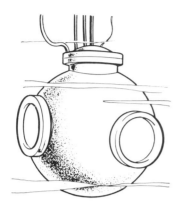

(a) Calculate the volume of the space inside the bell and also the volume of metal used in making it.
(b) Calculate the upthrust on the bell (equal to the mass of water displaced).
(c) Calculate the mass of the bell allowing 5 g/cm³ for the metal and 0·008 g/cm³ for the air inside.
(d) Discuss the results of (b) and (c).

17 A storage tank is made from a hemisphere joined to a cylinder as shown.

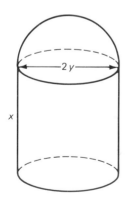

The diameter of both hemisphere and cylinder is 2y cm, and the height of the cylinder is x cm.
(a) Find a formula which expresses the ratio surface area: volume for the tank.
(b) Use your formula in the case x = 50 cm, y = 50 cm.

(c) Calculate a similar ratio for a tank which is the same size, but hemispherical at both ends.
(d) Discuss your results in relation to loss of heat from a hot-water storage tank.

◆ 18 The lampshade in the diagram has a top circumference of 50 cm and a bottom circumference of 80 cm. The sloping height is 30 cm.

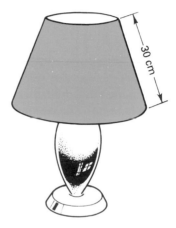

(a) Calculate the area of parchment used in making the lampshade.
(b) Calculate the smallest rectangular area from which the lampshade could be made (by cutting out).

◆ 19 The tuning of a radio is controlled by a cylindrical shaft of 4 cm length and 5 mm radius. This shaft has been cut leaving a plane rectangular surface (shown shaded).

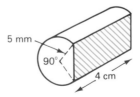

Calculate
(a) the volume of the shaft,
(b) the surface area of the shaft.

20 Use any method you like to estimate the area of this ellipse. It is suggested that $A = \pi ab$ could be a formula for the area of an ellipse. Do your results agree with this?

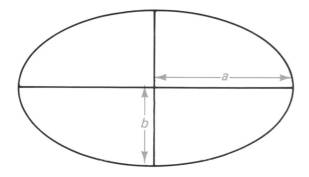

21 Water is carried in a main pipe whose diameter is 15 cm. The water flows along the pipe at 4 m/sec. Calculate the volume of water delivered per second. The pipe is broken during building site work and water is allowed to waste for 24 hours before the break is repaired. How much water is lost (in gallons)?

22 A market gardener needs a 4% solution (4 parts in 100 of water) of a chemical to deal with a plant disease. The chemical is supplied in 5 litre containers. The gardener knows she will need about 600 gallons of the solution altogether. How many containers of chemical should she buy?

23 (a) Calculate the total surface area of a square pyramid whose base is a square of side 8 cm and whose volume is 120 cm³.

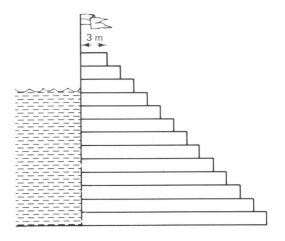

(b) The containing wall of a dam is shown. The height of the wall is 13 m and each layer of wall is 1 metre thicker than the layer above.
The wall is 50 metres wide altogether. Calculate the volume of the wall and also its mass if it is made of concrete with density 2·2 g/cm³.

24 **Channel tunnel expressway**
The proposal for the channel tunnel expressway consisted of twin tunnels, each 11·3 m in diameter and 48 km long. The disposal of the soil and rock would be spread over marshland to an average depth of 5 metres.
(a) Calculate the area which would be covered by the spoil.
(b) Estimate the number of train loads that would be needed to move the spoil, given that each train takes 40 trucks, each containing 22 tonnes [average density of spoil is 3·5 tonnes/m³].

Activities and investigations B

Competition quiz B

A reads out the questions headed 'A's questions for B' and B writes down the answers. Ten minutes are allowed for this. Then B takes the book and reads out the questions headed 'B's questions for A'. Again ten minutes only are allowed. The two people together then use the answers on p 420 to score their answer sheets. The winner is the person with most marks.

A's questions for B

1 What is the perimeter of a rectangle?
2 What is the area of a rectangle with sides equal to a cm and b cm?
3 What is the area of a triangle, base b cm and height h cm?
4 What is the way to find the area of any parallelogram?
5 What is the area of a trapezium, whose parallel sides are a cm and b cm?
6 What shaped rectangle with perimeter 44 cm has the largest area?
7 What shaped triangle, area A cm^2, has the smallest possible perimeter?
8 How many metres are there in 1 kilometre?
9 How many cm^2 in 1 m^2?
10 How many inches in 1 yard?
11 How many square inches in a square foot?
12 How many kg in 1 tonne?

B's questions for A

1 What is the perimeter of a square, side 5 cm?
2 What is the length of side of a square whose area is A cm^2?
3 A triangle has base x cm and height x cm, what is its area?
4 What is the area of a parallelogram base b cm and height h cm?
5 What shape(s) has area equal to 'half the sum of the parallel sides $\times$ distance between them'?
6 What is the area of a rhombus whose diagonals are $2a$ cm and $2b$ cm?
7 A right-angled triangle has perpendicular sides of length 4 cm and 6 cm. What is its area?
8 How many millimetres in a metre?
9 How many centimetres in 1 kilometre?

A's questions for B (cont.)

13 How many pounds in 1 kg?

14 Which months of the year have 30 days?

15 How many seconds in 1 hour?

16 How many days does it take for the earth to complete one orbit round the sun?

17 How many square metres in 1 hectare?

18 What is the volume of a cuboid, length l cm width w cm and height h cm?

19 What is the volume of a prism, length l cm with cross section area equal to A cm²?

20 What is the area of a circle whose diameter is d cm long?

21 If the diameter of a circle is multiplied by its circumference, the result is 4 × what?

22 What is the volume of a cylinder whose base radius is r cm and height = $2r$ cm?

23 What is the curved surface area of a cylinder whose base radius is r cm and height = $2r$ cm?

24 A mother-elephant, weight 4 tonnes, has a baby half her height. Roughly how much does the baby weigh?

B's questions for A (cont.)

10 How many inches in 1 metre?

11 How many grams in 1 kg?

12 How many grams in 1 lb?

13 How many pounds in 1 cwt?

14 How many days in a leap year?

15 How many minutes in a full day?

16 Roughly how long does it take the moon to complete one orbit round the earth?

17 How many square yards in 1 acre?

18 What is the length of side of a cube whose volume is 27 m³?

19 The area of cross section of a prism, volume V cm³, is A cm². What is its length?

20 What is the diameter of a circle whose circumference is 160 cm?

21 What is the volume of a cylinder 1 mm thick whose radius is 12 cm?

22 The curved surface area of a cylinder is A cm² and its radius is r cm. What is its height?

23 A tree trunk is 20 ft long with circumference 10 ft. What is the volume of wood in the trunk?

24 A young giraffe is 12 ft tall. It weighs 7 cwt. Its father is 18 ft tall. Estimate his weight.

The tangram

You probably know the tangram puzzle. It can be very helpful in reminding you about different areas.
This 'tangram' square is 8 cm by 8 cm.
Calculate the area of the square and the areas of each of the seven pieces. Cut out a tangram square and mark each piece with its area.

Tangram game

Each player has a set of tangram pieces with the areas marked on them. A starts by playing any piece from her set and B then plays a piece from his.

- If B's piece has a greater area than A's, B keeps them both.
- If A's piece has a greater area than B's, A keeps them both.
- If both pieces have the same area they are removed from the game.

The player who has just won a piece leads the next round. The winner is the player with the largest area of tangram pieces.

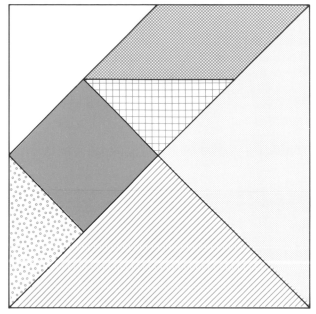

You can develop this game by changing the rules or by dividing the smallest pieces into equal parts (or in any other way that interests you).
Can you divide the square equally between 2, 3 or 4 people?

Puzzles and investigations

These puzzles and investigations will strengthen your understanding of Topic B. Work with a friend. Discuss the problem thoroughly before you attempt your solutions.

1   The fly on the cuboid

A fly lands on a cuboid at A. He wants to go to E.

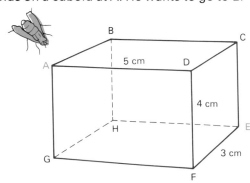

(i) What is his shortest route if he never leaves the surface of the cuboid?
(ii) What is his longest route if he stays on the edges and never repeats a journey?
(iii) How long in cm are his longest and shortest routes?

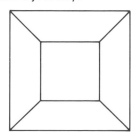

What has this shape got to do with problem (ii)?

65

2 The missing square

● Start with an 8 × 8 square and cut it into four parts marked 1, 2, 3, 4, like the diagram.
● Arrange them in a 5 × 13 rectangle.

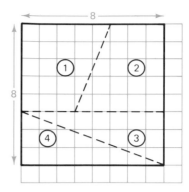

What is the area of the square?
What is the area of the rectangle?
Where **does** the extra square come from?

You can make a similar puzzle out of a 13 × 13 square or out of a 21 × 21 square.

?? What is special about the numbers 5, 8, 13, 21, . . . ?

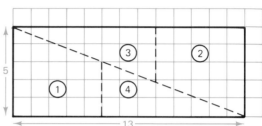

If you enjoyed doing this make a large puzzle to take home and intrigue your family!

3 Pin board . . . and a puzzle

Simple pinboard and rubber band experiments will remind you of all the rules for finding areas.

The areas shown in the figure are 15 sq units, 18 sq units, 16 sq units and 12 sq units.
Which is which?

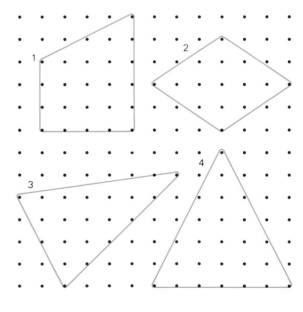

Puzzle

Now find squares with exact areas which are
(i) 20 square units,   (ii) 40 square units,   (iii) 27 square units.

4 Pythagoras ... a new look

You all know Pythagoras' theorem: 'The square
on the hypotenuse equals the sum of the
squares on the other two sides', and you know
its picture.

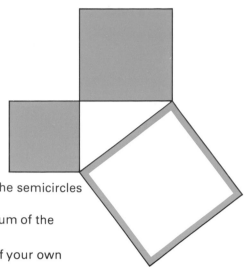

Investigate Pythagoras' theorem for other shapes.

- The equilateral triangle on the hypotenuse is equal to the
  sum of the equilateral triangles on the other two sides.
- The semicircle on the hypotenuse is equal to the sum of the semicircles
  on the other two sides.
- The regular pentagon on the hypotenuse is equal to the sum of the
  regular pentagons on the other two sides.

Draw diagrams first. Test Pythagoras' theorem for shapes of your own
choice! Can you cut them to fit?

5 Shapes in shapes

You can see an equilateral triangle in a square but it is possible to draw one with a bigger area.

?? Can you find the largest triangle that will fit
   into the square?

?? Can you find the largest square that will fit
   into an equilateral triangle?

?? Every triangle has a biggest square inside it.
   Can you find a way to draw it?

?? Every circle has a biggest rectangle inside it.
   Can you find it?

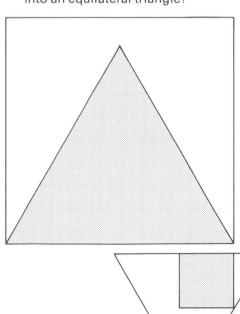

6 Pyramids in a cube

The diagram shows that six equal pyramids can be fitted into a cube.

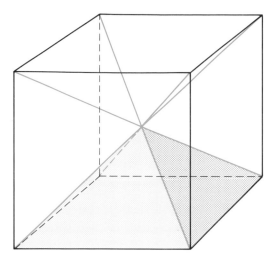

Make a model of this. Choose your own dimension for your cube.

Hint: The sloping edges of the pyramids will all be (0·866 × the edge of the cube).

[If you make the cube as a box you should be able to fit the pyramids in exactly.]

Five tetrahedra will fit exactly into a cube, as shown in the diagram.

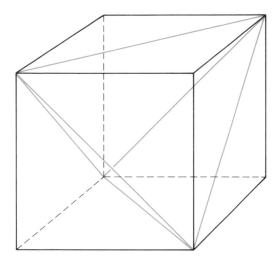

Four of the tetrahedra are all the same size. One tetrahedron is regular (all its sides are equal in length).
Make a model of this situation. Choose your own dimension for the cube.
[If you make the cube as a box you should be able to fit the tetrahedra inside.]

7 A strange shape?

Work out the shape of a solid which would pass exactly through these three holes.

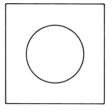
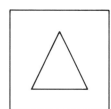
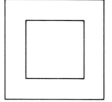

8 Volume investigations

An open box is made by cutting four equal squares from the corners of a square sheet of cardboard. The sides are then folded up.

?? What is the volume of space in the largest box that can be made from a sheet cardboard 100 cm²?

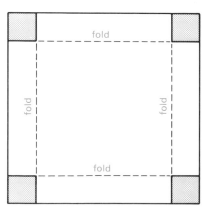

[You can go further and consider starting with a rectangle instead of a square.]

9   The largest volume?

The volume of an ordinary tin can is given by the
formula $V = \pi r^2 h$.
The area of metal sheet used in making the tin is
$A = 2\pi r(r + h)$.

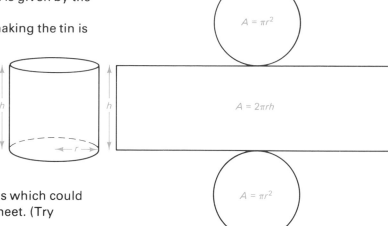

Investigate the volumes of tin cans which could
be made from 100 cm² of metal sheet. (Try
different values for r and h).

Hint: Choose r and h but make sure that
        $2\pi r(r + h)$ is not more than 100.

Team problem solving

When problems are tackled in industry or business the work is usually done
by a team of people, rather than just one person alone. You should therefore
get used to working with other people. The examination encourages this and
it is possible to get some of your marks from work done on a problem
together with other students.

In this section I have suggested a number of problems that can be tackled at
school, making use of mathematics that you already know. You will find
that working on these problems helps a great deal in understanding and
remembering the ordinary mathematics. This work will, therefore, help you
to get better marks in the examination papers as well as marks for special
project work.

Project 1   Rationalising car parking space

Time allowed: 4 double periods

Most schools and colleges are short of car parking space. You could
undertake a study which aims to make more space available for staff cars.
You will need to make a plan of the space available. You will need
information on size of cars, visitors to school, part-time teachers etc. Your
end-product would be a report which would

(a) summarise the information you have found out;

(b) make suggestions and recommendations to help with the problems;

(c) include maps and data.

Project 2 Packaging in the food industry

Time allowed: 4 double periods

This is an investigation of the shapes used in packaging food. You can organise the team to investigate different types of packaging—boxes, bottles, cans, etc. The end-product should be a report plus an exhibition (or poster) so the other students can share in your discoveries.

Look for . . .
- Sizes which are used more often than others.
- Relationships (e.g. is it true that most tins are as tall as their diameters?).
- Packaging . . . how are boxes folded? How does this relate to the way they are filled in the food factory?
- Rules (e.g. some liquids are never packed in glass bottles).
- Waste of resources.

Think about . . .
- The relationship between packaging and transport.
- The relationship between packaging and storage.

Add your own interesting discoveries.

Project 3 Measurement of trees

If you go to school in an area where there are some large trees you might be interested to investigate some of the ideas below.

Problem 1 Finding the height of a tree. I leave you to invent your own methods for doing this.

Problem 2 Estimating the volume of wood in a tree trunk. [Particularly important in forestry.] Use your estimating method to find the largest tree in the neighbourhood.

Problem 3 A mature oak or beech tree requires a lot of ground space. Compare the spaces occupied by different types of large trees.

Product You should present your work as
 (i) methods used,
 (ii) results,
(iii) conclusions.

Project 4   Making a useful plan

Time allowed: 4 double periods

A plan of a school can be very useful, particularly to new pupils; so can a plan of a town centre, especially if the car parks and main shopping areas are marked. The only equipment needed are a surveyor's tape and an instrument for measuring horizontal angles, which can be very simple.

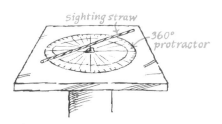

Stage 1: Decide with the rest of your team what plan you want to make.

Stage 2: Ask the teacher for the equipment you need.

Stage 3: Make a 'plan of action'. This will list what everyone is expected to do and when their work will be ready.

Stage 4: Collect up everyone's results and prepare the final piece of work (i.e. the plan itself).

Some suggestions:

(a) Plan of your school.

(b) Plan of a local sports centre.

(c) Plan of the town centre.

(d) Plan of an indoor shopping centre.

(e) Plan of the school library (don't make too much noise!).

(f) Plan of the maths department.

(g) Plan of a local park.

(h) Plan of a nearby F.E. college.

Notes: (i) You may need to standardise your pace. This is done by counting the number of steps you take to walk exactly 100 metres ... and back again. First measure the 100 metres with the surveyor's tape. Walk normally without stretching. The length of your pace will be $200/n$ where n is the number of steps you have taken. Repeat as many times as necessary until you get the same result for $200/n$ twice in a row. Record the length of your pace somewhere safe as you will use it in your work.

(ii) Don't choose too difficult a plan unless you are prepared to work very hard in your own time.

(iii) Make use of existing plans to check your work if they are available. You may find that you can make an existing plan much easier to use.

(iv) When you have made your plan you can use it for other projects. For example, you could study the fire hazards in your school (are there any bottle-necks?) or ways to reduce traffic along the corridors by changing the use of rooms.

Project 5   Fuel consumption

Investigate the fuel consumption of cars, motorbikes, lorries, trains, coaches, aircraft.

- Compare the fuel costs of travel per passenger mile by different methods of transport.
- Compare the fuel consumption of different types of car at different speeds. (Obtain data from brochures and advertisements.)

Suggestion: use graphs.

Present your results in a form that can be understood easily by non-mathematical people.

- As a team, try to find some ideas which would save fuel
   (i) for private car owners,
   (ii) in public transport,
   (iii) in the transport industry.

Note: You will probably need some help from your teacher in collecting data.

Project 6   The channel tunnel

You will need the book 'Channel Fixed Link' (prepared for DoT by Land Use Consultants). Study some of the problems associated with the channel tunnel using the book as a source of data. Present your results to the rest of the class as a summary.

Some suggestions . . .

? What to do with the earth that is to be dug out in the construction of the tunnel. Estimate quantities.
? What quantity of air will need to be pumped through?
? Arrangements to prevent large traffic problems at both ends.
? Number of passengers and weight of freight to be transported (one train every 30 minutes?).
? Costs and recovery of money by charges.

Further ideas for projects*

Measuring things which are very small . . .

(a) Find the thickness of a piece of paper.
(b) Estimate the volume of a drop of water.
(c) Measure the cross section of a pin.
(d) Investigate measuring instruments and gauges (refer to CDT department).

Analysis of newpapers. Work out how much of the paper is devoted to news, sport, pictures, gossip, adverts, etc. (using either column length or area as a measure).

Measurements used in medicine and health care. [Especially useful for people planning to become nurses, doctors, health workers.]

Investigation into the transport industry. Sizes of lorries and vans, packaging of containers, etc.

* These projects could be either for teams or individuals

Worked answers to examination questions B

These are discussions of the examination questions B. Make sure you understand the answer and that you have a copy of it in your own book or file. Some of the calculator sequences may not fit your calculator exactly. If this is the case write out the calculator sequence which gives the correct answer on your own machine.

1 The volume of a cube is 28 cm³. Calculate its surface area and the length of each edge.

Edge = $\sqrt[3]{28}$ cm = 3·04 cm   (correct to 2 decimal places)
Surface = $6 \times 28^{\frac{2}{3}}$ = 55·33 cm²   (correct to 2 decimal places)

Since the solid is a cube the edges will each be the cube root of the volume.
$V = 28 \Rightarrow l = \sqrt[3]{28}$ ... 28 $\boxed{x^{1/y}}$ 3. $\boxed{=}$
or 28 $\boxed{x^y}$ 0·3333 $\boxed{=}$ if you do not have $x^{1/y}$ functions.

Each face will have an area which is the square of the edge.
There are six faces altogether so ... $A = 6 \times [(28)^{1/3}]^2$.
Both answers can be found from one calculator sequence:

28 $\boxed{x^{1/y}}$ 3 $\boxed{=}$ $\boxed{x^2}$ $\boxed{\times}$ 6 $\boxed{=}$
   ↑   ↑
  edge   surface area

2 (a) Calculate the area of this shape.

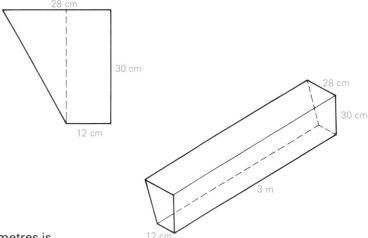

(b) A concrete beam of length 3 metres is made with this shape as cross section. Calculate in cubic metres, the volume of concrete in the beam.

(c) The concrete has a density of 4·5 g/cm³. What is the mass of the beam?

Area: 600 cm²   volume: 0·18 m³   mass: 0·81 tonnes

(a) There are many ways of finding the area so I have given two. Either will do.

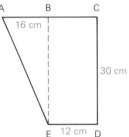

Area of BCDE = 360 cm²
Area of △ABE = $\frac{1}{2}$ × 16 × 30 = 240 cm²
Total area = 600 cm²

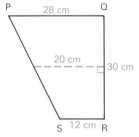

Since PQRS is a trapezium:
Area = $\frac{1}{2}$(28 + 12) × 30
$\qquad$ = 20 × 30
$\qquad$ = 600 cm²

The area is the average of the parallel sides times the perpendicular distance between them.

(b) The volume of the prism equals area of cross section × length.
V = 600 cm² × 300 cm = 180 000 cm³
$\qquad\qquad\qquad\quad$ = 0·18 m³
As the question asks for volume in metres cubed, remember that
1 000 000 cm³ = 1 m³

(c) The mass = volume × density
$\qquad\qquad$ = 180 000 × 4·5 g
$\qquad\qquad$ = 810 000 g
$\qquad\qquad$ = 0·81 tonnes
● Density can be expressed as 4·5 g/cm³ or 4·5 tonnes/m³

3 A gardener has a lawn 20 m long by 8 m wide. He wants to put fertilizer on his lawn and his gardening book advises 50 g/m².
(a) What weight of fertilizer should be buy?
(b) When he goes to the shop he can only get a packet weighing 5 kg and he spreads this. What is the average weight of fertilizer on each m²?

(a) 8 kg $\quad$ (b) 31·25 g

The area of the lawn is 20 × 8 = 160 m².
Weight of fertilizer required is thus 160 × 50 = 8 000 g = 8 kg.
If he can only buy 5 kg he will only be able to spread $\frac{5}{8}$ of 50 g on each m².
$\frac{5}{8}$ × 50 = 31·25 g per m²

4 (a) Show that the area between two
concentric circles, radius r and R is
$\pi(R + r)(R - r)$.

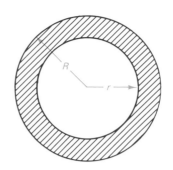

(b) Calculate the volume of material in a
cylindrical pipe, 1 metre long whose
thickness is 2·5 cm and whose external
diameter is 18 cm.

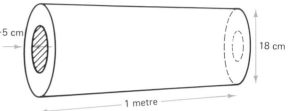
2·5 cm / 18 cm / 1 metre

(a) Area of large circle = πR^2
Area of small circle = πr^2
Area of ring = $\pi R^2 - \pi r^2 = \pi(R^2 - r^2)$
= $\pi(R + r)(R - r)$

(b) 12 174 cm^3

(a) Note that the whole argument is required for the answer as this
question says "Show that ... ".

(b) First find the area of cross section by using the formula in (a). You
need to find R and r first.
Clearly $R = 9$ cm and $r = 6·5$ cm.
$A = \pi(9 + 6·5)(9 - 6·5) = \pi \times 15·5 \times 2·5$ cm^2
Volume = area of cross section × length
= $\pi \times 15·5 \times 2·5 \times 100$
= 12 174 cm^3

5 A rhombus is cut from a regular hexagon,
side 3 cm, leaving a shape as shown (a
concave regular hexagon).
(a) Find the area of the shape.
(b) If the shape is cut out and folded it can
be made into a square pyramid (without
a base). What is the height of this
pyramid?

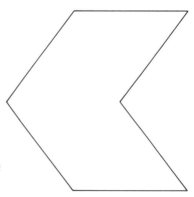

(a) 15·59 cm^2 (b) 2·12 cm

(a) The shape is made up of 4 equilateral triangles of side 3 cm.
Each triangle's area is $\frac{1}{2} \times 3 \times 3 \times \sin 60°$ (from the formula
$\frac{1}{2}ab \sin C$).
Thus the whole area is $4 \times \frac{1}{2} \times 3 \times 3 \times \sin 60° = 18 \sin 60$ cm^2
= 15·59 cm^2

(b) The height of the pyramid is also the height of a triangle whose base is a diagonal of the pyramid's base and whose sides, XY and XZ, are each 3 cm long.

YZ is also a diagonal of a square, side 3 cm, so its length is $3\sqrt{2}$ cm.

Pythagoras (inverse) shows that there is a right angle at X.

So (i) YZ is the diagonal of a square side 3 cm (which we knew anyway),

and (ii) h is half of the other diagonal, so

$$h = \frac{3\sqrt{2}}{2} = 2 \cdot 12 \text{ cm.}$$

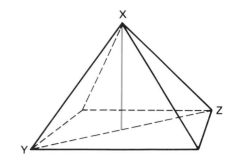

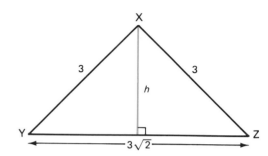

Note: There are many ways of approaching the above problem and you should discuss them with your teacher. One of the most interesting is to realise that the pyramid is half of a regular octahedron.

The symmetry demonstrates that the height of your pyramid must be half a diagonal of the square base.

Make a regular octahedron and study it.

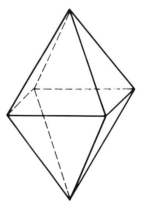

6 A cardboard box is made from a single piece of cardboard. The net is made by cutting out the shaded places in the diagram on the left. It is then folded to make the box on the right.

(a) What was the area of the original sheet of cardboard?

(b) What is the surface area of the box?

(c) What is the volume of the box?

(a) 234 cm² (b) 94 cm² (c) 60 cm³

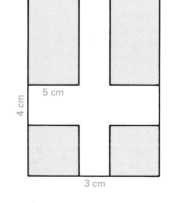

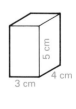

This question requires a little thought.
There must be two 3 cm × 4 cm faces
                two 3 cm × 5 cm faces
            and two 4 cm × 5 cm faces
It is possible to deduce the length of the cardboard to be 18 cm and its width to be 13 cm.
[The deduced measurements are shown in colour.]

(a) Area of card = 13 cm × 18 cm = 234 cm².

(b) Surface of box = 2(12) + 2(15) + 2(20) cm²
                   = 94 cm².

(c) Volume = 3 cm × 4 cm × 5 cm = 60 cm³.

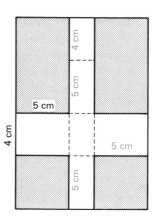

The value of (b) can be checked by subtracting the areas shaded from 234 cm², ie 234 − 2(45) − 2(25) and this should equal the surface area of the box.

7 (a) Calculate the perimeter and area of a rhombus with diagonals 20 cm and 21 cm.

(b) What is the difference between this area and that of a square with both diagonals equal to 20·5 cm?

(a) Perimeter = 58 cm   Area = 210 cm²   (b) 0·125 cm²

Pythagoras' theorem is used to find a side of the rhombus.

$$\text{Side} = \sqrt{10^2 + (10\cdot5)^2}$$
$$= \sqrt{100 + 110\cdot25}$$
$$= \sqrt{210\cdot25} = 14\cdot5 \text{ cm}$$

Perimeter = 4 × 14·5 = 58 cm
Area = $4 \times \frac{1}{2} \times 10 \times 10\cdot5$ = 210 cm²

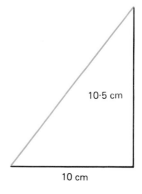

For the square, the side = 10·25 × $\sqrt{2}$ = 14·495689
    While the area = 2 × 10·25 × 10·25 = 210·125 cm²
Thus the square is 0·125 cm² larger in area, but its perimeter is 0·017 cm smaller than the rhombus.

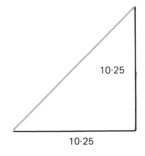

8 This diagram shows a lawn in the shape of a rectangle from which two semicircles have been removed. The diameters of the semi-circles are 11 m and 7 m. Take π as $\frac{22}{7}$ to calculate the perimeter and area of the lawn.

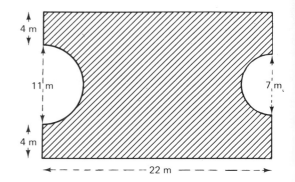

Perimeter = 92·3 cm   Area = 351·25 cm²

The perimeter consists of the two long straight edges, the four short straight edges and the two semicircles.
Perimeter = 44 + 8 + 12 + ($\pi \times 5\cdot5 + \pi \times 3\cdot5$)
           = 64 + $\pi \times 9$ 64 ⊞ 22 ⊟ 7 ⊠ 9 ⊜
           = 92·3 cm
The area is the area of the whole rectangle minus the two semicircles.
Area = 22 × 19 − [$\frac{1}{2}\pi \times 5\cdot5^2 + \frac{1}{2}\pi \times 3\cdot5^2$]
     = 418 − (47·5 + 19·25) = 351·25 cm²

● It is essential to write these things down in the examination.

9 A woman builds a concrete ramp to get her car over the pavement. The ramp is a triangular prism as shown.
(a) Calculate the volume of concrete required to make the ramp. Give your answer in m³.
(b) The concrete is made from cement and sand in the ratio 1:3·5 by volume. How much cement is needed?

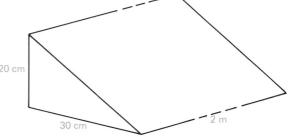

(a) 0·06 m³   (b) Volume of cement = 0·0133 m³

The cross section is a simple half rectangle.
Its area is $\frac{1}{2} \times 20 \times 30 = 300$ cm².

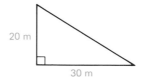

The volume of the prism is found by multiplying area of section by length:
V = 300 × 200 = 60 000 cm³
In cubic metres, 1 m³ = 10⁶ cm³, so 60 000 cm³ = 60 000 ÷ 10⁶ m³
                                              = 0·06 m³
Watch out for units! The length of the prism must be in the same units as the cross section. Thus I have changed 2 m into 200 cm when

calculating the volume. This is then converted into cubic metres because the question demands it.

Cement : Sand = 1 : 3·5 so that the volume of cement is 1/4·5 or $\frac{2}{9}$ of the total volume . . .
$\frac{2}{9} \times 0·06 = 0·01333 \ldots$ cubic metres.

10 A circular pack of cheese is 1·4 cm thick. It contains six cheeses and the radius of the pack is 6·5 cm.
  (a) The top of each portion is completely covered by a label. Calculate the area of one label (correct to 1 decimal place).
  (b) Calculate the total volume of cheese in the pack.
  (c) Calculate the cost/100 g given that the density of cheese is 0·9 gm/cm³ and the cost of the whole pack is £1.20.

  (a) 22·1 cm²   (b) 185·8 cm³   (c) 72p

  Consider the whole circular pack of cheese.
  Area of top $= \pi r^2 = \pi \times (6·5)^2 = 132·7$ cm²
  Surface area of 1 label = area ÷ 6 = 22·1 cm²
  Volume of cheese = area × thickness
    $= 132·7 \times 1·4 = 185·8$ cm³
  Mass of cheese = volume × density
    $= 185·8 \times 0·9 = 167·2$ g.   This costs 120p.
  Thus 100 g costs $\dfrac{100}{167·2} \times 120 = 71·75$ or   72p.

11 A tree trunk has a circular core of average radius 30 cm. Each year its diameter increases by 7%.
  (a) Calculate the diameter of the tree two years after the core is formed.
  (b) What is the volume of wood in the first 4 metres of its trunk at this time?

  (a) 68·69 cm   (b) 1·48 m³

  This is like a compound interest question.
  The diameter increases 7% each year.
  Thus, at the end of the second year the diameter is $60 \times (1·07)^2 = 68·69$ cm

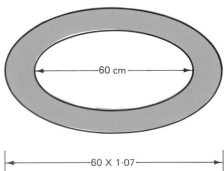
60 cm

60 × 1·07

The volume is $\pi r^2 h$.
Thus $V = \pi \times (68·69 \div 2)^2 \times 400$ cm³
  $= \dfrac{\pi \times 34·345^2 \times 400}{1\,000\,000}$ m³
  $= 1·48$ m³
  $\pi \;\boxed{\times}\; 34·345 \;\boxed{x^2}\;\boxed{=}\;\boxed{\times}\;400\;\boxed{=}\;\boxed{\div}\;10\;\boxed{x^y}\;6\;\boxed{=}$

12 A swimming pool is 10 m wide and 25 m long. The depth of the water
increases uniformly from the shallow end, where the water is
1·5 metres deep, to the deep end where the depth is 2·5 metres.
   (a) Calculate the volume of water in the pool.
   (b) When the pool is emptied for cleaning, water passes through a pipe
   8 cm in diameter at 1 metre/second. How long does it take to
   empty the pool?

(a) 500 m³   (b) 27·6 hours

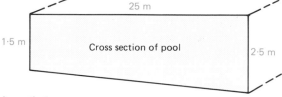

25 m

1·5 m

Cross section of pool

2·5 m

   (a) The cross section area of the pool is
   average depth × length. This equals
   2 × 25 = 50 m². The volume of water
   equals cross section × width =
   50 × 10 = 500 m³
   (b) Each second a cylinder of water, radius 4 cm, length 1 m passes
   through the pipe, ie $\pi \times 16 \times 100$ cm³.
   Time to empty the pool is therefore

$$(500 \times 10^6) \div (\pi \times 16 \times 100) \text{ seconds}$$
$$= (500 \times 10^6) \div (\pi \times 16 \times 100 \times 3600) \text{ hours}$$
$$= 27 \cdot 6 \text{ hours}$$

On my calculator ... 500 [Exp] 6 [÷] π [÷] 16 [÷] 36 [Exp] 4 [=]

500 [Exp] 6   puts 500×10^6 into the calculator.

   ● Care with units

13 P, Q, R and S are the mid points of the sides
of a quadrilateral ABCD.
Find the relationship between the area of
PQRS and the area of ABCD.

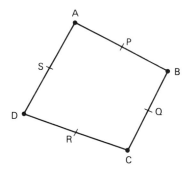

The area of PQRS is exactly half that of
ABCD.

Since no details of ABCD are given, the
question suggests that the relationship will
be the same for all quadrilaterals.
Investigating a rectangle shows that PQRS
is $\frac{1}{2}$ ABCD in this case.

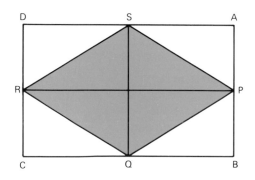

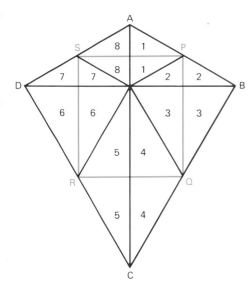

The above diagram shows the eight pairs of equal area triangles in ABCD. One of each pair is inside PQRS.

Note: Proof is not required as the question says 'Find ... '.

14 The cuboid in the diagram has sides of length 3 cm, 4 cm and 5 cm.

(a) Calculate the distance from one corner to the opposite one (eg E to C or D to F)

(b) Find the shortest distance from E to C, keeping to the surface of the cuboid.

(a) $\sqrt{50}$ (b) $\sqrt{74}$

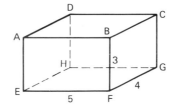

(a) Consider $\triangle$EGC. $\hat{F}$ and $\hat{G}$ are right angles.

$EG^2 = 5^2 + 4^2$

$EC^2 = EG^2 + 3^2 = 5^2 + 4^2 + 3^2$

$EC^2 = 50 \Rightarrow EC = \sqrt{50}$

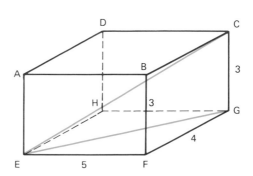

(b) Think about the cuboid opened out into its net. The shortest distance from E to C is across AB as shown. This length is $\sqrt{5^2 + 7^2} = \sqrt{74}$. The other route is longer. [You might try to find an even shorter route by opening up the cuboid in a different way.]

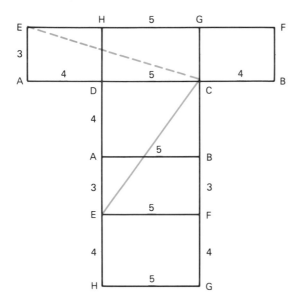

15 Two oranges are bought and compared. The first has an external diameter of 7 cm, 2 mm thick peel and costs 8p, while the second has external diameter of 9 cm, 4 mm thick peel and costs 12p. Which orange is the better value for money, given that only the fruit is used?

12p orange is better value

The volume of fruit in each orange is calculated. Then the number of cm³ per penny is found.
The tabulation of this question will not earn marks but it makes you less liable to error.

		8p	12p
diameter	=	7 cm	9 cm
radius	=	3·5 cm	4·5 cm
internal radius	=	3·3 cm	4·1 cm
volume	=	$\frac{4}{3}\pi \times 3\cdot3^3$	$\frac{4}{3}\pi \times 4\cdot1^3$
calculated V	=	150·53 cm³	288·7 cm³
volume per 1p	=	$\frac{V}{8} = 18\cdot8$ cm³	$\frac{V}{12} = 24\cdot06$ cm³

Clearly the larger orange gives more fruit per penny.

16 The metal used in making the walls of a
spherical diving bell is 8 cm thick. The
internal radius of the bell is 1·02 m.

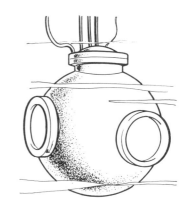

   (a) Calculate the volume of the space inside
   the bell and also the volume of metal
   used in making it.
   (b) Calculate the upthrust on the bell (equal
   to the mass of water displaced).
   (c) Calculate the mass of the bell allowing
   5 g/cm³ for the metal and 0·008 g/cm³
   for the air inside.
   (d) Discuss the results of (b) and (c).

   (a) 4·445 m³, 1·13 m³   (b) 5·575 tonnes   (c) 5·685 tonnes
   (d) (b) and (c) are very close so that it is easy to move the diving bell
   down into the sea.
   Note that this question has not made any allowance for different
   density of glass, etc.

   1∅ Internal radius 1·02 m
   2∅ Internal volume = $\frac{4}{3}\pi r^3 = \frac{4}{3}\pi(1·02)^3 = 4·445$ m³
   3∅ External radius 1·10 m
   4∅ External volume = $\frac{4}{3}\pi r^3 = \frac{4}{3}\pi(1·1)^3 = 5·575$ m³
   5∅ Upthrust = 5·575 tonnes
   6∅ Volume of metal . . . 4∅ − 2∅ . . . = 1·130 m³
   7∅ Mass of metal = 1·130 × 5 = 5·65 tonnes
   8∅ Mass of air = 0·008 × 4·445 = 0·036 tonnes
   9∅ Mass of bell . . . 7∅ + 8∅ . . . 5·686 tonnes

17 A storage tank is made from a hemisphere
joined to a cylinder as shown.
The diameter of both hemisphere and
cylinder is 2y cm, and the height of the
cylinder is x cm.

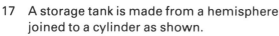

   (a) Find a formula which expresses the
   ratio surface area : volume for the tank.
   (b) Use your formula in the case $x = 50$ cm,
   $y = 50$ cm.
   (c) Calculate a similar ratio for a tank which
   is the same size, but hemispherical at
   both ends.
   (d) Discuss your results in relation to loss of
   heat from a hot-water storage tank.

   (a) $\dfrac{3(3y + 2x)}{y(3x + 2y)}$ (b) $\dfrac{3}{50}$ (c) $\dfrac{6(2y + x)}{y(4y + 3x)}, \dfrac{18}{350}$
   (d) The tank with only one hemisphere has a greater surface area/
   volume ratio and so will lose heat more quickly.

This question is best organised by a tabulation.

radius: y

height of cylinder: x

	one sperical end	two spherical ends
Volume	top: $\frac{2}{3}\pi y^3$ cylinder: $\pi y^2 x$	both ends: $\frac{4}{3}\pi y^3$ cylinder: $\pi y^2 x$
Surface area	top: $2\pi y^2$ cylinder: $2\pi yx$ base: πy^2	top: $2\pi y^2$ cylinder: $2\pi yx$ bottom (spherical): $2\pi y^2$
SA/V	$\dfrac{\pi y(3y + 2x)}{\frac{1}{3}\pi y^2(2y + 3x)}$	$\dfrac{2\pi y(2y + x)}{\frac{1}{3}\pi y^2(4y + 3x)}$
Simplified ratio	$\dfrac{3(3y - 2x)}{y(2y + 3x)}$	$\dfrac{6(2y + x)}{y(4y + 3x)}$
If $x = 50$, $y = 50$	$\dfrac{3}{50} \times \dfrac{250}{250} = \dfrac{3}{50} = \dfrac{21}{350}$	$\dfrac{6}{50} \times \dfrac{150}{350} = \dfrac{18}{350}$

18 The lampshade in the diagram has a top circumference of 50 cm and a bottom circumference of 80 cm. The sloping height is 30 cm.

(a) Calculate the area of parchment used in making the lampshade.

(b) Calculate the smallest rectangular area from which the lampshade could be made (by cutting out).

Area of parchment = 1 950 cm²   Area of rectangle = 2 770 cm²

The solution of this problem depends on drawing a good diagram and then developing, step by step.

1∅ Find the length of XA and XB (marked x). XDC is an enlargement of XAB.

11 So $\dfrac{x}{50} = \dfrac{x + 30}{80}$

12 $\Rightarrow 80x = 50(x + 30)$

13 $\Rightarrow 30x = 1500$

14 $\Rightarrow \quad x = 50$

2∅ The result $x = 50$ shows that $\hat{X}$ is special. It is the angle that gives arc length equal to radius. This angle is 57·3°. [The exact value of the angle is $\dfrac{360}{2\pi}$ and it is called 1 radian.]

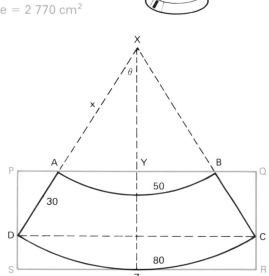

3∅ Area of any sector is $\frac{1}{2} \times$ radius $\times$ arc

31 Area of sector AXB $= \frac{1}{2} \times 50 \times 50 = 1250$ cm^2

32 Area of sector CXD $= \frac{1}{2} \times 80 \times 80 = 3200$ cm^2

33 Area of ABCD $= 3200 - 1250 = 1950$ cm^2

4∅ PQRS is the smallest rectangle from which the parchment can be cut. The problem is to find lengths QR and RS.

41 QR $=$ YZ $=$ XZ $-$ XY

42 XZ $= 80$ cm

43 XY $= 50 \cos \theta$ where $\theta = \frac{1}{2}$ AX̂B.

44 XY $= 50 \cos \frac{1}{2} \left(\dfrac{360}{2\pi} \right) = 50 \cos \dfrac{90}{\pi}$

   $= 43{\cdot}88$ cm ... $90 \boxed{\div} \pi \boxed{=} \boxed{\cos} \boxed{\times} 50 \boxed{=}$

45 YZ $= 80 - 43{\cdot}88 = 36{\cdot}12$ cm

46 RS $=$ DC $= 2 \times 80 \sin \dfrac{90}{\pi}$

   $= 76{\cdot}71$ cm ... $90 \boxed{\div} \pi \boxed{=} \boxed{\sin} \boxed{\times} 160 \boxed{=}$

47 Area of PQRS $= 36{\cdot}12 \times 76{\cdot}71 = 2\,770$ cm^2

Notes: (a) This question requires a number of different mathematical skills and is revising trigonometry as well as mensuration.

   (b) With your calculator it is just as easy to use $90/\pi$ for the angle as to make an approximation to $\frac{1}{2}$ (57·3°), and the result is more accurate.

19 The tuning of a radio is controlled by a cylindrical shaft of **4 cm** length and **5 mm** radius. The shaft has been cut leaving a plane rectangular surface (shown shaded). Calculate

(a) the volume of the shaft,

(b) the surface area of the shaft.

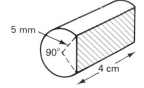

Volume: 2 856·2 mm^3 Surface area: 1368·1 mm^2

1∅ Area of cross section is $\frac{3}{4}$ of the circle plus the right angled triangle.

11 $A = \left(\frac{3}{4} \times \pi \times 25 \right) + \dfrac{25}{2} = 71{\cdot}4$ mm^2

2∅ Volume $= A \times l = 71{\cdot}4 \times 40$ mm^3 ... $= 2856$ mm^3
   [4 cm $\rightarrow$ 40 mm]

3∅ Surface area is made up of 4 distinct areas.

   (i) the curved part ($\frac{3}{4}$ of the curved surface of a cylinder),

   (ii) & (iii) the ends of the shaft,

   (iv) the flat part.

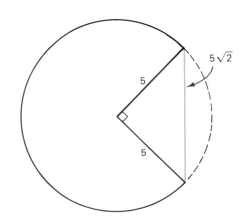

31 Curved area =
$(\frac{3}{4} \times 2 \times \pi \times 5 \times 40)$ mm² = 942·5 mm²
32 Ends ... 2 × 71·4 = 142·8 mm²
33 Flat rectangle $5\sqrt{2} \times 40$ = 282·8 mm²
34 Total area = 1368·1 mm²

20 Use any method you like to estimate the
area of this ellipse. It is suggested that
$A = \pi ab$ could be a formula for the area of
an ellipse. Do your results agree with this?

πab gives a good estimate of the area

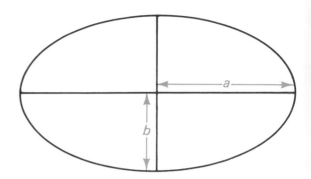

It is only necessary to measure one quarter
of the ellipse. This shape can be divided in
various ways. I have divided the base into
6 parts each approximately 6 mm wide.
This gives six trapezia whose areas are found
by 'average height × base'.

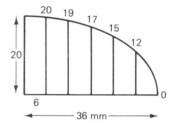

   6 × 20 6 × 19·5 6 × 18 6 × 16 6 × 13·5 6 × 6
  (120 + 117   +   108 + 96 + 81   +   36) = **558 mm²**

Total area of ellipse ≃ 4 × 558 = 2232 mm²

$\pi ab = \pi \times 20 \times 36$ = 2262 mm²

Thus πab gives a result which is very close to my experimental result.

● A good ruler is a great help in this question.

21 Water is carried in a main pipe whose diameter is 15 cm. The water
flows along the pipe at 4 m/sec. Calculate the volume of water
delivered per second. The pipe is broken during building site work and
water is allowed to waste for 24 hours before the break is repaired.
How much water is lost (in gallons)?

(a) 70·6 litres per second   (b) 1 341 803 gallons

The water delivered per second consists of a cylinder 4 m long with
15 cm diameter.
Volume = $\pi \times (7·5)^2 \times 400$ ... keeping cm as unit
       = 70 685 cm³
       = 70·6 litres per second.
Volume of water lost = 70·6 × 60 × 60 × 24 litres in 24 hours
             = 6 099 840 litres
Since 1 gallon = 4·546 litres
Volume lost = 6 099 840 ÷ 4·546
         = 1 341 803 gallons

22 A market gardener needs a 4% solution (4 parts in 100 of water) of a chemical to deal with a plant disease. The chemical is supplied in 5 litre containers. The gardener knows she will need about 600 gallons of the solution altogether. How many containers of chemical should she buy?

22 containers

600 gallons of solution = 600 × 4·546 = 2 727·6 litres
4% solution ... 2727·6 × 0·04 litres of chemical
Number of 5 litre containers = (2727·6 × 0·04) ÷ 5
= 21·82
So 22 containers are needed.

23 (a) Calculate the total surface area of a square pyramid whose base is a square of side 8 cm and whose volume is 120 cm^3.

(b) The containing wall of a dam is shown. The height of the wall is 13 m and each layer of wall is 1 metre thicker than the layer above.
The wall is 50 metres wide altogether. Calculate the volume of the wall and also its mass if it is made of concrete with density 2·2 g/cm^3.

(a) 174·4 cm^2
(b) Volume = 5 850 m^3
Mass = 12 870 tonnes

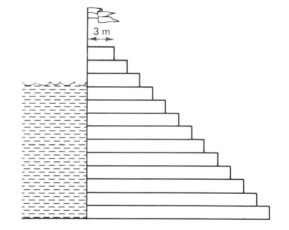

The approach to this problem is first to find the height of the pyramid and then the altitude of one triangular face. The surface area can then be calculated.

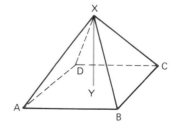

1Ø Volume of a pyramid =
$\frac{1}{3}$ × area of base × height
11 $120 = \frac{1}{3} \times 64 \times h$
12 $h = 360 \div 64 = 5\cdot625$ cm.
2Ø Y is the centre of the square base, T is the centre of AB, YT = 4 cm.
21 From Pythagoras' theorem in △XYT
$XT = \sqrt{XY^2 + YT^2}$
$= \sqrt{(5\cdot625)^2 + 4^2}$
22 $\Rightarrow XT = 6\cdot9$ cm

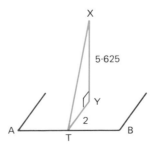

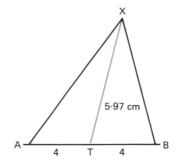

30 Area of △AXB = $\frac{1}{2}$ × base × altitude
$= \frac{1}{2} \times 8 \times 6 \cdot 9$
$= 27 \cdot 6 \text{ cm}^2$

31 Surface area of
pyramid = (4 × 27·6) + 64

sloping sides   base

32 Total surface = 174·4 cm²

(b) The thickness of each 'step' is 1 metre.
Area of section = (3 + 4 + 5 + ... + 15) × 1 = 117 m²
Volume of wall = 117 × 50 = 5 850 m³
Mass of wall   = 5 850 × 2·2 tonnes
               = 12 870 tonnes
This question ignores the problem of the 'ends' of the wall.

24 Channel tunnel expressway

The proposal for the channel tunnel expressway consisted of twin
tunnels, each 11·3 m in diameter and 48 km long. The disposal of the
soil and rock would be spread over marshland to an average depth
of 5 metres.
(a) Calculate the area which would be covered by the spoil.
(b) Estimate the number of train loads that would be needed to move
the spoil, given that each train takes 40 trucks, each containing
22 tonnes [average density of spoil is 3·5 tonnes/m³].

(a) Approximately 2 km² (1·92 km²)   (b) 38 291 train loads

(a) Volume of spoil = $2 \times \pi \times \left(\frac{11 \cdot 3}{2}\right)^2 \times 48\,000 \text{ m}^3$

$= 9\,627\,599 \cdot 182 \text{ m}^3$
$\simeq 9\,627\,600 \text{ m}^3$

Area of land covered = V ÷ 5
$= 1\,925\,520 \text{ m}^2$
$= 192 \text{ hectares}$
$= 1 \cdot 92 \text{ km}^2$

(b) Each train would take 880 tonnes of spoil
Total mass of spoil = 9 627 600 × 3·5 tonnes
Number of trains   = mass of spoil ÷ 880
= 38 291 train loads

Notes: (i) These figures would be rounded to roughly 2 km² and
40 000 train loads as the estimates would all be
approximations.
(ii) It is interesting to work out how many years it would take to
move the spoil at (say) 1 train every hour. Possibly this
could be compared with the number of lorry journeys
needed if the spoil were to be moved by road!

Topic C   The world of money

Contents

Obtaining money; taxation; spending money; housing; buying food; saving and borrowing; making financial decisions

Self assessment

As you know, the purpose of this task is to find out whether or not you need revision on Topic C. If not you can go straight on to the next topic. There is no time limit on this task.

- Make a table in your book, like the one on page vi. You need space for 28 questions.
- Write down your answers to all the following questions.
- When you have finished calculate your score from the answers on page 421.
- If you score more than 80% go on to Topic D self assessment (pp. 127–136).

1 George and Abdul do the same job but George is paid £205 a week while Abdul is paid £11 000 a year. Who is better paid and by how much?

2 The rate for working on a telephone switchboard is £5·40 per hour for a 36-hour week. Extra time is paid at £8·10 per hour (time and a half). An operator works 51 hours in one week. How much does he earn?

3 The average weekly wages for miners in different countries are given in the table.
   (a) Which miners earn the highest wages?
   (b) Which miners are paid the least?

Country	Basic weekly wage (average)	Currency	Rate of exchange for £1
France	1900 F	franc	11·2
Germany	1073 DM	Deutschmark	3·7
Spain	40 000 p	peseta	270
Italy	425 000 L	lira	2500
UK	£180	pound	1

4 A girl is paid £132 before tax each week. Her employers change their payment system to monthly payments by cheque. How much is her new monthly payment before tax?

5 A job carries a salary of £8250 p.a. Work out the income tax you would expect to pay if you have a personal allowance of £3000 and the rate of tax is 30%.

6 Fostershire Council rates are £1.40 in the £1. Wayne lives in Fostershire in a flat whose rateable value is £350. How much does he have to pay in rates?

7 The table below gives the weekly wages and total allowances for three workers. Work out the income tax deducted per week for each person.

Name	Allowances	Income
Ali	£3000	£120 per week
Gill	£4850	£170 per week
Dave	£4500	£190 per week

8 Mr Peabody earns £10 500 a year and Mrs Peabody earns £12 450 a year. They each claim an allowance of £2400 (the personal allowance). Copy and complete the calculations below.

	Earnings	Allowances
Mr P:	£10 500	£2400
Mrs P:	£12 450	£2400

Total earnings	……	(a)
Total allowances	……	(b)
Taxable income	……	(c)

Tax payable at 30% is £…… (d)

9 A new tennis racquet costs £75 + VAT (15%). What is the cost including VAT?

10 What is the total cost including VAT at 15% of a repair job on a car? The bill is made up of
Parts … £65 + VAT
Labour … £40 + VAT

11 A radio costs £155·25 including VAT (at 15%). What is the cost before tax?

12 The price of a cooker including VAT at 15% is £322. What difference will it make to the price if VAT is raised to 25% at the next budget?

13 At the butcher's meat is sold fresh, or frozen in large quantities. 5 lb of minced beef (frozen) costs £3·95. Fresh minced beef costs 95p per lb. How much money is saved by buying the 5 lb pack?

14 The diagram shows the readings on Mrs Khan's electricity meter on 1 July and 1 October. How many units had been used?

| 1 | 2 | 5 | 9 | 8 | 1 July

| 1 | 3 | 1 | 7 | 9 | 1 October

The bill includes a fixed charge of £7·50 and a charge of 6·5p per unit. What is the total bill for the quarter?

15 A family's income is £160 per week. They spend the amounts shown below:
Food, £36; Transport; £16·50; Rent, £45;
Fuel, £17·20; Rates, £15.
How much money is left over for other things?

16 It is said that 'two can live as cheaply as one'. Make a list of the expenses which would be the same for two people as for one. Make another list of those items which could not be shared.

17 Wire netting costs £45 for 50 metres. How much would you expect to pay for 20 ft?
[1 metre = 3·3 ft.]

18 An ordinary tube of toothpaste costs 85p for 150 ml. The same toothpaste in a 'dispenser' costs £1·40 for 200 ml. Which is better value?

19 At Christmas a box of apples weighing 20 kg can be bought for £14. How does this compare with another box weighing 28 lb which costs £10? [1 kg = 2·205 lb]

20 Salt can be bought in 250 g, 500 g or 2 lb packets. The prices are 25p, 40p and 88p. Which is the best value for money?
[1 kg = 1000 g = 2·205 lb]

21 A pair of boots, usually £38·50, is offered for sale at £27. How much has been knocked off the price?

22 The usual price for some cassette tapes is £7·70 for a packet of 5. They are offered for sale at 30% discount. What is the discounted price?

23 Most people are drawn to a 'special offer' because they think it is a bargain. The truth may be that the article is on special offer because it is hard to sell. What would you think of these special offers … ?

A car costing £100.

A record costing 25p.

A suit costing £20.

Shoes costing £1 per pair.

24 A typewriter can be bought for £160 cash or on hire purchase by either
(a) 12 payments of £16 per month, or
(b) 18 payments of £12·50 per month, or
(c) 24 payments of £9·50 per month.
Work out the additional cost for each type of HP payment. Which method of payment would you choose? Give your reasons.

25 Ms McQueen has £750 in a savings account. The account pays 6% interest per annum. How much does the money earn in interest during 3 years?

26 Mr King borrows £260 from his bank. The rate of interest is 16% p.a. What interest is payable after 1 year? Mr King leaves the loan for five years without paying any interest. How much does he have to pay to clear the debt then? [Remember: The bank adds the interest to the loan each year.]

27 David is working at a job which pays him £140 a week (after tax). He puts 20% of his wages into a building society each week. How long will it be before he has saved £500, not counting the interest?

28 Pat and Gill are saving to buy a flat. They save £1400 each and leave it invested for five years at 8% compound interest. Copy and complete the table to show how their money grows during the five years.

	Balance on 1 Jan	Interest at 8% p.a.	Balance on 31 Dec
1987	£2800	£224	£3024
1988	£3024	£241·92	
1989			
1990			
1991			

Key facts C

This set of key facts is divided into seven sections; there is a lot of information in this topic which will be useful to you all your life, as well as in passing your examinations.

C.1 Obtaining money

All people, once they are responsible for themselves, need money to live on.

Money comes from: wages … money paid each week
salary … money paid each month   Employment
profit … the money made by a business

'social security' ... unemployment benefit, etc.
pensions ...paid to old people, disabled people, widows, etc. } No employment

- All of these payments are called income.
- Money saved up in the bank or invested is called capital. Capital is also invested in your own home if you own it.

Exercise C.1

1 Tim works a 38 hour week at £4·25 per hour. How much does he earn (before tax)?   C

2 Calculate the wages earned:
   (a) 14 hours' cleaning at £3·35 per hour.
   (b) 28 hours' petrol pump work at £3·60 per hour.
   (c) 16 hours' operating a switchboard at £4·40 per hour.
   (d) 12 hours' babysitting at £1·25 per hour.
   (e) 36 hours' paint-spraying at £5·25 per hour.
   (f) 14 hours' overtime hairdressing at £2·40 × $1\frac{1}{2}$ per hour.
   (g) 42 hours' labouring at £4·60 per hour.   C

3 Two friends Clio and Claude clean cars at weekends. They earn an average of £2 per car. How many cars do they need to clean in order to earn £120 each?   C

4 Ann works in a shoe shop and earns £2·10 per hour for a 35 hour week and double time for a 7 hour Saturday shift. How much does she earn in a full week?   C

5 What is the weekly rate of pay for a job that pays £4200 p.a. (including holidays)?   C

6 The job in question 5 consists of 48 weeks each of 35 hours. What is the hourly rate of pay (ignoring holidays)?   C

7 Sarah earns £4 per hour for a basic 30 hour week and £6·50 per hour for week-end overtime. How much does she earn altogether in a week in which she works 12 hours at the weekend?   C

8 A big store runs a commission scheme for its sales assistants. They are paid £3·75 per hour for a 38 hour week and 2% of the value of the goods they sell as commission. Leroy sells goods worth £3800 in one week. How much does he earn altogether in the week?   C

9 A pair of friends run a car repair business. They complete work worth £480 in a month. Their overheads cost them £40 a week. What is their profit for the month?   C

10 A disabled person receives £36 per week disability pension and also earns £185 a week for a season of 16 weeks in the summer. When he is not working he receives £78 per week social security.
   (a) What are his earnings for the whole year?
   (b) What are his average earnings per week for the year?   B

C.2 Taxation

People who earn money are made to give a share of it for the common good. They pay income tax. The money is used for defence, education, health, building homes and paying social security and pensions (among other things). This money is spent by the government.
Householders also have to pay a local tax called rates. This tax is based on the size of the home (whether owned or rented). Businesses also pay this local tax.
The following are the main taxes paid to the government.

C.2.1 Income tax

In 1985, income over £2205 p.a. was taxed at a basic rate of 30%.

Examples

1 In 1985/86 Mr Jones earned £7000 p.a.

Personal allowance	£2205	
Taxable income	£4795	£7000 − £2205
Tax payable	£1438·50	£4795 × 0·3

2 Ms Evans earned £12 500 p.a. in 1985/86

Personal allowance	£2205	
Taxable income	£10 295	£12 500 − £2205
Tax payable	£3088·50	£10 295 × 0·3

3 Ms Keene earned £87·50 per week in 1985/86

Annual income	£4550	£87·5 × 52
Personal allowance	£2205	
Taxable income	£2345	£4550 − £2205
Tax payable	£703·50	£2345 × 0·3
Tax each week	£13·53	£703·50 ÷ 52

- Allowances for a married couple were £3455 in 1985/86.
- If you are buying your own home by means of a mortgage the interest is allowed against income. [This is calculated by the building society, and your mortgage repayments are adjusted.]
- Allowances and rates of tax are set each year in the budget. [All examples are based on the tax year 1985/1986, when the basic rate of tax was 30%. In 1986/1987 the rate changed to 29%. You can rework the examples for the year in which you use this book!]

C.2.2 Local tax

People pay for local services such as libraries, street lighting, refuse collection (dustmen) and so on by means of 'the rates'. This tax is based on the size of the home you live in, whether it is owned or rented. Businesses also pay rates.

Each property is given a rateable value. The tax payable is then calculated from this value, as in these examples.

Examples

1 Ms King rents a flat ... The rateable value is £440. The rate is 150p in each pound. So the tax payable is £660 (440 × £1·50)
2 Bird & Wolfe own a factory ... The rateable value is £4750. The rate is 136p in each pound. So the tax payable is ... £6460 (4750 × £1·36)

Notes: (i) Different places have different rates in the pound. The rate is set by the Council.
   (ii) This system of taxation is not very satisfactory and is expected to be reformed soon.

C.2.3 VAT

VAT—value added tax—is a tax on spending. Everything you buy (except food, children's clothes and books) has tax added to the cost. This tax is passed on to the government. The rate of VAT is 15% at present (1986).

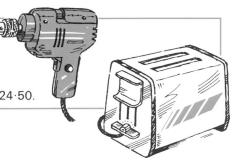

> **Examples**
> 1   An electric drill costs £36 + VAT.
>   Total cost = £36 + £5·40=£41·40 including tax.
> 2   A toaster costs £24·50 including tax.
>   The total price = cost before tax £21·30 + VAT £3·20 = £24·50.

Useful rules

1: To find tax from pre-tax cost: multiply by 0·15
2: To find total cost from pre-tax cost: multiply by 1·15
3: To find pre-tax cost from total cost: divide by 1·15
4: To find tax from total cost:
        (i) divide by 1·15 ... gives pre-tax cost
   then (ii) multiply by 0·15 to give tax.

> **Example**   Using rules 3 and 4 above.
>
> A cassette player costs £82 including tax.
> Cost before tax = £71.30   82 ÷ 1·15 = × 0·15 =
> VAT   = £10·70
>   ↑   ↑
>   Cost before   Tax
>   tax
>
> *Note*: The cost before tax plus the VAT will equal the cost including tax.
>   Use this fact as a check.

Additional hint: Every £1 of the pre-tax cost becomes £1·15 in the total cost. So dividing the total cost by 1·15 will tell you how many pounds there were in the pre-tax cost. (See function diagrams which follow.)

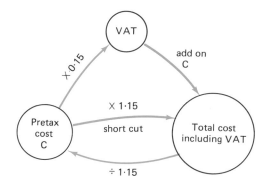

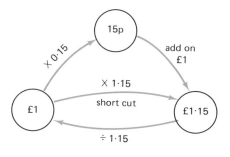

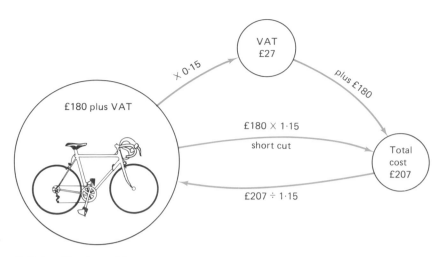

VAT
£27

× 0·15

plus £180

£180 plus VAT

£180 × 1·15

short cut

Total
cost
£207

£207 ÷ 1·15

C.2.4 National Insurance

National Insurance is a tax paid by workers and their employers. The amount payable depends on the weekly rate of pay.

> **Example**
>
> A person earns £120 per week.
>
> N.I. tax $\begin{cases} \text{The employee pays £8·98 per week} \\ \text{The employer pays £7·33 per week} \end{cases}$
>
> so the government collects £16·31 per week in N.I. tax. This money is to provide old-age pensions, unemployment benefit and insurance to cover illness, etc.

C.2.5 Corporation tax

Corporation tax is collected from the profits of business. [In 1985 it was 40% for large businesses and 30% for small business.]

Exercise C.2

1 Calculate the VAT (at 15%) on
   (a) a hairdryer costing £22 before tax.
   (b) a carpet costing £160 before tax.
   (c) 1 tennis racquet, £38 before tax. C

2 Calculate the 1986/87 income tax (rate 29%) on the following, ignoring allowances.
   (a) Annual income of £6500 p.a.
   (b) Wages of £130 per week.
   (c) Salary of £840 per month.
   (d) Wages at £4·75 per hour. C

3 An industrial workshop has rateable value of £4000 p.a. Rates are payable at £1·20 in the pound. What is the rates bill p.a.? C

4 A food mixer costs £66 + VAT (at 15%). Calculate the full cost including tax. C

5 Four friends use the workshop in question 3 to set up a business. The rent of the workshop is £240 per month. How much do they have to pay each month in rent and rates altogether? C

6 Explain some of the things that taxes are spent on. C

7 Make a list of all the different sort of taxes people pay. [Where a person's money is spent by central government or local government for the benefit of the whole community.] C

8 Which of these two sewing machines is dearer:
  (a) a machine costing £285 including tax or
  (b) a similar machine costing £240 plus VAT (at 15%)?   C

9 A repair bill for a motorcycle comes to £66·70 including VAT (at 15%). How much of the bill is tax?   C

10 A hairdresser's salon has an annual rates bill of £852. With rates at £2·40 in the pound, what is the rateable value of the salon?   B

C.3   Spending money

A family with two children spends most of its money on the home. The table below gives the average percentages (for 1978) for the United Kingdom. Today's figures will be roughly the same.

Money spent per week (%)

	Housing	15·2%	...	55°
	Fuel, light and power	5·6%		
	Food	25·6%	...	92°
	Drink	4·2%		
	Tobacco	3·1%		
	Clothes and shoes	9·0%	...	32°
Furniture, washing machine, TV, etc. }	Durable goods	6·7%		
Crockery, hobbies etc. }	Other goods	7·8%		
	Transport and vehicles	13·1%	...	48°
Holidays, bank interest, hairdressing, etc. }	Services, etc.	9·7%	...	35°
		100%		

This pie chart shows the main items of expenditure for a family with 2 children.

In 1978 the average total spent in a week was £95·05; by 1985 this was £190 per week per family.

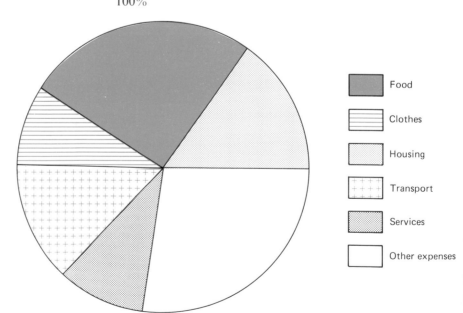

Food
Clothes
Housing
Transport
Services
Other expenses

Example

A family with two children and an income of £220 per week.*

Estimate of money spent on housing...15·2% × £220 = £33·44
Estimate of money spent on food　...25·6% × £220 = £56·32
Estimate of money spent on clothes ...　9% × £220 = £19·80

* Based on the average pattern of spending for 1978.

Exercise C.3

1 A family spends 18% of its income on entertainment. The total income is £360 per week. How much is spent on entertainment? C

2 A miner earning £260 per week gives half the money to his wife for household expenses and pays £48 rent and rates. How much is left for other bills and his own spending? C

3 Three friends go on a camping holiday. They spend £80 on equipment, £65 on travel, £130 on food, drink and entertainment and £45 for the camp site. How much does the holiday cost each of them? C

4 A family allocates £36 per week for food. By Friday £26·50 has been spent. How much is left for the weekend? C

5 Make a list of all the expenses you would expect to pay if you moved into a flat with a friend. C

6 A newly married couple take home £410 per week. They are buying a flat which costs £280 a month altogether (including rates). What percentage of their take home pay is spent on the flat? C

7 Make a pie chart which shows the ways in which you spend your own money each week. B

C.4　Housing

People either rent their homes or buy them by means of a mortgage. It is always worth thinking of buying your own home: you will be investing your money in something which you will eventually own.

Example　*A tale of two flats*

Helen and Jim rent their flat for £54·50 per week excluding rates. Charles and Sue are buying their flat, in the same block as Helen and Jim. They pay £256 per month mortgage interest, £40 per month for an Endowment Assurance Policy to repay the capital of £22 000 they have borrowed to buy the flat. They also pay rates of £480 per year.

Helen and Jim

Charles and Sue

Each month ...

Helen and Jim pay ...	Charles and Sue owe ...
£54·5 × 52 ÷ 12 = £236·17	£256 + £40 = £296
	But 30% of the £256 is recovered
	in income tax. So they pay
	£296 − (30% of £256) = £219·20

So Charles and Sue pay less than Helen and Jim each week.

Ten years on ... Both families are expecting a second child and need a larger flat. Their positions are very different.

Helen and Jim have paid £54·50 a week for 10 years ... £54·5 × 52 × 10 = £28 340!!!

After paying all that money they own nothing! [And they may have paid more than this if their rent has risen.]

Charles and Sue have paid £219·20 per month for 10 years ... = £26 304.

But (i) their flat will have increased in value by about 6% each year.

Value of flat
... £22 000 × (1·06)^{10} = £39 398   [22 000 × 1·06 x^y 10 =]

Also (ii) their assurance policy will be worth about 70% of the money they have paid for it.

Value of policy ...	£3360	[£40 × 12 × 10 × 0·70]
Total value of policy and property ...	£42 758	[£39 398 + £3360]
Original mortgage ...	−£22 000	
	£20 758	

So Charles and Sue have £20 758 out of the £26 304 they have spent so far!!!
This money will help them to buy a larger flat.

Study the calculations in the example above. They are probably the most important calculations you will ever do.

Exercise C.4

1   A furnished flat in Birmingham costs £70 per week to rent (including rates). How much is this a year?   C

2   Mr and Mrs Morris are 12 weeks behind with their rent (£37·50 week). How much do they owe their landlord?   C

3   Mrs Osapu takes a lodger. She charges £32·50 per week. How much is this for a full year?   C

4   Flat 140, Topmast Point costs £42·50 per week and is shared by three friends. They have to pay rent 12 times a year on the 1st of each month. Tracey, one of the friends, collects the rent from the other two. How much should she collect each month?   C

5   Bill and Sue are students each with grants of £2100 p.a. to cover three 12-week terms. How much do they have to spend each week?   C

6   What is the most Bill and Sue could pay for rented rooms while they are at college?   C

7   Mike and Jim are both planning to get married. Mike has saved £3000 and Jim has saved £2500 for a home. They are both able to get 95% mortgages. What is the most expensive place each of them can buy (without considering their future wives' earnings)?   C

8 Mr and Mrs McDove buy a house for £40 000. They manage to borrow 90% of the money from a building society. How much money do they have to find for the deposit? C

9 Sarah has found a flat for £45 per week but she must find (a) three months rent in advance, and (b) a deposit of £250 in case of damage. How much does she need altogether? C

10 Captain Blogger lives in a house boat. His mooring fees are £3·50 per day. He also has to pay £650 a year for maintenance. How much does his home cost a year? C

11 A one-bedroom flat in London cost £36 000 to buy in 1985. Find the cost of the same flat two years later if prices rise by 15% each year. B

12 List some of the points that people should consider when deciding whether to rent or buy their home. B

C.5 Buying food

Since so much money is spent on food it is worth thinking about it. Here are some things to consider.

(i) Planning what you eat can save money.

(ii) Raw foods, such as fresh vegetables, meat, fish, etc., are usually cheaper than processed foods (such as ready-cooked pizzas, fish fingers, cakes, biscuits and tinned fruit). Fresh food can also be better for you!

(iii) Buying larger quantities because they are relatively cheaper does not always save money. Some food may be wasted.

(iv) Time spent shopping around can save quite a lot of money. Buying in markets can be good value but be careful. 'Bargains' can be very wasteful. [Those apples may be very cheap but you may have to throw many of them away!]

C.5.1 Conversions

Ounces	Pounds	Kilograms	Grams
1	0·0625	0·028	28·35
16	1	0·454	454
35·28	2·205	1	1000
3·5	0·22	0·01	100

ml	Litres	Pints	Gallons
1000	1	1·76	0·22
570	0·57	1	0·0125
4550	4·55	8	1

When shopping, the following rough conversions will be useful.

1 kilogram is just over 2 lb (10% more)*
1 pound is about 450 g
1 ounce is 28 g (about 30 g)
1 gallon is $4\frac{1}{2}$ litres
1 litre is $1\frac{3}{4}$ pints

* To change price per lb to price per kg, just double and add 10%.

Example

Bananas are 78p per lb: $78 \xrightarrow{\times 2} 156 \xrightarrow{+10\%} 171 \cdot 6p$ per kg

C.5.2 Comparing values

There are two ways to compare values.
Method 1: Compare the prices per unit measure (i.e. weight or volume).
Method 2: Work out what quantity you can buy for £1.

Example

A pint of cooking oil costs £1·58.
900 ml of the same oil costs £3·25.

Method 1: Price per unit
First convert the pint to millilitres using the table above:
1 pint = 570 ml.
570 ml costs 158p → l ml costs 0·277p
900 ml costs £3·25 → 1 ml costs 0·361p
The 900 ml bottle of oil is much dearer (30% dearer).*

Method 2: Quantity for £1
£1·58 buys 0·57 litres → £1 buys 0·36 litres = 360 ml
£3·25 buys 900 ml   → £1 buys 276 ml
The smaller bottle buys more for £1 (30% more).*

* Do you notice anything odd about the results of these two calculations? Is this a coincidence?

Exercise C.5

Part 1

1 Which is more, 400 g or 1 lb?   C
2 Which is more, 4 oz or 150 g?   C
3 Which is more, 1 km or 1000 yards?   C
4 Which is more, 5 litres or 1 gallon?   C
5 Which is faster, 75 m.p.h. or 100 km.p.h.?   C
6 Which is deeper water, 150 m or 500 ft?   C
7 Which is higher, an aircraft at 35 000 ft or one at 10 000 metres?   C
8 Which of these weights is roughly the same as $\frac{1}{2}$ lb:
(a) 2 kg, (b) 500 g, (c) 250 g, (d) 50 g?   C
9 Use the conversion table to convert 50 kilograms to pounds.   C

10 A bottle of mineral water contains 1400 ml and costs 69p. A 5-litre container of the same water costs £1·65. How much money is saved by buying the 5-litre container?   C
11 Mr Wakefield loves bargains. He bought a 50 kg sack of apricots for £8 but $\frac{3}{4}$ were rotten. What is the real price per kg? How does this compare with the usual price of 80p per pound?   C
12 A litre is equal to $1\frac{3}{4}$ pints. A pint carton of milk costs 30p. What would you expect 1 litre of milk to cost?   C
13 What is the weight of 5 litres of water (in kg)?   C

14 Crude petroleum oil weighs 1·2 kg/litre. Estimate the weight of a load of 1 million gallons carried by a petrol tanker. [1 gallon = 4·5 litres.] C

15 Explain how your weight in kilograms could be used to find your volume in cubic centimetres. (Remember your density is the same as that of water!) C

Part 2

1 Frozen beans cost £3·75 for a 6 lb pack. How much is this per pound? C

2 Mars bars are sold on special offer at £1·80 for 12 bars. How much does one bar cost? C

3 Frozen broccoli is sold at £1·25 per pound or £6 for a 5 lb pack. How much do you save (per lb) by buying the large pack? C

4 Which is the better value for money … a large bottle of sauce at 98p for 800 g, or a small bottle of sauce at 49p for 450 g? C

5 A small packet of washing powder costs 75p for 930 g, while a big packet of the same powder costs £2·10 for 2200 g. Which is the better value for money? C

6 A particular brand of paint comes in 3 sizes. Compare the price per litre for each size. Is it always best to buy the cheapest? Explain your answer. C

7 A packet of nuts costs 75p for 100 g. What would you expect 1 kg to cost? Would you expect 1 tonne of nuts to be 1000 times the price of 1 kg? Give your reasons. C

8 Think of some products where the large size costs the same or less than the small one. C

9 Frozen peas cost £4·25 for a 5 kg pack. What weight can be bought for £1? C

10 Fish fingers are packed in a packet of 12. The pack weighs 650 g and costs £1·80. What is the price of the fish per kilogram? C

11 Fresh cod costs £1·95 per pound while a 400 g pack of frozen cod costs £2·20. Which is dearer, fresh or frozen cod? B

C.6   Saving and borrowing

The first thing to understand is the relationship between borrower and lender.

Borrower ⟶ pays interest ⟶ Lender
Borrower ⟵ lends money ⟵ Lender

When you save you lend money to
[bank
business
building society
government]
They pay you interest!
… You are the lender or investor.

When you borrow from a
[bank
business
building society
finance company]
You pay them interest!
… You are the borrower.

The amount of interest paid or earned depends on
(i) the amount you borrow or invest.
(ii) the rate of interest, and
(iii) the time for which the money is borrowed or invested.

Examples Saving

1 Jeanette saves £200 in a deposit account at the bank for 4 years. The rate of interest is 8% p.a.
Each £1 grows to £1·08 in a year, including interest.

$$£200 \xrightarrow{\times 1·08} £216 \xrightarrow{\times 1·08} £233·28 \xrightarrow{\times 1·08} £251·94 \xrightarrow{\times 1·08} £272·10$$

After 1 year   After 2 years   After 3 years   After 4 years

Jeanette's savings earn £72·10 over the four years.

2 Kim has bought £250 of National Savings Certificates and keeps them for the full five years. How much are they worth if the interest rate is 7·85% p.a.? [$£250 \times (1·0785)^5 = £364·79$.]

3 Gary saves £180 in his post office account every month for a year. He is saving up to get married.
Each month he earns interest on the money already in the account and invests another £180.

	At beginning of month		
	New money added	Total in account	Interest earned at $\frac{1}{2}$% per month	Total in account at end of month
1st month	£180	£180	£0·90	£180·90
2nd month	£180	£360·90	£1·80	£362·70
3rd month	£180	£542·70	£2·71	£545·41
4th month	£180	£725·41	£3·63	£729·04
5th month	£180	£909·04	£4·55	£913·59
6th month	£180	£1093·59	£5·47	£1099·06
7th month	£180	£1279·06	£6·40	£1285·46
8th month	£180	£1465·46	£7·33	£1472·79
9th month	£180	£1652·79	£8·26	£1661·05
10th month	£180	£1841·05	£9·21	£1850·26
11th month	£180	£2030·26	£10·15	£2040·41
12th month	£180	£2220·41	£11·10	£2231·51

This calculation is long and slow because each month is taken separately.
Gary has saved £2231·51 instead of just 12 × £180 (= £2160), i.e. an extra £71·51 in interest.

Examples Borrowing

1   Samantha has a £250 overdraft at the bank. They charge her interest at
    15% p.a. until she has paid it off. The interest is calculated daily.

    Rate of interest 15% per year $= \dfrac{0\cdot15}{365}$% per day.

    Daily interest on Samantha's £250 overdraft is
    (£250 × 0·15) ÷ 365 = £0·10 (or 10p per day).
    This is one of the cheapest ways of borrowing money.

2   Geoff uses a credit card. If he does not pay back all he has spent at the
    end of the free credit period he is charged 2·5% interest per month.
    He has bought a hi-fi for £280 using his credit card and only paid back
    £28. So £252 is left outstanding as a debt. He is charged
    £252 × 0·025 = £6·30 interest for the month.
    [On an overdraft at 15% he would have paid
    (£252 × 0·15) ÷ 365 × 30 = £3·11.]
    Paying bills by credit card is an expensive way of borrowing money.

3   Pat and Paul have decided to buy a flat together and have borrowed
    £28 000 from a building society. The rate of interest is 11% so the interest
    each month is (£28 000 × 0·11) ÷ 12 = £256·67.

Important questions to ask when you borrow money

(i)   Can you afford to pay the interest?
(ii) How will you pay back the loan?
(iii) Is the rate of interest too high?
(iv) Do you really want the thing you are buying?

To protect people from 'loan sharks', companies
are forced by law to show the true rate of interest
on all loans. This is the APR—the annual
percentage rate—so look out for it! Any APR
above 30% is very expensive.

Exercise C.6

1   Calculate the interest earned when £400 is
    saved for a year at 12%.   C

2   Calculate the interest that has to be paid
    on a 1 year loan of £500 at 14% p.a.   C

3   A woman borrows £5200 to buy a car
    over three years. Interest at 12% for each
    year is added to the cost of the car. What
    is the total cost she has to pay?   C

4   The same woman pays off her debt in 36
    equal monthly payments. What is each
    payment?   C

5   Show how £1 grows in the first five years
    of compound interest at 8% p.a.   C

6   Chris saves £800, left to him by his
    granny, at 9% p.a. compound interest. If
    he leaves the money for five full years
    what amount of interest is earned?   C

7   Charley King borrows £600 from his bank
    for two years. The rate of interest is 18%
    p.a. How much does he have to pay back
    to clear the loan?   C

8   Anthea uses her credit card to buy a
    holiday costing £450. She pays £45 back
    each month and interest at 2% per month
    on the money she still owes. Make a table
    showing the first 3 months' repayments
    and interest payments.   B

C.7 Making financial decisions

If something is cheap you will not necessarily buy it just for that reason.
Often you will decide what you want and then find a way to pay for it.
It is important to be able to understand printed information about money
whenever it occurs. The following example is about choosing a holiday.

Paradise Island Holidays

Cost per person, including return flight

	7 nights	*14 nights*	*21 nights*
Self-catering	£285	£385	£490
* Hotel B & B	£320	£450	£550
** Hotel B & Eve. Meal	£345	£525	£650
*** Full residence	£365	£575	£715

From the table you can see that 7 nights at a two-star hotel, with bed and
breakfast and evening meal costs £345 per person.

You can also see that you can save £60 per person by taking 'self-catering'
accommodation. [This could be a chalet or a flat.] So if 5 people were going
on this holiday, the 'self-catering' package is £300 cheaper. On the other
hand, you would get all your meals in the hotel for the extra £20 per person.
But ... is it worth it? Would you want to take all your meals at the same hotel?
Suppose they are not very good?

Another fact that can be seen from the table is that a two-week self-catering
holiday costs just £20 more than full residence for one week in a three-star
hotel, and so on.

The golden rule is to take time to decide when making financial decisions and
get all the information you can.

Exercise C.7

Using the table given in the example 'Paradise Island Holidays', describe
how you would choose a holiday if you had £500 to spend. [Remember,
you will need spending money while you are away. Also consider you
have a total of 4 weeks holiday in a year. Perhaps you will take time off to
do other things?]

Examination questions C

The following examination questions are typical of the ones you can expect in your final examination. Fully worked out answers are given on pages 117–124, but don't look at them until you have attempted all the problems in this section. You will be expected to use a calculator but remember that accurate answers are the only way to get full marks, so check carefully. Questions of this type always have a lot of words so make sure you read each question carefully and make use of all the information given.

1 A paperback textbook costs £1·85p.
  (a) Calculate the cost of 7 of these books.
  (b) When I pay for these with a £20 note, what is the correct change?

2 Two friends go out for a meal. The cost before VAT is £14·50. VAT is 15%.
  (a) Calculate the VAT to be added.
  (b) Calculate the total cost of the meal including VAT.

May Flower Restaurant

五月花饭馆

Set meal for two/three   £5 per person

Boiled rice, roast duck, greens with
oyster sauce, steamed fish, Chinese tea

Chinese beer   £1.00

Wine per glass (red/white)   85p.

Fruit: litchis, mango etc. £1.00

VAT extra (15%)

3 Seven days' 'bed and breakfast' cost £105. Calculate the cost of 10 days' 'bed and breakfast' at the same rate.

4 A man and woman and their two children went on a package tour to Moscow. The cost was £350 per person with 10% discount for children.
  (a) Calculate the cost for the whole family.
  While they were in Moscow they went to the Kremlin three times, at a cost of 5 roubles per person each time.
  (b) How much did their Kremlin visits cost in pounds if £1 = 1·3 roubles?

5 Mei-Li went on a skiing holiday to France. She took £60 spending money which she exchanged for francs at 11 francs to £1.
  (a) How many francs did she get?
  When she gets home again she has 250 F left.
  (b) How much is this worth in pounds, at 12 F = £1?

6 Mr and Mrs Sharp want to insure the contents of their home. Their belongings are valued at £8300. [This is what it would cost to replace everything if it were burnt.] The rate is 37p per £100. What will the insurance cost?

7 Mr and Mrs McLean won £3000 on the football pools. Instead of spending it they deposited it straight away in a building society. The interest rate was $8\frac{1}{2}$% p.a., calculated half-yearly. What was their prize worth after three years?

8 George is an insurance salesman and his friend Sandra works in the head office of the same company. In the same week … George earned a basic wage of £75 plus 8% commission on sales totalling £3800. Sandra earned £5·75 an hour for a 35-hour week plus 6 hours' overtime at time and a half. What did they each earn that week?

9 A bubble bath is offered at a 'bargain' price of £1·25 for 50 ml. The bottle holds 7 'measures'. What is
  (a) the cost per litre of the liquid?
  (b) the cost per measure of the liquid?

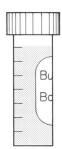

10 In 1985 a woman and her husband together earned £18 000 p.a. Their combined personal allowances came to £4410. [They were taxed separately.] They were also paying 12% interest on their mortgage of £22 000. In 1985/1986 income tax was charged at 30% of taxable income.
 (a) Calculate the interest they paid on their mortgage.
 (b) Calculate their taxable income.
 (c) Calculate the tax they had to pay in 1985/86 [30p in the £1].

11 Mrs James shares a flat with her son. The rateable value of the flat is £350. The local rate is 140p in the pound.
 (a) Calculate the rate payable.
 (b) Calculate the increase that will be payable if the rates go up by 25p in the pound.

12 Tim and Jim started a decorating business after leaving college. They borrowed £6000 from the bank to buy equipment and a van. The bank charges 16% compound interest and expects them to pay back £120 per month of the loan as shown on the loan statement.

T.Smith and J.Jones   LOAN ACCOUNT

Date	Debit	Debit	Credit	Balance
1 Sept				6000 OD
30 Sept	Interest	80		6080 OD
	Repayment		120	5960 OD
31 Oct	Interest	79.46		6039.46 OD
	Repayment		120	5919.46 OD

 (a) What do you notice about the interest payments?
 (b) Explain how the interest is calculated.
 (c) Complete the next four lines of the loan account [the entries for November and December].

13 Lucy is left £7000 by her grandfather (lucky girl!). She decides to either
 (a) invest the money at $8\frac{1}{2}$% p.a. interest and draw the interest at the end of year, or

 (b) invest the money at 8% p.a. in a scheme where interest is added to capital each year.
Calculate the interest she would receive under each scheme over 5 years. Which is the better of the two, do you think? Give your reasons.

14 A special shampoo comes in three sizes. The quantities and prices are shown in the diagram. Which of the three is the best value for money?

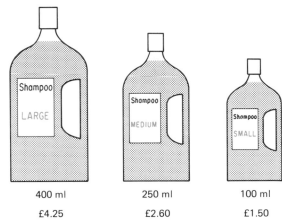

400 ml	250 ml	100 ml
£4.25	£2.60	£1.50

15 A firm which has been paying wages weekly goes over to a monthly system. Wages are transferred into the employees' bank accounts on the last day of each month. How much should be transferred each month to
 (a) a secretary who was earning £125 a week (after tax)?
 (b) a manager earning £8950 p.a. (after tax).
 (c) a driver who was earning £85 a week plus £32 overtime?

16 A shop pays its assistants £95 per week basic plus £4·50 an hour for overtime. The assistants also earn commission: $1\frac{1}{2}$% of the value of the goods they have sold is added to their wages.
Ali works 6 hours' overtime in one week and sells £1350 worth of goods. What are his total wages for that week?

17 Stephanie earns £185 a week as a designer.
 (a) What is her annual income before tax?
 (b) If she has a total of £4800 allowances, how much income tax will she pay (at 30%) a year?
 (c) How much tax will she pay each week?

18 The price of a motorbike is £4800 including VAT at 15%. How much VAT has been paid?

19 A travel agent is giving $12\frac{1}{2}$% discount on all holidays over £250. What will be the discounted prices of these holidays?
(a) Two weeks in Istanbul: £650.
(b) Eight days in Leningrad: £380.
(c) Twelve fabulous days on a Nile cruise: £950.
(d) A weekend for two in Paris: £180.

20 Use the table to answer the following questions.
(a) A fridge–freezer costs £285. Susan pays £85 cash down and the balance on hire purchase over 18 months. What are the monthly payments?
(b) Desirée can only afford to pay about £5 per month for a camera, after paying a deposit of £20. What is the price of the most expensive one she can buy?
(c) Is it cheaper to take a longer hire purchase agreement than a shorter one? Give reasons for your answer.

| Balance of cash price to pay | 12 months | | 18 months | | 24 months | |
	Total HP cost	Monthly payment (12)	Total HP cost	Monthly payment (18)	Total HP cost	Monthly payment (24)
10	11·28	0·94	11·88	0·66	12·72	0·53
20	22·56	1·88	23·76	1·32	25·20	1·05
50	56·28	4·69	59·40	3·30	62·64	2·62
100	112·56	9·33	118·80	6·60	125·04	5·21
200	225·00	18·75	237·50	13·20	250·08	10·42
500	562·80	46·90	594·00	33·00	626·40	26·20
1000	1125·60	93·30	1118·00	66·00	1250·40	52·21
2000	2251·20	186·60	2236·00	132·00	2500·80	104·42

Activities and investigation C

Competition quiz C

A's questions for B

Wages ... rates and taxes ... borrowing

1 Which pays more, £6500 p.a. or £125 per week?
2 A boy earning £120 per week gets a 15% rise. What is his new wage?
3 A woman changes to 'part time' when she has a baby. Her wages drop from £8400 to £5000 p.a. How much less does she earn each month?
4 The rateable value of a farm is £960 p.a. The farmer pays £2 rates in the pound but is allowed a 15% agricultural discount. How much does he pay each year?
5 A flat costs £3750 p.a. to rent plus £850 rates. How much is this per week?

B's questions for A

Wages ... rates and taxes ... borrowing

1 An apprentice starts at £65 per week. How much more will she earn per week when she becomes a craftswoman at £8500 p.a.?
2 A boy gets £325 per month before tax plus £60 a month overtime. What does he earn in a year?
3 A girl on £6000 p.a. gets a 15% rise. What is her new salary?
4 A couple's income is £320 per week. How much is this per calendar month?
5 A worker has £62 per week deducted from a wage of £210. What is her take-home pay?

A's questions for B (cont.)

6 A librarian earns £725 before tax each month. Total deductions are £211. What is his take-home pay?

7 The rent of a flat includes rates of £16 a week. The total paid is £75 per week. How much is the rent?

8 The rateable value of a house is £600 p.a. and the rates payable are £900. What rates are payable on a flat whose rateable value is £440?

9 What is 15% of £240?

10 What would be the interest payable on a one year loan of £500 at 18% interest p.a.?

11 A credit card company charges 2% interest per month on a loan of £800. What rate is this per year?

12 Which type of borrowing would you expect to be most expensive?
(a) Mortgage with building society.
(b) Bank loan.
(c) Credit card.

B's questions for A (cont.)

6 A nurse earns £6500 p.a. but has £45 per week deducted for his accommodation. How much is his pay per month (before tax)?

7 A new video recorder costs £280 plus 15% VAT. How much does it cost including tax?

8 A woman pays 30% basic rate tax on her taxable income of £7200. How much tax does she pay?

9 Is it true that 25% of £60 is the same as 60% of £25?

10 Calculate one year's interest on £7000 borrowed at 13% p.a.

11 A couple borrow £6000 to buy a car on H.P. They pay £3600 interest altogether over three years, which is added to the £6000 at the beginning. How much does the car cost per month?

12 How would you use APR if you wanted to borrow some money?

Learning games

1 Snip

The purpose of this game is to make you very efficient at working out 'value for money' calculations.

Materials

The game is played with a pack of special cards which you will have to make first. There are 36 cards altogether in the pack, three cards for each commodity.
Choose twelve commodities and find out the usual sizes and prices in the supermarket. Then make up sets of cards for each commodity like the ones in the example.

Example

The commodity is toothpaste: sizes and prices are given.

Playing the game

1: Shuffle and deal the cards face down in two sets of 18. Each player takes one set of cards.
2: The players turn up a card each (as in snap). When two cards of the same commodity are turned up together, as long as one player says 'snip', the player with the better value for money card wins the cards that have been turned up so far.

Example

First method

80 g for £1·60 ⇒ 1 g for 2p
                 ⇒ 25 g for 50p

So the large toothpaste is cheaper by 25p and B takes the cards.

Second method

25 g for 75p ⇒ 1g for 3p
             ⇒ 80g for £2·40

So the large is cheaper by 80p and B takes the cards.

[Both methods give the right answer—the large is better value—but the figures are different. How interesting!]

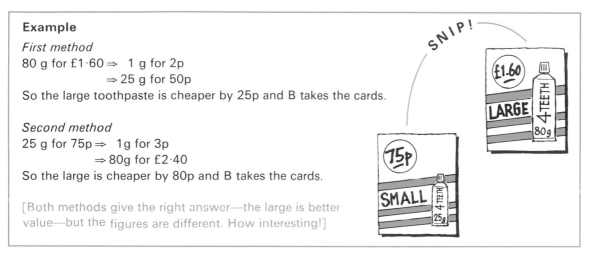

3: The game ends when one player has all the cards.
You can develop this game by adding more cards and by changing the rules.

2 Gone shopping ... or spend, spend spend!

Make double sized copies of the following cards.

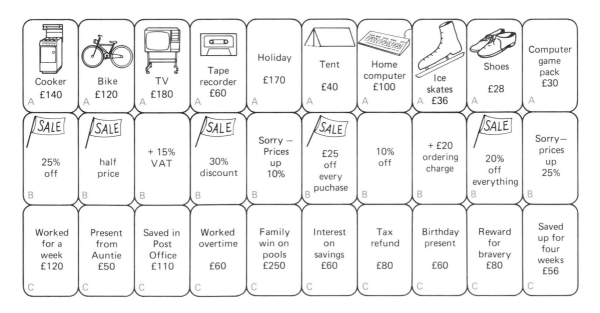

A	Cooker £140	Bike £120	TV £180	Tape recorder £60	Holiday £170	Tent £40	Home computer £100	Ice skates £36	Shoes £28	Computer game pack £30
B	SALE 25% off	SALE half price	+ 15% VAT	SALE 30% discount	Sorry — Prices up 10%	SALE £25 off	10% off	+ £20 ordering charge	SALE 20% off everything	Sorry— prices up 25%
C	Worked for a week £120	Present from Auntie £50	Saved in Post Office £110	Worked overtime £60	Family win on pools £250	Interest on savings £60	Tax refund £80	Birthday present £60	Reward for bravery £80	Saved up for four weeks £56

How to play

(i) The cards are placed face down in three piles, A, B and C.

(ii) A player takes one card from each pack. If he or she can buy the A card with the help of the B and C cards he or she keeps the A card and the others are replaced. If not, all three cards are replaced.

(iii) The piles are shuffled and the other player has a turn.

The winner is the player who manages to buy the most things.

3 Town Hall spending

People who become local councillors have the power to spend our money on local services such as education, transport, housing, etc. If the people do not like the way their money is spent they can dismiss the councillors by voting for someone else at the local elections. This board game shows how local government might spend money.

How to play

Use M+ and M−

Each player has a counter at start. They take it in turns to throw a die. They start with £56m and follow the instructions each time their counter lands. The winner is the player with most council money left after an agreed time (20 minutes to half an hour).

Team games

Hurdle race

This race will improve your speed at answering questions on money. [Try playing without a calculator!] The race is for four people and a 'Controller'. It can be played with 3 or 4 players only, but one person must by the Controller. The rules are given for four players.

How to play

Four 'question cards' marked A, B, C, D on one side are placed face down and shuffled. Each player picks a card to decide which set of questions to answer. Once the race has started each player answers the first question and brings the answer to the Controller, who checks it against the answers on page 423. If the answer is right, the player moves on to the next question. If not he or she has to have a second attempt. If this is also incorrect the player moves on to the next question.

Order of approach to the Controller
When a player has finished a question he or she puts their question card in line on the table in front of the Controller. The Controller deals with the cards in order. This saves argument about who is next.

Scoring

Each player scores one point for each correct answer and loses one point for each wrong answer (after 2 attempts). There is a bonus of 5 points for completing all the questions first. The race stops when one person has completed their last question.

I suggest that the Controller prepares a score sheet before the start of the race.

Replay

The race can be run again (if there is time) by rotating the cards so that a new person becomes Controller and everyone has a new set of questions.

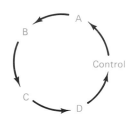

A
1 What change would you expect from £10 after spending £6·14?
2 What is the cost of 4 pairs of socks at £3·29 per pair?
3 What is the difference between 48 + (12 ÷ 6) and (48 + 12) ÷ 6?
4 What is the cost of 12 HP payments of £8·50 per month?
5 A job pays £85·50 per week. How much is this per year?
6 Calculate the 15% VAT on a camera costing £65 all together.
7 What is the cost in a '25% off' sale of a coat usually £26?
8 What interest is earned on £200 in a year at 14% p.a.?
9 What is the annual cost of a loan of £400 at 2% per month simple interest?
10 Which is better value: 1 kg of soap powder for 80p or 400 g for 40p?
11 What is the value of $(256)^{\frac{1}{2}}$? It is a whole number.
12 What sum of money could be shared exactly between 4, 5 or 8 people?

B
1 What change would you expect from £10 after spending £5·35?
2 What is the cost of 4 pairs of socks at £2·89 per pair?
3 What is the difference between 50 + (6 ÷ 2) and (50 + 6) ÷ 2?
4 What is the cost of 12 HP payments of £6·75 per month?
5 A job pays £76·50 per week. How much is this per year?
6 Calculate the 15% VAT on a tennis racquet costing £72 all together.
7 What is the cost in a '25% off' sale of a shirt usually £18?
8 What interest is earned on £400 in a year at 16% p.a.?
9 What is the annual cost of a loan of £400 at $1\frac{1}{2}$% per month simple interest?
10 Which is better value: 1 kg of nuts for £1·20 or 200 g for 40p?
11 What is the value of $(343)^{\frac{1}{3}}$? It is a whole number.
12 What sum of money could be shared exactly between 2, 3 or 5 people?

C
1 What change would you expect from £10 after spending £3·82?
2 What is the cost of 4 pairs of socks at £3·07 per pair?
3 What is the difference between 28 + (4 ÷ 8) and (28 + 4) ÷ 8?
4 What is the cost of 12 HP payments of £9·25 per month?
5 A job pays £83·20 per week. How much is this per year?
6 Calculate the 15% VAT on a cassette player costing £140 all together.
7 What is the cost in a '25% off' sale of a suit usually £88?
8 What interest is earned on £600 in a year at 12% p.a.?
9 What is the annual cost of a loan of £400 at $1\frac{1}{4}$% per month simple interest?
10 Which is better value: 1 kg of coffee at £11·20 or 200 g for £2·00?
11 What is the value of $(225)^{\frac{1}{2}}$? It is a whole number.
12 What sum of money could be shared exactly between 3, 5 or 7 people?

D
1 What change would you expect from £10 after spending £7·22?
2 What is the cost of 4 pairs of socks at £2·76 per pair?
3 What is the difference between 18 + (9 ÷ 3) and (18 + 9) ÷ 3?
4 What is the cost of 12 HP payments of £7·50 per month?
5 A job pays £92·60 per week. How much is this per year?
6 Calculate the 15% VAT on a pair of walking boots at £96 all together.
7 What is the cost in a '25% off' sale of a tea-set usually £35?
8 What interest is earned on £500 in a year at 8% p.a?
9 What is the annual cost of a loan of £400 at $1\frac{3}{4}$% per month simple interest?
10 Which is better value: 1 kg of butter at £2·00 or 250 g for 90p?
11 What is the value of $(216)^{\frac{1}{3}}$? It is a whole number.
12 What sum of money could be shared exactly between 3, 5 and 8 people?

Practical work

The only way to learn about money is by finding things out for yourself. You should carry out at least two of the following study projects. For each project, decide if it is best to work alone, in pairs, or in groups, for greatest efficiency.

1   What do you cost your parents?

Work out an estimate of how much you cost to keep for a year.
Don't forget to include a share of food, heat, rent or mortgage, travel,
telephone, TV licence, as well as pocket money, clothes, haircuts and holidays.
You will be surprised how valuable you are.

2   How wages have changed

Using grandparents and other older people as sources of information, find out
how wages have changed for various jobs. You can ask them how much they
earned when they started work, when they were married and so on. They may
well remember the cost of commodities such as bread, beer and housing at
that time and you should use this information in presenting your results. This
will give a feeling of the 'real value' of money.

One way of assessing how well-off people are is to work out how many hours
of work they need to do to earn enough money to buy a holiday or pay the
rent or mortgage. You will certainly find that some things have got much
cheaper on this basis.

3   Food prices

(a) Make a survey of food prices in your area. Choose selected items and
     compare the prices in different shops. Some suggested items are:
     butter, margarine, tinned products, eggs, cereals, pulses [dried beans,
     etc.], vegetables, fish and meat.
     Present your results so that differences stand out.

Consider these statements in the light of the results of your survey.

 (i) Supermarkets are cheaper than open markets.
 (ii) Fresh fruit and vegetables cost the same wherever you buy them.
(iii) Differences in price are greater for expensive foods than for cheap foods.

(b) Design a full week's menu for two people including breakfast, lunch and
     evening meal. Estimate the total cost for the week. Would feeding a family
     of four lead to any saving of money?

4 Finances of owning and running a car (or motorbike)

(a) Investigate the cost of buying and running a car for a year.
Allow for depreciation (30% of cost price per year if you buy new), maintenance, insurance, petrol, HP interest, tax.
Investigate and compare the costs for new and secondhand cars, big and small cars.

(b) Would it be possible to run a car if you only had £20 per week to spare?

5 Borrowing

Most adults borrow money one way or another. They borrow money to buy homes (mortgages) and also to buy cars, furniture and household goods (hire purchase or bank loan). Another way of borrowing is to use a credit card. Some methods of borrowing are much more expensive than others. Most expensive of all are the 'loan sharks'—companies who charge very high rates of interest—although their adverts may make them seem very appealing.

In this project find out all you can about the different ways of borrowing money. Banks and building societies will give you free information and your teacher will also be able to help you. Don't forget to look at the advertisements for loans in your local newspaper.

Remember the true cost of loans can be compared by using the APR [the annual percentage interest rate]. By law, all loan arrangements must state the APR. Investigate the APRs for building societies, banks (overdrafts and personal loans), credit cards and hire purchase. Watch out for extra costs such as 'arrangement fees' or 'commission'.

Worked answers to examination questions C

1 A paperback textbook costs £1·85.
  (a) Calculate the cost of 7 of these books.
  (b) When I pay for these with a £20 note, what is the correct change?

  (a) £12·95   (b) £7·05

  7 books at £1·85 will cost £1·85 × 7 = £12·95.
  The change will be £20 − £12·95 = £7·05.

2 Two friends go out for a meal. The cost before VAT is £14·50. VAT is 15%.
  (a) Calculate the VAT to be added.
  (b) Calculate the total cost of the meal including VAT.

  (a) VAT £2·18   (b) Total cost £16·68

  The VAT is 15% of £14·50: 0·15 × £14·5 = £2·18.
  This has to be added to the £14·50: £14·50 + £2·18 = £16·68.

May Flower Restaurant
五月花饭馆

3 Seven days' 'bed and breakfast' cost £105. Calculate the cost of 10 days' 'bed and breakfast' at the same rate.

  £150

  First find the cost per day.
    Cost per day is £105 ÷ 7 = £15.
    Cost for 10 days is £15 × 10 = £150.

4 A man and woman and their two children went on a package tour to Moscow.
  The cost was £350 per person, with 10% discount for children.
  (a) Calculate the cost for the whole family.
  While they were in Moscow they went to the Kremlin three times, at a cost of 5 roubles per person each time.
  (b) How much did their Kremlin visits cost in pounds if £1 = 1·3 roubles?

  (a) Cost of tour £1330   (b) Cost of visits to Kremlin = £46·15

  2 adults cost £700
  2 children cost £630   90% of £700
  Total cost is £1330.

  Easily done on my calculator as
  350 ☒ 2 ⊞ 350 ☒ 2 ☒ 0·9 ⊜

  The Kremlin visits cost 20 roubles each time.
  Cost for 3 visits = 60 roubles
  In pounds: 60 roubles = £60 ÷ 1·3
                    = £46·15.

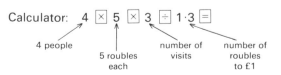

Calculator: 4 ☒ 5 ☒ 3 ÷ 1·3 ⊜

4 people   5 roubles each   number of visits   number of roubles to £1

5 Mei-Li went on a skiing holiday to France. She took £60 spending money which she exchanged for francs at 11 francs to £1.
(a) How many francs did she get?
When she gets home again she has 250 F left.
(b) How much is this worth in pounds, at 12 F = £1?

(a) 660 F   (b) £20·83

(a) Each £1 is worth 11 francs, so £60 = 60 × 11 F = 660 francs.

(b) Each 12 F buys £1 back, so 250 F will buy £250 ÷ 12 = £20·83.

Note: The 'buying price' and 'selling price' for francs [or any other foreign currency] are not the same. This is because the banks take a profit on the exchange. On a cross-channel ferry going from France to England the ship's purser buys francs for pounds. He sells francs to people going the other way. Very good business indeed when you think that the boat may cross to and fro six times in one day!

6 Mr and Mrs Sharp want to insure the contents of their home. Their belongings are valued at £8300. [This is what it would cost to replace everything if it were burnt.] The rate is 37p per £100. What will the insurance cost?

£30·71

This is a very easy question. Each £100 of their property costs 37p to insure.
£8300 = 83 × £100
So the cost would be 37p × 83 = £30·71.

7 Mr and Mrs McLean won £3000 on the football pools. Instead of spending it they deposited it straight away in a building society. The interest rate was $8\frac{1}{2}\%$ p.a., calculated half yearly. What was their prize worth after three years?

£3851·04

The interest rate is $8\frac{1}{2}\%$ p.a. payable half yearly. So in each half year £1 grows to £1·0425. There are 6 half years in three years so each £1 grows to $(1·0425)^6 = 1·283\,67\ldots$
£3000 grows to £3000 × $(1·0425)^6$ = £3851·04   Calculator: 1·0425 ⊠ ⊠ 3000 = = = = = =
                                                         or 3000 ⊠ 1·0425 x^y 6 =

Note: $8\frac{1}{2}\%$ p.a. usually is taken to equal $4\frac{1}{4}\%$ every half year if interest is payable half yearly.

You can see the money growing half yearly in this table:
  £3000
  £3127·50 after 6 months
  £3260·42 after 1 year
  £3398·99 after $1\frac{1}{2}$ years
  £3543·44 after 2 years
  £3694·04 after $2\frac{1}{2}$ years
  £3851·04 after 3 years

Note: This question is rather hard because the half-yearly payments can lead to mistakes.

8 George is an insurance salesman and his friend Sandra works in the head office of the same company. In the same week ... George earned a basic wage of £75 plus 8% commission on sales totalling £3800. Sandra earned £5·75 an hour for a 35-hour week plus 6 hours' overtime at time and a half. What did they each earn in that week?

George: £379   Sandra: £253

George's commission comes to 8% of £3800: $0·08 \times £3800 = £304$.
George earns $£304 + £75 = £379$.

        ↑   ↑
  Commission basic wage

Sandra earns 35 hours at $£5·75 = £201·25$
and 6 hours at $£5·75 \times 1·5$ $= £51·75$
Sandra's total wage is £253.
The calculations can both be done in one sequence if you have a scientific calculator.

George: 75 [+] 3800 [×] 0·08 [=]
Sandra: 35 [×] 5·75 [+] 6 [×] 1·5 [×] 5·75 [=]

Note: It works out the same if you count Sandra's overtime as 9 hours at
£5·75, i.e. multiply her number of hours' overtime by $1\frac{1}{2}$.
Her wages are then found to be $44 \times £5·75 = 253$.]
                  ↑
               (35 + 9)

9 A bubble bath is offered at a 'bargain' price of £1·25 for 50 ml. The bottle holds seven 'measures'. What is
(a) the cost per litre of the liquid?
(b) the cost per measure of the liquid?

(a) £25   (b) 18p

(a) 50 ml cost £1·25
    1 litre = 1000 ml
        = 20 × 50 ml.
    So 1 litre costs $£1·25 \times 20 = £25$.
(b) Simple. The bottle costs £1·25
    Each measure costs $£1·25 \div 7 = £0·178 ...$
                        = 18p (rounding to nearest penny).

10 In 1985 a woman and her husband together earned £18 000 p.a. Their combined personal allowances came to £4410. (They were taxed separately.) They were also paying 12% interest on their mortgage of £22 000. In 1985/1986 income tax was charged at 30% of taxable income.
(a) Calculate the interest they paid on their mortgage.
(b) Calculate their taxable income.
(c) Calculate the tax they had to pay in 1985/86 [30p in the £1].

(a) £2640   (b) £13 590   (c) £4077

This is an important calculation if you want to check how much income tax you should pay.

(a) Interest is 12% on £22 000 = 0·12 × £22 000
$$= £2640.$$

(b) The taxable income is found by subtracting the allowances from the income:
£18 000 − £4410 = £13 590.

(c) The tax is 30p for every pound of taxable income:
0·30 × £13 590 = £4077.

11 Mrs James shares a flat with her son. The rateable value of the flat is £350. The local rate is 140p in the pound.
(a) Calculate the rate payable.
(b) Calculate the increase that will be payable if the rates go up by 25p in the pound.

(a) £490   (b) £87·50

(a) The rates that have to be paid are 140p for every £1 of rateable value:
1·40 × £350 = £490.

(b) If the rates increase by 25p, this will mean an extra 25p will have to be paid for every £1 of rateable value:
0·25 × £350 = £87·50.

Note: The new total rates payable would be £490 + £87·50 = £577·50, but this was not asked for in the question.

12 Tim and Jim started a decorating business after leaving college. They borrowed £6000 from the bank to buy equipment and a van. The bank charges 16% compound interest and expects them to pay back £120 per month of the loan as shown on the loan statement.
(a) What do you notice about the interest payments?
(b) Explain how the interest is calculated.
(c) Complete the next four lines of the loan account. [The entries for November and December.]

T.Smith and J.Jones   LOAN ACCOUNT

Date	Debit	Debit	Credit	Balance
1 Sept				6000 OD
30 Sept	Interest	80		6080 OD
	Repayment		120	5960 OD
31 Oct	Interest	79.46		6039.46 OD
	Repayment		120	5919.46 OD

(a) The interest payment reduces as the loan is paid back.
(b) The rate is 16% p.a. This is treated as $\frac{16}{12}$% per month.
Interest = Outstanding loan × 0·16 ÷ 12.
(c) 30 Nov.   interest   £78.93D   £5998·39 OD
         repayment   £120C   £5878·39 OD
    31 Dec.   interest   £78·38D   £5956·77 OD
         repayment   £120C   £5836·77 OD

Interest on 30 November: £5919·46 × 0·16 ÷ 12 = £78·93.
Interest on 31 December: £78·93 × 0·16 ÷ 12 = £78·38.

13 Lucy is left £7000 by her grandfather (lucky girl!). She decides to either
  (a) invest the money at $8\frac{1}{2}$% p.a. interest and draw the interest at the end of
      the year, or
  (b) invest the money at 8% p.a. in a scheme where interest is added to capital
      each year.
  Calculate the interest she would receive under each scheme over 5 years.
  Which is the better of the two, do you think? Give your reasons.

  (a) £2975   (b) £3285   The second scheme earns more interest but in the
      first scheme Lucy has use of the money earlier.

  (a) Interest of £7000 × 0·085 will be paid for each of the five years. Total
      interest is £7000 × 0·085 × 5 = £2975.
  (b) After 5 years the £7000 will have grown to £7000 × $(1·08)^5$ = £10 285. Of
      this, £3285 is interest.

14 A special shampoo comes in three sizes. The
  quantities and prices are shown in the
  diagram. Which of the three is best value for
  money?

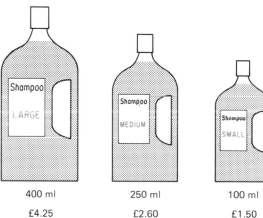

400 ml	250 ml	100 ml
£4.25	£2.60	£1.50

The 250 ml size is the cheapest.
400 ml costs £4·25 → £10·625 per litre, since 1 litre = 2·5 × 400 ml, 1 litre
costs 2·5 × £4·25.
250 ml costs £2·60 → £10·40 per litre, since 1 litre = 4 × 250 ml.
100 ml costs £1·50 → £15 per litre, since 1 litre = 10 × 100 ml.

15 A firm which has been paying wages weekly goes over to a monthly
  system. Wages are transferred into the employees' bank accounts on the
  last day of each month. How much should be transferred each month to
  (a) a secretary who was earning £125 a week after tax?
  (b) a manager earning £8950 p.a. after tax?
  (c) a driver who was earning £85 a week plus £32 overtime?

  (a) £541·67   (b) £745·83   (c) £507 less tax

  (a) The secretary earns £125 a week. In a year he would earn
      £125 × 52 = £6500. Divided into 12 equal payments this becomes
      £6500 ÷ 12 = £541·67 per month.
  (b) £8950 per year becomes
      £8950 ÷ 12 = £745·83 per month.
  (c) The total wages come to £117 per week. In a year (if the driver keeps up
      the overtime) she will earn £117 × 52 = £6084.
      Divided into twelve equal payments this becomes £6084 ÷ 12 = £507 per
      month.

Notes: (i) The answers take no account of National Insurance deductions and assumes that holidays are taken with pay.

(ii) The driver in part (c) will have tax deducted monthly. It is not possible to say how much without more information. The answer assumes the same amount of overtime is worked every week of the year.

(iii) All the above calculations can be done directly on the calculator but if you make a mistake you will get no marks unless you have shown the stages.

(a) 125 $\boxed{\times}$ 52 $\boxed{\div}$ 12 $\boxed{=}$ 541·67

(b) 8950 $\boxed{\div}$ 12 $\boxed{=}$ 745·83

(c) 85 $\boxed{+}$ 32 $\boxed{=}$ $\boxed{\times}$ 52 $\boxed{=}$ $\boxed{\div}$ 12 $\boxed{=}$ 507

16 A shop pays its assistants £95 per week basic plus £4·50 an hour for overtime. The assistants also earn commission: $1\frac{1}{2}$% of the value of the goods they have sold is added to their wages. Ali works 6 hours' overtime in one week and sells £1350 worth of goods. What are his wages for that week?

£142·25

Ali earns	£95·00	basic
6 × £4·50	£27·00	overtime
and 0·015 × £1350	£20·25	commission
Total for week	£142·25	less tax

Calculator: 95 $\boxed{+}$ 6 $\boxed{\times}$ 4·5 $\boxed{=}$ $\boxed{+}$ 0·015 $\boxed{\times}$ 1350 $\boxed{=}$ £142·25

● See Note (iii) in question 15.

17 Stephanie earns £185 a week as a designer.
   (a) What is her annual income before tax?
   (b) If she has a total of £4800 allowances, how much income tax will she pay (at 30% per year)?
   (c) How much tax will she pay each week?

(a) £9620   (b) £1446   (c) £27·81

(a) £185 × 52 = £9620.
(b) Her allowances are £4800 so her taxable income is
   £9620 − £4800 = £4820.
   At 30% her tax will be 0·3 × £4820 = £1446.
(c) Her weekly tax will be £1446 ÷ 52 = £27·81.

The question doesn't ask for it, but her take-home pay will be
£(185 − 27·81) − National Insurance contribution = £157·19 − Nat. Ins.
i.e. about £150 per week.

18 The price of a motorbike is £4800 including VAT at 15%. How much is the VAT?

£626·09

£4800 is 115% of the price before VAT.
Price before VAT is £4800 ÷ 1·15 = £4173·91.

So VAT = £4173·91 × 0·15
       = £626·09 ... 15% of the pre-tax price
Check: £4173·91 + £626·09 = £4800.

Beware of the trap. The VAT is not 15% of £4800: the £4800 includes the VAT already.
[Check 'Key facts' section C.2.3 on VAT.]

19 A travel agent is giving $12\frac{1}{2}$% discount on all holidays over £250. What will be the discounted prices of these holidays?
(a) Two weeks in Istanbul, £650.
(b) Eight days in Leningrad, £380.
(c) Twelve fabulous days on a Nile cruise: £950.
(d) A weekend for two in Paris: £180.

(a) £568·75   (b) £332·50   (c) £831·25   (d) £180

(a) Price is £650. Discount = £650 × 0·125 = £81·25.
     Discounted price: £650 − £81·25 = £568·75.
(b) Price is £380. Discount = £380 × 0·125 = £47·50.
     Discounted price: £380 − £47·50 = £332·50.
(c) Price is £950. Discount = £950 × 0·125 = £118·75.
     Discounted price: £950 − £118·75 = £831·25.
(d) No discount because only holidays over £250 earn discount.

Note: There is a short cut to find the discounted prices: $12\frac{1}{2}$% discount means
      £1 → 87·5p. So multiplying the cost by 0·875 produces the discounted
      price.

Calculator: Use constant multiplier   0·875 ☒ ☒ 650 ☐ 380 ☐ 950 ☐

                                   (a) Istanbul
                                       (b) Leningrad
                                            (c)Nile

The 'Blue Mosque',
Istanbul

20 Use the table to answer the following questions.
  (a) A fridge–freezer costs £285. Susan pays £85 cash down and the balance on hire purchase over 18 months. What are the monthly payments?
  (b) Desirée can only afford to pay about £5 per month for a camera, after a deposit of £20. What is the price of the most expensive one she can buy?
  (c) Is it cheaper to take a longer hire purchase agreement than a shorter one? Give reasons for your answer.

Balance of cash price to pay	12 months		18 months		24 months	
	Total HP cost	Monthly payment (12)	Total HP cost	Monthly payment (18)	Total HP cost	Monthly payment (24)
10	11·28	0·94	11·88	0·66	12·72	0·53
20	22·56	1·88	23·76	1·32	25·20	1·05
50	56·28	4·69	59·40	3·30	62·64	2·62
100	112·56	9·33	118·80	6·60	125·04	(b) 5·21
200	225·00	18·75	237·50	(a) 13·20	250·08	10·42
500	562·80	46·90	594·00	33·00	626·40	26·20
1000	1125·60	93·30	1118·00	66·00	1250·40	52·21
2000	2251·20	186·60	2236·00	132·00	2500·80	104·42

(a) £13·20   (b) £120·00   (c) No it is not cheaper. You pay less each month but you have to pay more instalments. The total cost is more for a longer agreement.

(a) Susan still has to pay another £200 after putting down £85 as deposit. Under an HP agreement this will cost 18 monthly payments of £13·20 each.

(b) Desirée's monthly payment of £5·21 will allow her to borrow £100. Her deposit of £20 makes that up to £120 maximum for her camera.

Topic D **Geometry**

Content

Lines, angles and intersections; rectilinear shapes; circles; transformations; solids; nets.

Self assessment

The purpose of these three tasks is to find out whether you need revision on topic D or whether you can go on to the next revision topic. There is no time limit on these assessments.

When you have finished part I, check your score (answers on p. 423). Then try parts II and III (answers on pp. 423–425). If you score more than 80% go on to topic E and come back to topic D later (if you have time).

If you score less than 80% you should work your way through the revision of this topic.

Part I

1 The value of *x* is
   A 10°   B 70°
   C 50°   D 150°

3 Only one of the figures below is rectilinear. Which one is it?

A

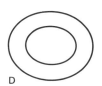

B

2 AD is not parallel to BC because
   A CÂD = CB̂D
   B CÂD ≠ CB̂D
   C CB̂D ≠ AD̂B
   D AĈB = AD̂B

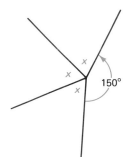

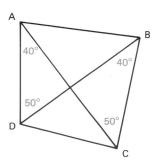

[≠ means 'not equal to']

4 BÂC + ACB = 90° because
A AĈB > BÂC
B The angles of a triangle add up to 180°.
C The exterior angle of a triangle is the sum of the opposite interior angles.
D $a^2 + c^2 = b^2$.

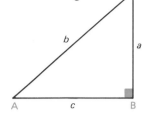

5 Which statement is not true?
A There are no right-angled triangles in the diagram.
B There are no rhombuses in the diagram.
C There are no equilateral triangles in the diagram.
D There are five different sizes of isosceles triangles in the diagram.

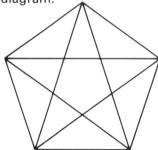

6 Which of these statements is not true about an isosceles triangle?
A The base angles are equal.
B The perpendicular bisector of the base passes through the vertex.
C All the angles are equal.
D All the angles add up to 180°.

Vertex

Base angles

7 If a right-angled triangle is also isosceles, its angles are
A 60°, 60°, 60°   B 60°, 90°, 30°
C 45°, 90°, 45°   D 60°, 90°, 120°

8 Any quadrilateral ABCD is drawn. The midpoints of its sides are marked P, Q, R, S. The new quadrilateral PQRS must be
A a rhombus.   B a rectangle.
C a parallelogram.   D a square.

9 Make a list of all the different sorts of quadrilateral you know.

10 A quadrilateral is drawn with opposite sides equal. It must be
A a square.   B a rectangle.
C a rhombus.   D a parallelogram.

11 ABCD is a rhombus. AD̂B = 28°.
(i) What other angles are 28°?
(ii) What is the size of CÂD?
(iii) What is the size of BCD?

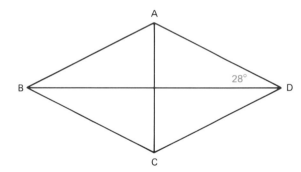

12 Which one of the following shapes is impossible to draw?
A A parallelogram with angles of 90°.
B A rhombus with two axes of symmetry.
C A rectangle with all its sides equal.
D A rectangle with one diagonal longer than the other.

13 What is the size of each interior angle of a regular pentagon?

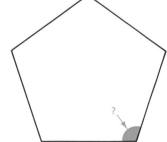

14 Every quadrilateral has two diagonals. How many diagonals has
(i) a pentagon   (ii) a hexagon?

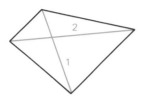

15 This polygon has 7 sides.
(i) How many triangles are formed if each vertex of the polygon is joined to O?
(ii) What is the total of all the angles in these triangles?
(iii) Deduce the sum of the angles of the polygon.

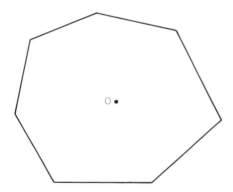

16 A circle is drawn with radius 8 cm.
(i) What is the length of the longest chord that can be drawn across the circle?
(ii) What is the special name of that chord?

17 Draw a circle and mark the following things on it, so that they can be seen clearly:
(i) the circumference;   (ii) a segment;
(iii) a sector;   (iv) an arc.

18 The number π connects two measurements on a circle by the formula $X = \pi Y$.
What are X and Y?

19 (i) How many axes of symmetry can be drawn on a circle?
(ii) What can you say about all the axes of symmetry?

20 The diagram shows a circle, centre O. A chord PQ has been drawn and the axis of symmetry is also shown. Write down all you know about the triangle OPQ.

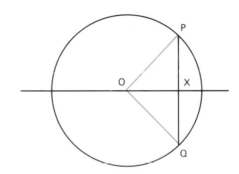

Part II

1 AB is the diameter of the circle, C lies on the circumference. Calculate (i) $\hat{C}$;   (ii) $\hat{B}$.

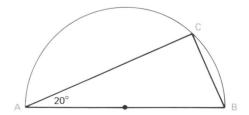

2 (a) Name two cyclic quadrilaterals in the diagram.
  (b) Calculate $\hat{C}$ and $\hat{D}$.
  (c) What can you deduce about $D\hat{E}C$ and $D\hat{B}C$?

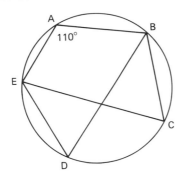

3 Which of the following statements are true?
$\hat{E} = \hat{D}$ $\hat{D} = \hat{C}$ $\hat{E} = \hat{C}$
Give a reason for your answer.

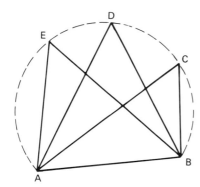

4 (i) Which two lines are tangents to the circle?
  (ii) What can you say about their lengths? Give a reason for your answer.

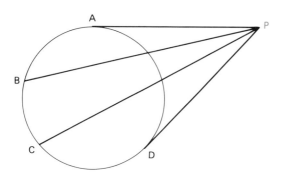

5 Copy the diagram on to squared paper and draw the reflection of the coloured shape in the y axis.

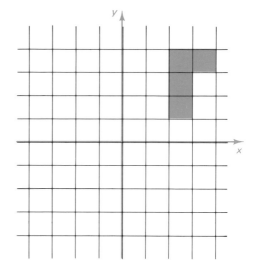

6 Which of these statements are true for the diagram?
  A Triangle 2 is a reflection of triangle 1.
  B Triangle 5 is a reflection of triangle 2.
  C Triangle 3 is a reflection of triangle 5.
  D Triangle 4 is a reflection of triangle 2.

◆7 (a) Calculate BÂD.
(b) Find AB̂D.
(c) Find AĈD.

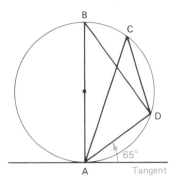

8 If the square is reflected in the line $y = x$ find
(i) the coordinates of the four corners of the image square;
(ii) the coordinates of the centre of the image square.

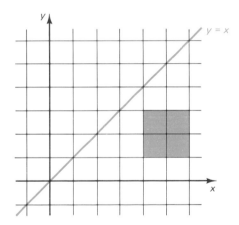

9 AB is the axis of symmetry of a shape. One half of the shape is shown in colour. Draw the complete shape.

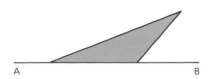

10 (i) Copy the rhombus and mark two axes of symmetry.
(ii) Which shapes are reflections in the axes of symmetry?
(iii) Copy and complete this sentence. 'For any rhombus ABCD, AC is always . . . to BD'.

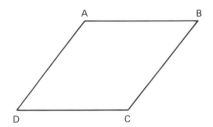

11 Which one of these shapes does not have a centre of rotational symmetry?
A rectangle   B parallelogram
C trapezium   D square

12 The triangle PQR is rotated through a half turn (180°) about O, the point (0, 0). What are the coordinates of P', Q', R'?

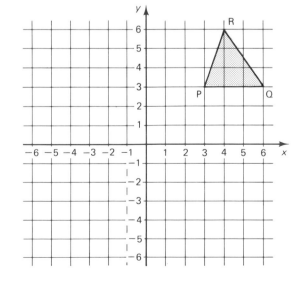

13 How many different translations can you see in this design?

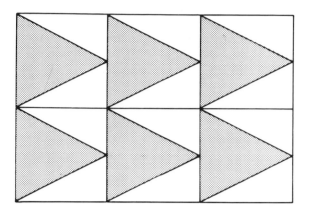

14 Which of the following will result in a translation?
   (i) A reflection in the x axis followed by a reflection in the y axis.
   (ii) A reflection in the y axis (x = 0) followed by a reflection in the line x = 3.
   (iii) A half turn with centre (0, 0) followed by a half turn with centre (3, 3).
   Use squared paper.

15 Read this description: 'A solid has faces, edges and vertices. All the faces have the same shape and all the edges have the same length. There are four vertices.'
   The solid is
   A a cube   B a cuboid
   C a square pyramid   D a tetrahedron

16 A can of soup is 20 cm high and 10 cm wide. What is the longest possible distance from a point on the top rim to a point on the bottom rim of the can?

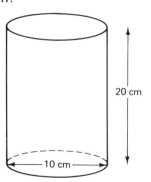

20 cm

10 cm

17 What solid shapes could be made from the nets below?

(a)

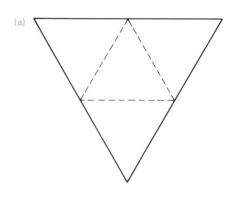

(b)

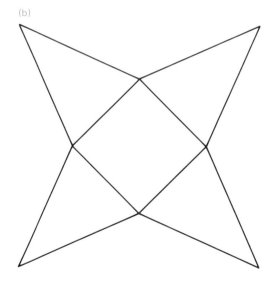

(c)

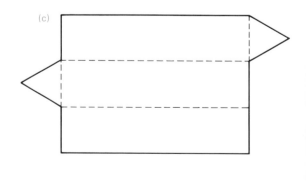

18 A man is trying to get a chest of drawers into the back of his van. The chest of drawers is a cuboid with diagonals 150 cm, 90 cm and 120 cm on its three faces. The space in the van is also a cuboid, 1·1 metres wide, 1 metre high and 1·5 metres long. Will he be able to get the chest into the van?
Explain your answer.

Part III

♦ **1** (a) ABC is any triangle.
Prove that AĈD − CB̂A + BÂC.

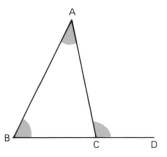

(b) OP, OQ, OR are radii of the circle.
Prove that QÔR = 2QP̂R.

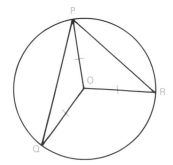

♦ **2** (a) X, Y are the mid-points of AB and AC.
Prove that XY is parallel to BC.
Suggested steps . . .
1∅ Draw a line parallel to BA, through C.
2∅ Extend XY until it meets 1∅.
3∅ Find a pair of congruent triangles.
4∅ Deduce a parallelogram.

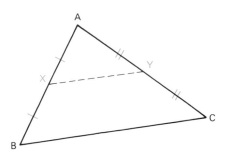

(b) Prove that the mid-points of the sides of any quadrilateral are the vertices of a parallelogram. What difference does it make if the quadrilateral is
  (i) a parallelogram   (ii) a rhombus
  (iii) a rectangle   (iv) a square.

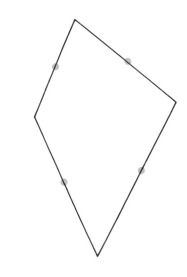

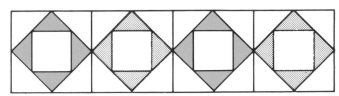

3 (a) The angles of a regular polygon are all 140°. How many sides has the polygon? [Give reasons for your answer].

(b) Calculate the area of the polygon given that each side is 8 cm in length.

Hint:

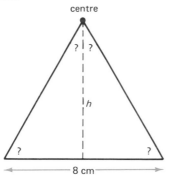

◆ 4 The length of the arc PQ is the same as the length of each radius.

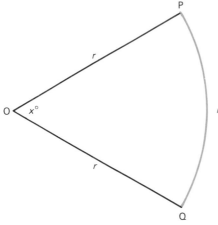

(a) Calculate the value of *x* in degrees. [This angle is called a radian.]

(b) Show that the area of the sector OPQ = $\frac{1}{2}r^2$. ie. Half the square of the radius.

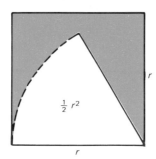

◆ 5 (a) $\hat{DAC} = \hat{DBC}$
Prove that the circle through B, C and D must also pass through A.

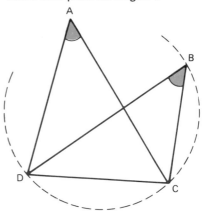

(b) The two angles are separated and placed over each other in a different position.

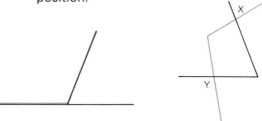

Prove that, wherever they are placed it is always possible to draw a circle which passes through X, Y and both angle vertices.

6 The quadrilateral PQRS has its sides extended until they meet at X and Y.

(a) In what ways does the figure SXQY resemble a quadrilateral.

(b) Investigate what happens to SXQY if PQRS is changed to a 'special' quadrilateral.

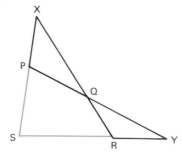

7 (a) Count the number of faces, vertices and edges of the fortress gate in the picture.

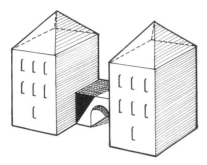

Does it satisfy Eulers formula
$$F + V = E + 2$$

(b) Show that Eulers formula is true for
 (i) a tetrahedron
 (ii) a pyramid on a square base.
(c) Design a solid with 9 faces and 9 vertices.

8 (a) What shapes would be exposed if the cube is cut with a plane
 (i) through AB and GH
 (ii) through the mid-points of AB, BC and BF.

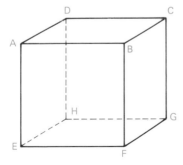

(b) How could the cube be cut to expose two hexagonal faces?
(c) What solid is formed by joining the mid-points of the faces of the cube? Describe the solid in as much detail as you can.

9 (a) Find a pair of congruent triangles in the figure. Give reasons for your choice. Can you make any deductions about the square AXYQ and the rectangle PQRS

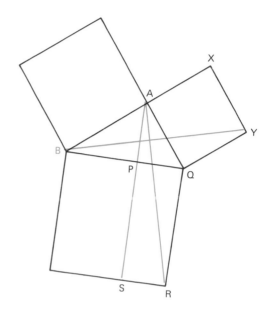

(b) List six pairs of congruent triangles in the figure.
PQRST is a regular pentagon.

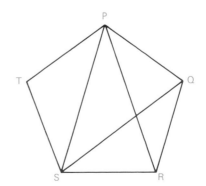

♦ **10** If two triangles have equal angles to one
another they are called similar triangles.
One triangle will be an enlargement of the
other.
This means that corresponding sides will be
in the same ratio.

$$\frac{AB}{PQ} = \frac{BC}{QR} = \frac{CA}{RP}$$

Also: Ratios of sides within each triangle
are the same.

$$\frac{AB}{AC} = \frac{PQ}{PR}, \quad \frac{AB}{BC} = \frac{PQ}{QR}, \dots \text{ etc.}$$

Corresponding sides are opposite
corresponding angles.

△ABC → △PQR

AB → PQ (opposite ▲)
BC → QR (opposite △)
CA → RP (opposite △)

(a) Find a pair of similar triangles in the
diagram below.

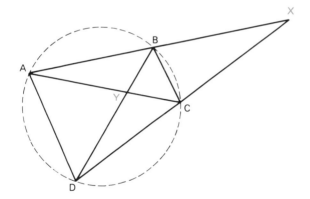

(b) Use the triangles you have found to
prove that XA · XB = XC · XD
[· means 'multiplied by']

(c) (i) All the lines drawn from a point P to
cut a circle have a ratio property in
common. What is it?

(ii) PT is a tangent to the circle. What
does the ratio property in (i) become
in this case?

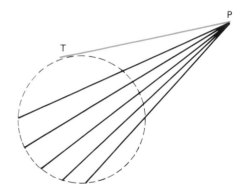

(d) Investigate the situation when P is
inside the circle.

Key facts D

D.1 Lines, angles and intersections

The fundamental 'building bricks' of geometry are
(1) lines and the angles between them, and
(2) points and the distance between them.
Make sure, as you read the following summary, that you really understand
the facts that are being presented.

D.1.1 Angles at a point add up to 360°

360°
angle

The angle on a straight line is 180°.
It makes no difference if lines are present.

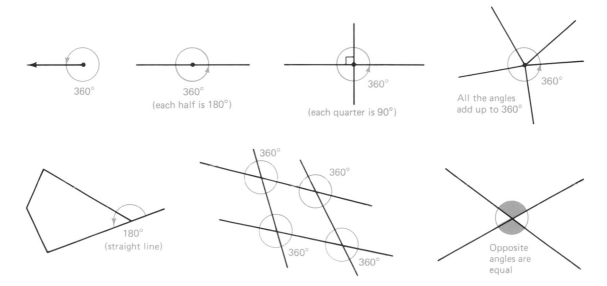

360°

360°
(each half is 180°)

360°
(each quarter is 90°)

360°
All the angles
add up to 360°

180°
(straight line)

360°

360°

360°

360°

Opposite
angles are
equal

D.1.2 Parallel lines make special angles

Parallel lines run in the same direction.

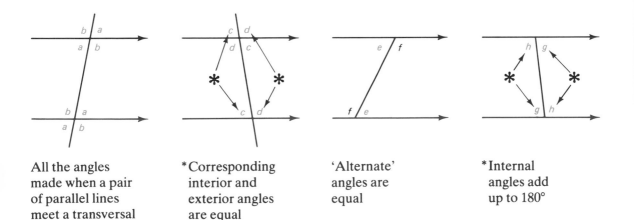

All the angles
made when a pair
of parallel lines
meet a transversal

*Corresponding
interior and
exterior angles
are equal

'Alternate'
angles are
equal

*Internal
angles add
up to 180°

Any line across parallel lines is called a transversal.

Exercise D.1

1 Calculate the size of the angles marked
a in the diagram. C

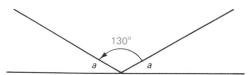

2 Which angles are 40° in this diagram? C

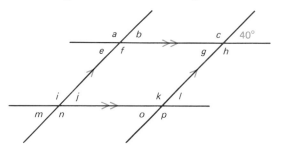

3 △ABC is isosceles. Calculate BÂC. C

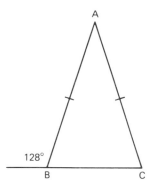

4 A quadrilateral ABCD has opposite
angles equal. Prove that ABCD must be
a parallelogram. B

D.2   Rectilinear shapes

Rectilinear shapes are made up entirely of straight lines. The usual
shapes are the ones that enclose space. You could think of important
rectilinear shapes that do not.

Examples
Capital letter, M X Z etc.
Electronic numbers.

$0\ 1\ 2\ 3\ 4\ 5\ 6\ 7\ 8\ 9$

Integrated circuits in electronic devices

Spirals

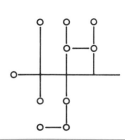

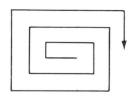

In geometry, however, the main shapes that we study are triangles (3 lines), quadrilaterals (4 lines) and polygons (more than 4 lines).

D.2.1 Triangles

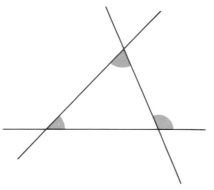

For every triangle:
  (i) there are three sides
 (ii) there are three internal angles
(iii) the three angles have a sum of 180°
(iv) every external angle is equal to the sum of the opposite internal angles
       [This follows from (iii): can you see why?]
 (v) the longest side must be shorter than the other two sides combined
(vi) the longest side is opposite the largest angle, etc.
       [What do you think 'etc.' means here?]

D.2.2 Special triangles

There are three special types of triangle you should know about: equilateral, isosceles and right angled

Properties to remember

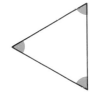

Equilateral
  (i) All sides are equal.
 (ii) All angles are 60°.
(iii) There are 3 axes of symmetry.
(iv) The bisectors of the vertices are also the perpendicular bisectors of the sides.

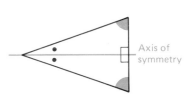
Three axes of symmetry

Isosceles
  (i) One pair of sides is equal.
 (ii) Angles opposite the equal sides are equal.
(iii) There is one axis of symmetry.
(iv) The bisector of the non-equal angle is also the perpendicular bisector of the side opposite to it.

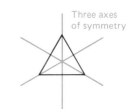
Axis of symmetry

Right angled
  (i) $a^2 + b^2 = c^2$ (Pythagoras' theorem).
 (ii) The sum of the other two angles is 90°.
(iii) Area $= \frac{1}{2}ab$.
(iv) The triangle divides into two similar ones.
 (v) The triangle divides into two isosceles ones.
(vi) O is the centre of the circle through the vertices.

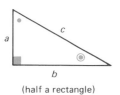
(half a rectangle)

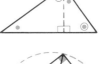
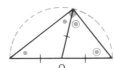

D.2.3 Quadrilaterals

A quadrilateral is formed when four straight lines intersect and enclose a space.
 (i) There are 4 sides and 4 vertices.
 (ii) The internal angles add up to 360°: $a + b + c + d = 360°$.
(iii) All quadrilaterals can be arranged in tessellations.

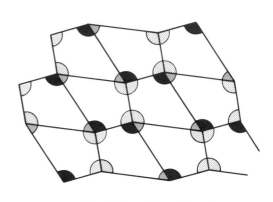

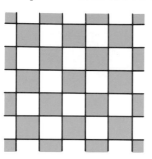

Tessellation with squares

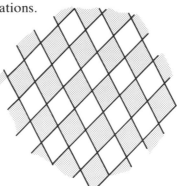

Tessellation with rhombuses

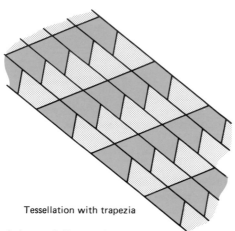

Tessellation with trapezia

Tessellation with quadrilaterals

D.2.4 Special quadrilaterals

Special quadrilaterals can be divided into two classes. Those which are
parallelograms (with both pairs of opposite sides parallel) and those
which are not.

Parallelograms

Rhombus: all sides equal

Rectangle: all angles equal

Square: all sides equal and
           all angles equal

Non-parallelograms

Trapezium

Isosceles trapezium

Kite

Cyclic quadrilateral

D.2.5   Properties of special quadrilaterals

These properties are worth remembering. The square is the most symmetrical.

Parallelogram

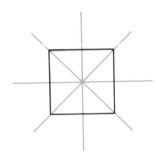

has opposite sides parallel
and ● opposite sides equal
     ● opposite angles equal
     ● diagonals bisecting each other
     ● rotational symmetry
     ● no axis of symmetry

Square

has all properties of parallelogram,
rectangle and rhombus

Kite

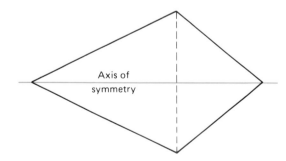

Axis of
symmetry

has two pairs of adjacent sides equal.
and ● one axis of symmetry
     ● one pair of equal angles
     ● perpendicular diagonals
     ● area equal to half the product of its
       diagonals (like the rhombus).

Rhombus

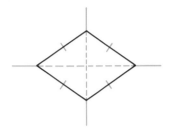

has all properties of parallelogram
and ● all sides equal
     ● diagonals are perpendicular
     ● diagonals bisect angles at vertices
     ● two axes of symmetry through vertices

Rectangle

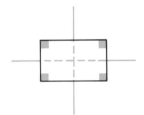

has all properties of parallelogram
and ● all angles equal to 90°
     ● diagonals equal in length
     ● two axes of symmetry through sides

Trapezium

has only one pair of parallel sides.

Isosceles trapezium

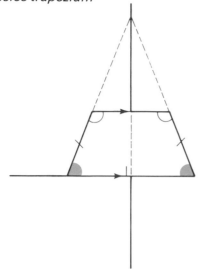

It is an isosceles triangle with its top cut off.
Also
● there are two pairs of equal angles
● the figure has one axis of symmetry
● the diagonals are equal

It is interesting that two parallel chords on a circle will always form an isosceles trapezium.

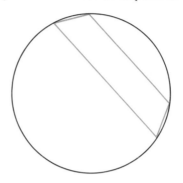

has a pair of parallel sides while the other two sides are equal.

◆ *Cyclic quadrilateral*

When four points on a circle are joined, a cyclic quadrilateral is formed.

Squares
Rectangles } are cyclic quadrilaterals
Isosceles trapezia

Parallelograms
Rhombuses
Kites } are not cyclic quadrilaterals
Ordinary trapezia

Try to draw them with all their vertices on a circle!

The diagonals of a cyclic quadrilateral show up interesting angle properties.

Lots of pairs of equal angles . . .

Four points on a circle

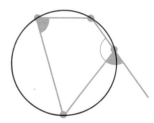

Cyclic quadrilateral:
● opposite angles add up to 180°
● each exterior angle is equal to the opposite interior angle

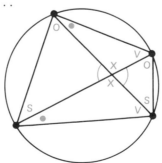

Can you discover any quadrilaterals which have not been included in this list.
If so, please write to the author!

D.2.6 Polygons

Closed rectilinear figures are called polygons, though some have special names. Triangles and quadrilaterals are themselves polygons.

Number of sides	Name of polygon
3	triangle
4	quadrilateral
5	pentagon ⎫
6	hexagon ⎬ worth remembering
8	octagon ⎭

Regular polygons have all sides equal and all angles equal.

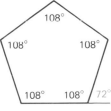

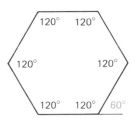

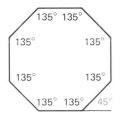

Regular pentagon   Regular hexagon   Regular octagon

- To find the angle of a regular polygon, first find the external angle.
  This will be $360°/n$ where n is the number of sides.
  The angle of the polygon is $180°$ − the external angle.
  [Check that this is correct for the regular pentagon (108°), regular hexagon (120°) and regular octagon (135°).]
Use the same method to find the interior angle of a regular 12-gon.

Exercise D.2

1 AB̂C and CX̂B are both right angles.
Calculate XB̂C, CÂB and AB̂X.

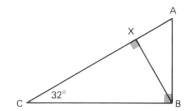

2 Make a list of all the special quadrilaterals you can see in the diagram.

C

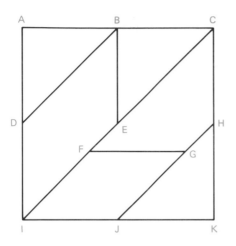

3 Calculate BÂD and DĈE. What other pairs of angles are equal in the diagram?

C

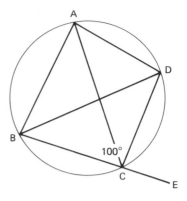

4 A polygon has fifteen equal sides. Calculate the size of its interior angles.

C

D.3 Circles

D.3.1 Parts of the circle

You should learn the meanings of the special circle words given below

centre
radius
diameter
circumference
arc
sector
chord
segment
tangent

and their relationships . . .

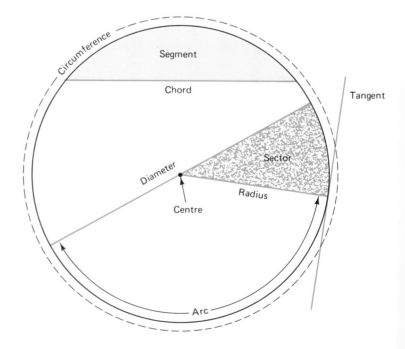

1: All points on the circumference are equal distance from the centre.
2: A radius is a straight line from the centre to the circumference.
3: A diameter is a straight line across the centre of the circle.
4: The diameter is twice as long as the radius.
5: The length of the circumference is π times the length of the diameter, or 2π times the length of the radius.
6: An arc is part of the circumference.

7: A sector is part of a circle between two radii.

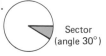

Sector (angle 30°)

8: A chord is the straight line between two points on the circumference.

Chord

9: A chord cuts a circle into two segments (while a diameter cuts a circle into two semicircles).

Minor segment

Major segment

10: A tangent touches a circle. The radius to its point of contact is perpendicular to the tangent.

D.3.2 Symmetry

Every circle has an infinite number of axes of symmetry. After a chord has been drawn on the circle there is only one axis of symmetry.

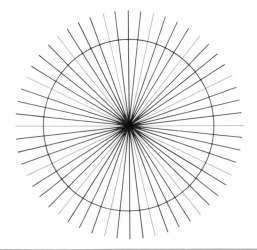

From the symmetry
(i) The perpendicular bisector of the chord will pass through the centre of the circle.
(ii) A line from the centre to the midpoint of the chord bisects the angle at the centre.

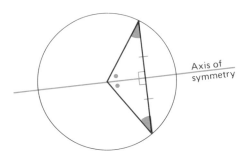

Axis of symmetry

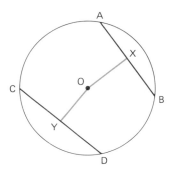

- AB and CD are equal chords: AB could be turned (about O) until it is exactly over CD.
- Equal chords are equal distances from the centre of the circle.

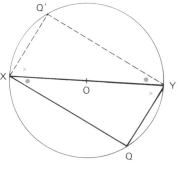

Axis of symmetry

- The figure has one axis of symmetry so OX = OY.

D.3.3 Angle in a semicircle

The angle in a semicircle must be a right angle and there are several ways of proving this.

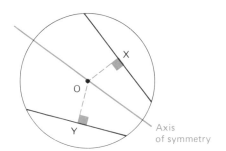

Proofs

1 Rotate △XQY about O through 180°.
XQYQ′ is a parallelogram with all four vertices on a circle.
XQYQ′ must therefore be a rectangle, so $\hat{Q} = 90°$.

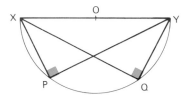

2 OX = OY = OP (all radii are equal).
△XOP and △YOP are isosceles so have equal base angles (shown as a, a, b, b)
$2a + 2b = 180° \Rightarrow a + b = 90°$.
Thus $\hat{P} = 90°$.

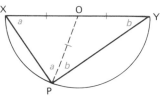

- You do not have to remember these proofs, but studying the proofs helps you to remember the important fact that the angle in a semicircle is 90°.

◆ D.3.4 Cyclic quadrilateral

A quadrilateral formed by joining up four points on a circle is called cyclic.
Every cyclic quadrilateral has special angle properties.

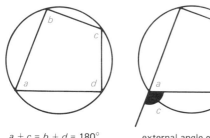
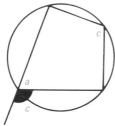
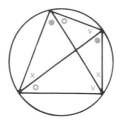

$a + c = b + d = 180°$
(proof below)

external angle equals opposite interior angle

If diagonals are drawn four pairs of equal angles are formed

Proof that opposite angles of a cyclic quadrilateral add to 180°

You do not need to learn this proof. It will, however, help you to remember the angle property.

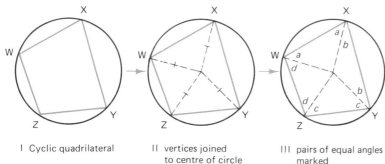

I Cyclic quadrilateral

II vertices joined to centre of circle forming four isosceles triangles

III pairs of equal angles marked

From figure III $2a + 2b + 2c + 2d = 360°$ ... angles in a quadrilateral
$$a + b + c + d = 180°$$
Both $\hat{X} + \hat{Z}$ and $\hat{W} + \hat{Y}$ are made up of $a + b + c + d$
So $\hat{X} + \hat{Z} = \hat{W} + \hat{Y} = 180°$

◆ D.3.5 Angles in the same segment

All the angles $\hat{P}, \hat{Q}, \hat{R}$ and $\hat{S}$ are equal. They are **all** equal to $180° - \hat{T}$. Can you see why?
Any point on the major arc from X to Y will have the same angle.

This situation is described by the theorem . . .
'Angles in the same segment are equal'.

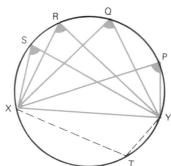

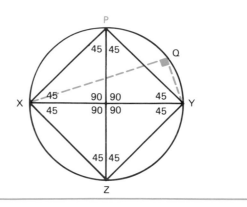

Special examples

1   Angle in a semicircle.
    It is obvious that $X\hat{P}Y = 90°$, so all
    other angles in the semicircle must
    be 90° (including $X\hat{Q}Y$).
2   Angles in a cyclic quadrilateral. [See
    section **D.3.4** diagram III]

D.3.6   Tangents

- Drawing a tangent to a circle selects one axis of
  symmetry.
  The tangent is perpendicular to the radius at
  the point of contact.
  Only one tangent can be drawn at a point on
  the circumference.
- Only two tangents can be drawn to a circle from
  a point outside.
  When the two tangents are drawn, the figure
  will have an axis of symmetry which will pass
  through
       (i) the centre of the circle,
  and (ii) the point where the tangents meet.

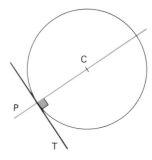

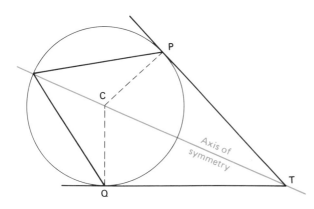

From this symmetry it can be seen that TQ = TP
(i.e. tangents to a circle from a point outside are
equal).
There are many other properties which follow
from this figure which you could explore. (Start
by putting $C\hat{T}P = a°$.)

◆D.3.7 Alternate segment theorem

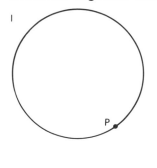

A circle is drawn

The tangent is drawn at P

A chord of the circle is drawn with one end at P

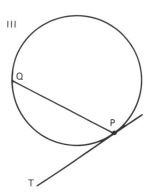

Any point X is chosen and PXQ is drawn.
Then $P\hat{X}Q = T\hat{P}Q$ wherever X is chosen.
This is known as the alternate segment theorem.
[What angle is equal to $X\hat{Q}P$?]

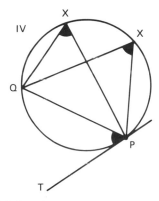

The following proof is given to help you grasp the theorem.
You should follow the proof and also check the theorem by careful drawing.

Proof of alternate segment theorem (in pictures)

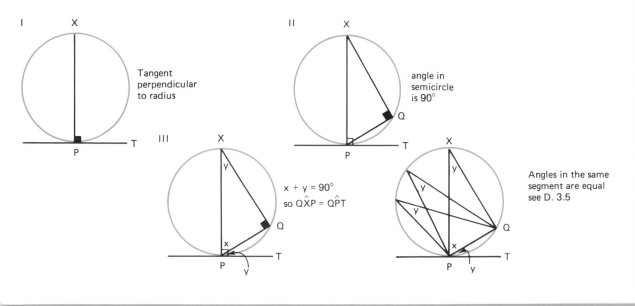

Tangent perpendicular to radius

angle in semicircle is 90°

$x + y = 90°$
so $Q\hat{X}P = Q\hat{P}T$

Angles in the same segment are equal
see D. 3.5

149

Exercise D.3

1 Draw a circle and add
   (a) a chord, (b) a diameter,
   (c) a sector.   C
   Label them clearly.

2 Given that $\hat{ADC} = 100°$ and $\hat{ACD} = 40°$
   calculate $\hat{DAC}$ and $\hat{DBC}$.   C

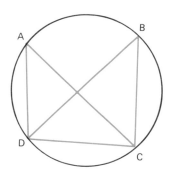

3 Copy the figure and mark in its axis of
   symmetry. Explain how you could find
   the exact centre of the circle by
   drawing.   C

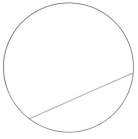

4 Draw the axes of symmetry for the
   following.
   (a) A circle where one tangent has
       been drawn.
   (b) A circle where two tangents have
       been drawn from a point outside
       the circle.
   (c) A circle where two tangents which
       do not meet have been drawn.   C

D.4 Transformations

Geometry can be looked on as a study of spatial patterns. Patterns are built
up by the movement of shapes, without changing the lengths or angles of the
shapes.
These movements are called isometric transformations. There are three types
which do not change size or angle: reflections, rotations and translations.

D.4.1 Reflections

Notes:
  (i) Triangle A'B'C' is called the 'image' of triangle ABC under reflection.
      This is because it is the mirror image of △ABC.
 (ii) AA', BB' and CC' have the axis as perpendicular bisector.

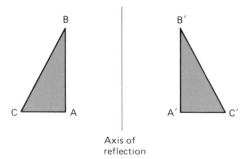

Axis of
reflection

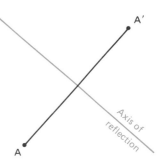

(iii) Geometrical reflection and mirror reflection are not quite the same thing. In geometry, both object ABC and image A′B′C′ are the same type of object, but a reflection of an object in a mirror is not the same type of thing as the object itself.

(iv) The reflection of A′ is A. Reflecting twice in the same axis takes you back to where you started.

D.4.2 Coordinates

The result of reflecting a point in an axis can be followed easily if the point is given coordinates.

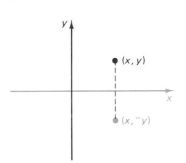

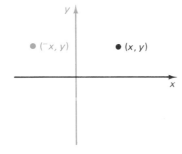

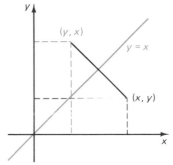

I $(x, -y)$ is the reflection of (x, y) in the x axis.

II $(-x, y)$ is the reflection of (x, y) in the y axis.

III (y, x) is the reflection of (x, y) in the line $y = x$.

You should practise reflecting points in different lines to make sure you know what is going on. Here are some to try.

(a) Reflect $(2, 3)$ in the x axis and the y axis.

(b) Reflect $(-2, 4)$ in the y axis and in $y = x$.

(c) Reflect $(2, 5)$ in the lines $x = 5$ and in $y = 3$.

D.4.3 Reflection and symmetry

If a figure has an axis of symmetry it can be reflected onto itself. △ABC will become △ACB after reflection in the axis of symmetry. Many designs make use of reflection.

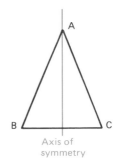

151

Example

These designs show clearly that two reflections
bring you back to the figure you started with.

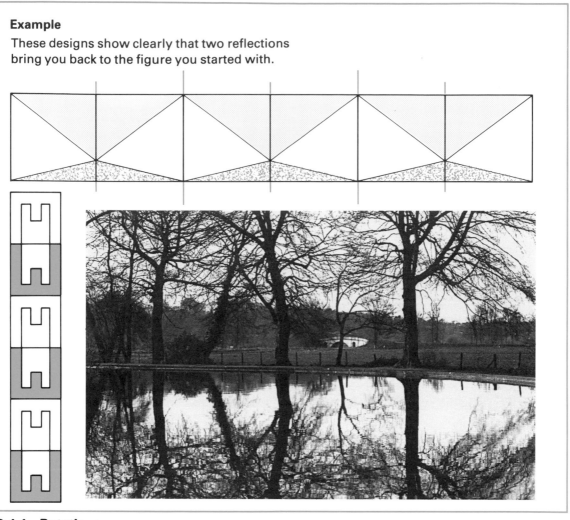

D.4.4 Rotations

Every rotation has a centre and an angle, and is either clockwise or
anticlockwise.

 Clockwise   Anticlockwise

Example

The flag has been rotated through 90° in an anticlockwise
direction about C.

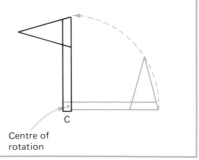

C

Centre of
rotation

The most important rotations for design are the half turn, quarter turn and rotation through 60°.

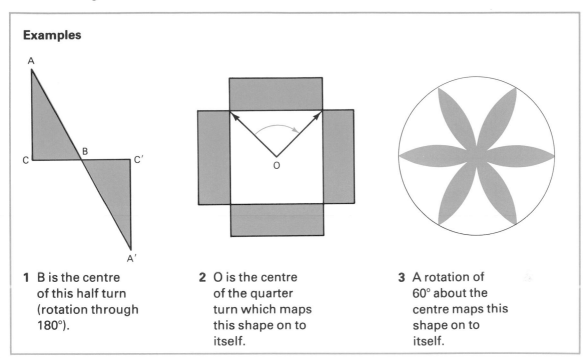

Examples

1 B is the centre of this half turn (rotation through 180°).

2 O is the centre of the quarter turn which maps this shape on to itself.

3 A rotation of 60° about the centre maps this shape on to itself.

D.4.5 Rotational symmetry

If a shape can be turned so that it covers its old position (as in Examples 2 and 3 in Section D.4.4), the shape has rotational symmetry.

- All parallelograms have rotational symmetry.
- All regular polygons have rotational symmetry and so do regular polygonal stars.

There are 5 different rotations which map the pentagon on to itself. We say the figure has rotational symmetry of order 5.

Any combination of a figure with its image from a half turn has rotational symmetry (see Example 1 in Section D.4.4 above).

Some letters of the alphabet have rotational symmetry.

- Rotational symmetry can be used to prove properties of shapes. For example, every parallelogram must have
  (i) opposite sides equal
  (ii) opposite angles equal, and
  (iii) diagonals which bisect each other at the centre of rotation.

A regular pentagon and its star

D.4.6 Coordinates and rotation

The half turn moves the point (x, y) to $(^-x, ^-y)$
e.g. $(3, 2) \rightarrow (^-3, ^-2)$.

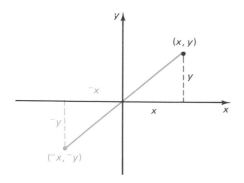

The anticlockwise quarter turn moves (x, y) to $(^-y, x)$
e.g. $(3, 2) \rightarrow (^-2, 3)$
.A second quarter turn will take you on to $(^-x, ^-y)$

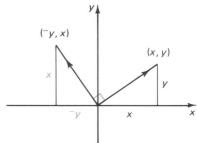

Example

The complete picture for (3, 2) turned anticlockwise is shown below.

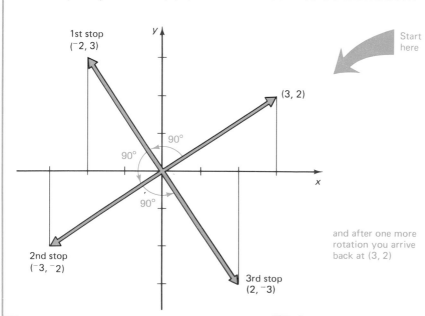

D.4.7 Translation

Translation is the simplest of the transformations. It happens when a shape is moved in any direction without turning.

A translation moves the point (x, y) to $(x + a, y + b)$.

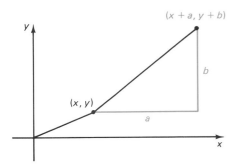

- A translation parallel to the x axis will map $(x, y) \to (x + a, y)$.
- A translation parallel to the y axis will map $(x, y) \to (x, y + b)$.

It is interesting to note that . . .　　two half turns produce a translation

and also . . .　　　　　　　　　　　two reflections in parallel axes produce a translation

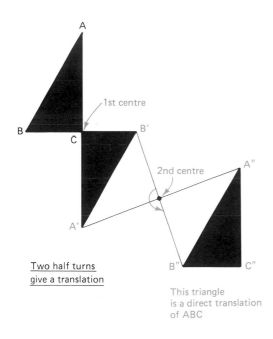

Two half turns
give a translation

This triangle
is a direct translation
of ABC

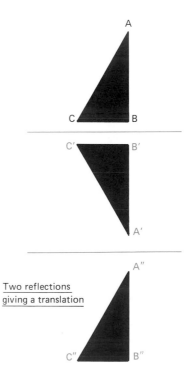

Two reflections
giving a translation

You might also like to show that a half turn can be produced by two reflections !!

Exercise D.4

1 Copy the figure and draw the reflection of ABCD in the axis.

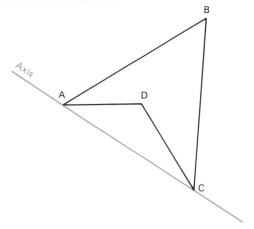

2 The line joining A (2, 3) and B (4, 5) is reflected in the *y*-axis. What are the coordinates of the midpoint of the reflected line? C

3 The triangle whose vertices are (2, 2); (2, 6) and (5, 2) is rotated anticlockwise through 90° about the point (0, 0). Draw a diagram to show the new position of the triangle. C

4 Identify these transformations as reflection, translation or rotation.
(a) A → F (b) C → G (c) E → D C

D.5 Solids

The solids you have to remember are

1: tetrahedron 2: cuboid 3: cube 4: prism 5: cylinder

One way of comparing solids is to compare edges, faces and vertices (corners).

D.5.1 Tetrahedron

Vertices at A, B, C and D . . .   4 altogether
Edges AB, AC, AD, BC, BD, CD . . .   6 altogether
Faces ABC, ABD, ADC, BCD . . .   4 altogether

The regular tetrahedron has all faces exactly the same shape (equilateral triangles) and all edges equal in length.

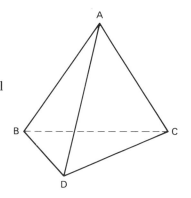

D.5.2 Cuboid

The cuboid is the ordinary 'brick shaped' solid. Each face is a rectangle.

Of the six faces,
two are $x \times y$
two are $x \times z$
two are $y \times z$ . . . 6 faces.

Of the twelve edges,
4 are x units long
4 are y units long
4 are z units long . . . 12 edges.
There are 8 vertices.

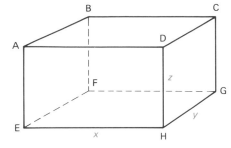

- There are 4 diagonals which pass through the centre of the cuboid.
- The cuboid has 3 axes of symmetry.

Faces	Edges		Vertices		Diagonals
ABCD	AB	CG	A	E	AG
BCGF	AD	DH	B	F	BH
FGHE	AE	EF	C	G	CE
EHDA	BC	EH	D	H	DF
ABFE	BF	FG			
CDHG	CD	GH			

D.5.3 Cube

The cube is the regular cuboid. Its faces are squares of the same size. All 12 edges are equal.
The cube has 13 axes of symmetry!! They all meet at the centre of the cube.

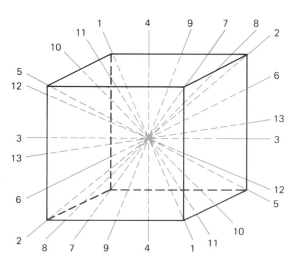

D.5.4 Prism

Any solid with a regular cross section is called a prism. A cuboid is a special case of a prism.

Examples

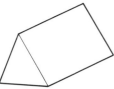

1 Cross section is a triangle.

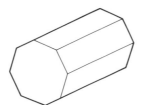

2 Cross section is a regular octagon.

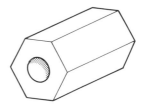

3 Cross section is a hexagon with circular hole.

• The volume of any prism is given by   Volume = Area of section × length

D.5.5 Cylinder

A cylinder is a prism (see Section D.5.4) with circular cross section.

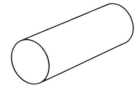

Exercise D.5

1 How many edges, vertices and faces are there in
(a) a cube   (b) a cuboid
(c) a tetrahedron
(d) a square-based pyramid?   C

2 Draw three different nets which could be made into cubes by folding and joining edges.   C

3 The net of a square pyramid is drawn by adding triangles to the sides of a square.
What can you say about the shapes of the triangles?
What can you say about the length of side of each triangle?   B

4 The three solids, cuboid, cylinder and triangular prism have one property in common. What is it? What formula for calculating volume would apply to all three solids?   B

D.6   Nets

If a solid is constructed out of flat card, the card shape used to make the solid is called the net.
Cube

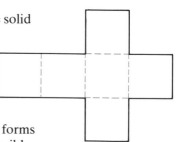

Several different forms of this net are possible.

Cuboid

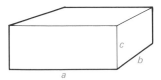

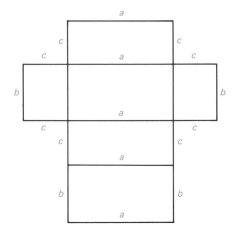

You can see that there are six
rectangles in this net:
$2 \times (a \times c), 2 \times (a \times b), 2 \times (b \times c)$

Prism (cylinder)

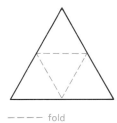

Regular tetrahedron

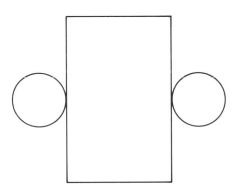

---- fold

Prism with hexagonal section

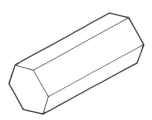

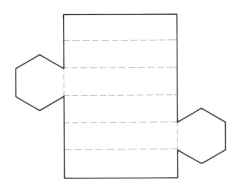

Examination questions D

The following questions are typical of the ones you can expect to find in your examination. Fully worked out answers are given on pages 182–199, but don't look at them until you have attempted the problems in this section. All diagrams should be drawn carefully using compasses and ruler and labelled clearly.

1 Draw an isosceles triangle with one side 5 cm long and at least one angle of 40°. Can you draw a second, different triangle from the same data?

2 O is the centre of the circle. Find an equation connecting x and y.

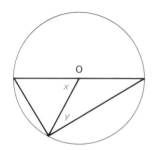

3 Calculate the values of s and t.

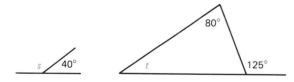

4 Find (i) The length of CH
(ii) The size of BĈH
Use the results to find BH.

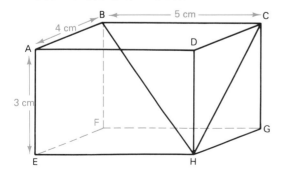

5 Draw a circle radius 4 cm. Draw
(a) a diameter,
(b) a chord perpendicular to the diameter, and
(c) a tangent at the end of the chord.

6 Calculate the value of y if △XYZ is isosceles.

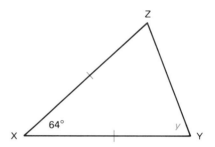

7 Which of the following is the right name for the figure PQRS?
(a) rhombus (b) rectangle
(c) parallelogram (d) trapezium

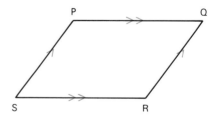

8 Draw any rectangle. Mark in
(a) the diagonals,
(b) the axes of symmetry, and
(c) the centre of rotational symmetry.

9 Copy the one figure from the three below which has rotational symmetry but no axis of symmetry.

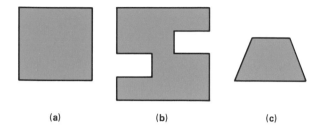

(a)   (b)   (c)

10 The diagram shows three telephone wires going from a pole to three different houses. Calculate *a*.

140°

130°

a

11 Write down the number of faces, edges and vertices for each of the figures below.

Tetrahedron

Cuboid

Pyramid on square base

12 TP and TQ are tangents to a circle with centre O. PȚO is 40° as shown. What are
(a) PȚQ   (b) TP̂Q   (c) PX̂T?

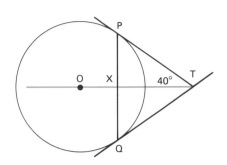

13 Calculate *x*, *y* and *z*.

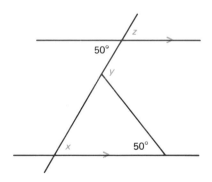

50°

z

y

x

50°

14 Calculate the values of *x* and *y*. Explain your reasoning carefully.

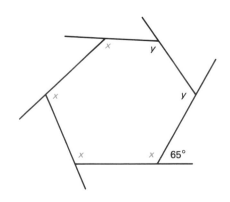

x   *y*

x   *y*

x   *x*   65°

15 Given that TA is a tangent to the circle at A, calculate the values of *p* and *q*.

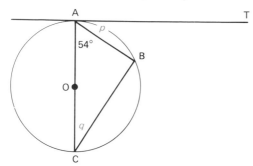

16 Measure the three angles of this triangle with your protractor. Comment on the results.

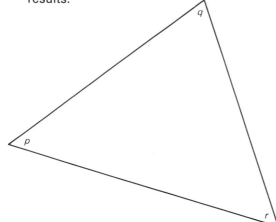

17 Draw the reflection of the coloured area in the axis.

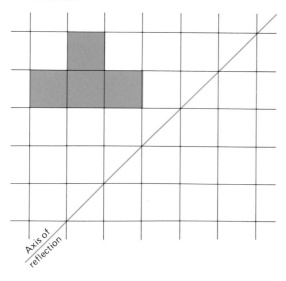

18 (a) What is the correct name for this shape?
(b) Show how it could be cut and rearranged into a parallelogram in two different ways.

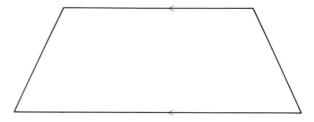

19 (a) Copy this simplified drawing of a house.
(b) Mark, in dotted lines, the unseen edges of the house.
(c) How many faces, edges and vertices does the house have?

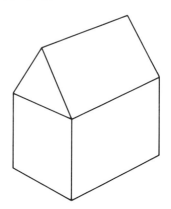

20 This shape is the net of a cube. Draw two more arrangements of six squares which will fold up into a cube.

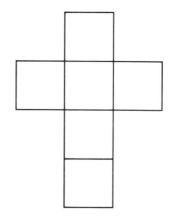

◆ 21 The only known facts about the triangles in the diagram are marked on them.
Is it possible that any pairs of triangles are congruent or similar?
Give reasons for your answers.

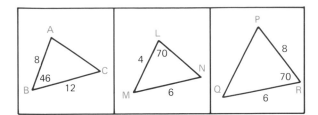

◆ 22 Triangle ABC has a right angle at C.
The lengths of the sides of △ABC are
AB = c cm
BC = a cm
CA = b cm.
(a) Find Â and B̂ and show that the figure consists of three similar triangles.
(b) BX = x cm. Show that
   (i) $cx = a^2$ (ii) $(c - x)c = b^2$
   Give reasons.

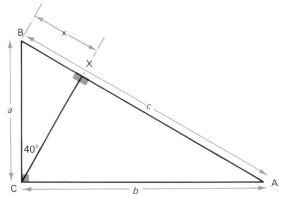

(c) Use the results (i) and (ii) to prove Pythagoras' theorem for △ABC. What changes need to be made in this question to prove Pythagoras' theorem for any triangle ABC, right angled at C?

◆ 23 (a) Prove that a quadrilateral whose opposite sides are equal must be a parallelogram.
(b) Prove that a parallelogram whose diagonals are equal must be a rectangle.

◆ 24 The semicircle shown is cut by a line XY (parallel to the base) which cuts the semicircle into two equal halves.

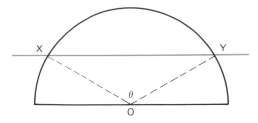

(i) Show that $\theta = 132 \cdot 35°$
(ii) Show that this value of θ fits the equation
$$\frac{\theta \times \pi}{180} - \sin \theta = \frac{\pi}{2}$$

Formulae: Area of a sector $= \frac{1}{2} r^2 \left[\dfrac{\theta \times \pi}{180} \right]$

Area of a $\triangle = \frac{1}{2} ab \sin C.$

◆ 25 XY is the perpendicular bisector of a line segment.
(i) P is any point on XY. Prove that PA = PB.
(ii) Q is not on XY. Prove that Q must be nearer to one of the points A,B than to the other.

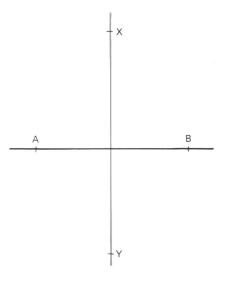

26 (a) Demonstrate how to bisect any angle using ruler and compass.
   (b) Draw accurate angles of
     (i) 90°   (ii) 45°   (iii) 60°
     (iv) 30°   (v) 75°.
     Explain the steps taken in each construction.

◆ **27** A theorem states ... 'The bisector of an angle of a triangle divides the opposite side in the ratio of the sides surrounding the angle'.
   (a) Test this suggestion by an accurate drawing.
   (b) Prove the theorem by considering the areas of the two parts of the original triangle.

◆ **28** A point A is chosen outside a circle. Lines from A meet the circle at B, C, D and E.
   (i) Given AB = AC prove AD = AE.
   (ii) Investigate a similar situation with A inside the circle.

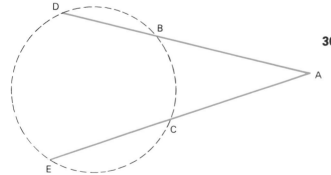

29 (a) Hexagons will form a tessellation and so will equilateral triangles. Construct a tessellation using a mixture of regular hexagons and equilateral triangles.
   (b) Investigate ways of constructing tessellations from a mixture of squares and equilateral triangles.

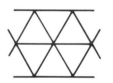

30 (a) What solid fits the following description?
    • It is not a prism.
    • It is not a pyramid.
    • It has no vertices.
    • It has one edge.
    • It has one plane (flat) face and one curved face.
    • The area of the curved face is double the area of the plane face.
   (b) List the number and type of faces, edges and vertices of the following objects.
    (i) A sharpened hexagonal pencil.
    (ii) A rugby football.
    (iii) A glass lens (convex).

Activities and investigations D

Are you in good shape?

A quiz on geometry names for 2 people . . . or maybe a panel game!
Each clue describes a geometrical shape. The name of the shape can be found
in the word list. It is also given jumbled up [as an anagram] so that you will
know if you have found the right answer. Try to complete this quiz in
30 minutes.

Clues		*Jumbled answers*
1	Solid with 12 edges.	DCBIOU
2	This shape can have lots of sides.	NYGPLOO
3	Its internal angles add up to 360°.	URARQDLELAITA
4	This quadrilateral has all its sides equal but not its angles.	HBRMSOU
5	A quadrilateral with 4 axes of symmetry.	ARQUES
6	This quadrilateral has all its angles equal but not its sides.	TGREALCEN
7	A closed shape made from one curved line and one straight line.	TMSGNEE
8	A quadrilateral with only one axis of symmetry.	ITKE
9	This shape has five sides and five vertices.	NTGPNEOA
10	A solid with four triangular faces.	NRTDAHERTOE
11	Part of a circle cut out by two radii.	CORSET
12	A quadrilateral with one pair of sides parallel.	PZITRAEMU
13	The shape you get if you cut the corners off question 5.	TGOANOC
14	A solid with a regular cross section.	SMIRP
15	The diagonals of this shape bisect each other [but they're not equal].	MERALOALRPLAG
16	Question 14 with a circular cross section.	EYINRDCL
17	The internal angles of this shape add up to 180°.	ENGLATIR
18	This question 17 has a pair of equal sides.	EESSSCLIO
19	The regular 3-sided polygon.	AL QUITE REAL ENGLATIR
20	A pyramid with a circular base.	ENOC

*Word list**

triangle	rhombus	sector
equilateral	kite	segment
isosceles	square	solid
right-angled	polygon	tetrahedron
quadrilateral	regular	pyramid
cyclic	pentagon	cube
trazepium	hexagon	cuboid
parallelogram	octagon	prism
rectangle	circle	cylinder
circumference	semicircle	cone

*Make sure you know the meaning of all these words.

Puzzles for two

This collection of puzzles will help you to remember important geometrical facts. They are also to be enjoyed.

1 Cut-and-rearrange

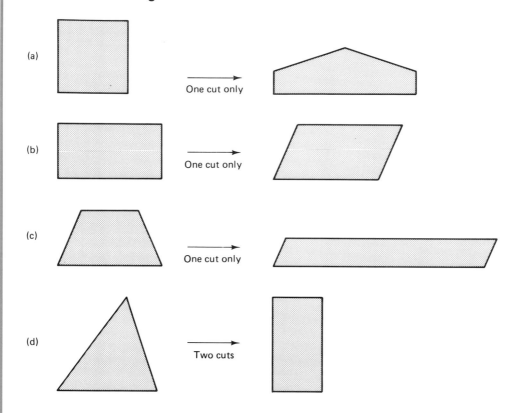

Design some more puzzles.

2 Cutting the circle

Can you design some more puzzles like this? Have a go.

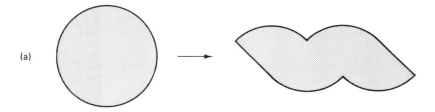

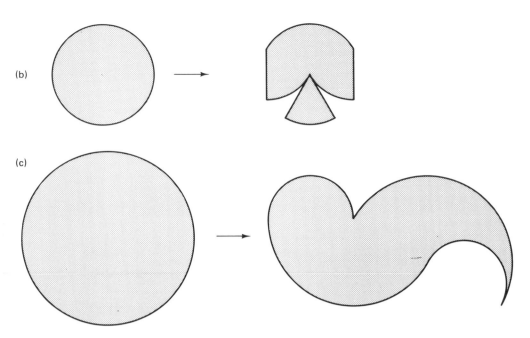

(b)

(c)

3 Cutting into half-size shapes

It is easy to cut triangles and rectangles into half-size copies of the original shapes.

(a) 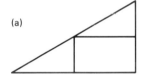   (b)

But what about these shapes . . . ?

(a) 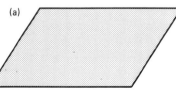   (b)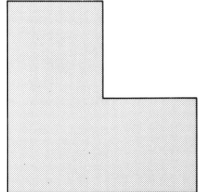

(c)

4 General puzzles

(a) Can you cut the cross so that it can be formed into a square?
[*Hint*: you can calculate the length of the side of the square first.]

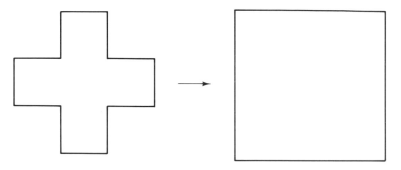

(b) The four pieces A, B, C and D can be arranged into another interesting figure. What is it?

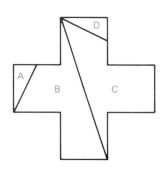

(c) Five triangles this size and shape can be arranged as a square, but one of the triangles will have to be cut first. Can you do it?

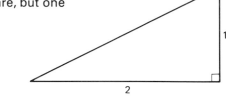

(d) This circle has been cut into 16 pieces with six lines. Can you use six lines to get more pieces than this?

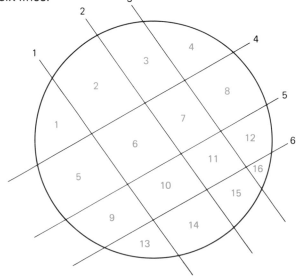

Games for two to four people

1 **All pent up** (two players)

All the angles in a pentagon are multiples of 36°.
The game is played with a die and two coloured pens.

How to play

Draw a regular pentagon of side 5 cm and join up the diagonals.
The players take it in turn to throw the die.
The score is then used to 'buy' angles:

    1 point of the die 'buys' an angle of 36°;

    2 points 'buys' 72°,

and so on.

[*Note*: 6 points can 'buy' either 6 angles of 36°, 3 angles of 72°, 2 angles of 108°, or a combination.]

Each player tries to win all the interior angles in a shape. When a whole shape is captured work out your score like this:

    for a triangle, score 3

    for a kite, rhombus and trapezium, 4

    and pentagons score 5.

    If you win all the angles at a point, score 6.

It is possible to capture several complete figures at the same time. In that case, all the scores are added up.

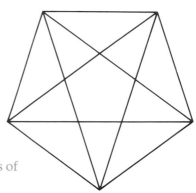

Example

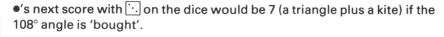

•'s next score with ⚁ on the dice would be 7 (a triangle plus a kite) if the 108° angle is 'bought'.

Four players

If four people want to play this game it is worth drawing an extended board. The rules are the same but there are more opportunities for scoring. (You can alter the rules to make the game more exciting or fast moving.)

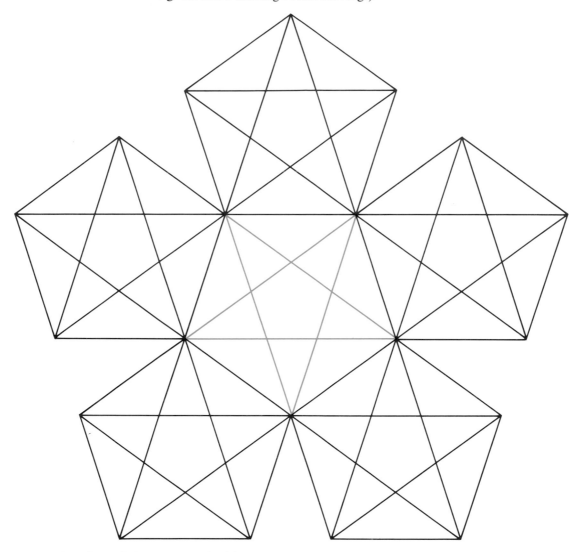

If you win coloured shapes score double.

2 Vector race game (up to four people)

This is one of the most exciting mathematical games I know. It is also very useful in understanding velocity and acceleration—things which everyone needs to understand when they learn to ride a bike or drive a car or motorbike.
You need . . . a different coloured pen for each player; and a large piece of squared paper.

How to play

A race course is drawn on squared paper (2 mm is easier to use than 1 mm).

Each player in turn moves by a vector $\begin{pmatrix} x \\ y \end{pmatrix}$—$x$ along y up.

The vectors are built up by adding 0, $+1$ or -1 to the x or y coordinate each time a player moves. If a player crosses the boundary of the course, this counts as a crash and the player is out of the race.

Example

The diagram shows the first four moves of a player whose moves were:

Start $\begin{pmatrix} 0 \\ 0 \end{pmatrix} \xrightarrow[+1]{+1} \begin{pmatrix} 1 \\ 1 \end{pmatrix} \xrightarrow[+1]{+1} \begin{pmatrix} 2 \\ 2 \end{pmatrix} \xrightarrow[+0]{+1} \begin{pmatrix} 3 \\ 2 \end{pmatrix} \xrightarrow[-1]{+0} \begin{pmatrix} 3 \\ 1 \end{pmatrix}$

Start

As you get more skilful you can increase the difficulty of the track with S bends and 'narrows'.

Design activities

1 Designing using a grid

Many designs are based on simple square grids. The design is built up in steps. This design is based on the 4-square grid.

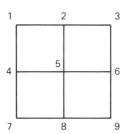

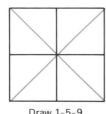

Draw 1–5–9
and 3–5–7

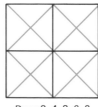

Draw 2–4–8–6–2

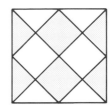

Colour in and rub
out unwanted lines

(a) Copy the patterns below. Start with a simple 4-square grid each time.

 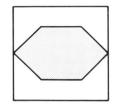 

(b) Invent three more designs on the 4-square grid.
(c) Investigate how these designs build up into larger patterns.
(d) Extend your investigations to the 9-square and 16-square grids.
(e) This design is made by repeatedly drawing the same line, in different positions, on a 25-square grid. Explore this method of designing.

(f) Similar patterns can be built on a grid of dots. [Patterns like this are made during Hindu festivals].

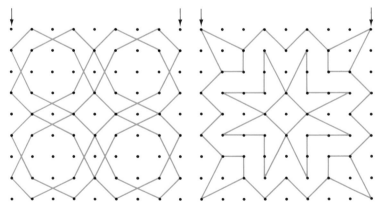

These patterns can be coloured in many different ways to emphasise different shapes.
Design some more patterns of your own. How do your designs relate to the grid patterns above?

2 Curves from straight lines

(a) As the ladder slips it seems to draw a perfect curve. Find out all you can about the curve.

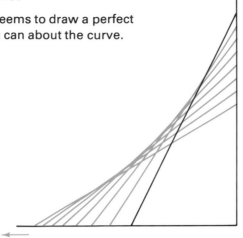

(b) Explore the situation of a ladder in a circle.

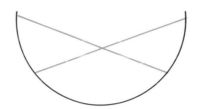

(c) Start off with a straight line LM and a point P. Draw a line from P to X (anywhere on LM). Draw a coloured line perpendicular to the line you have just drawn, through your point X. Follow the same procedure with other lines from P to LM.

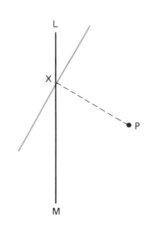

(d) Try a similar activity to (c) but put P inside a circle, and make X any point on that circle.

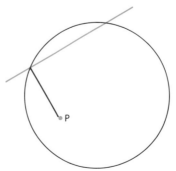

(e) Following on from (d), try a similar exploration with P outside the circle.
(f) Find out how the curves below are being constructed. They you can invent some different ones for yourself.

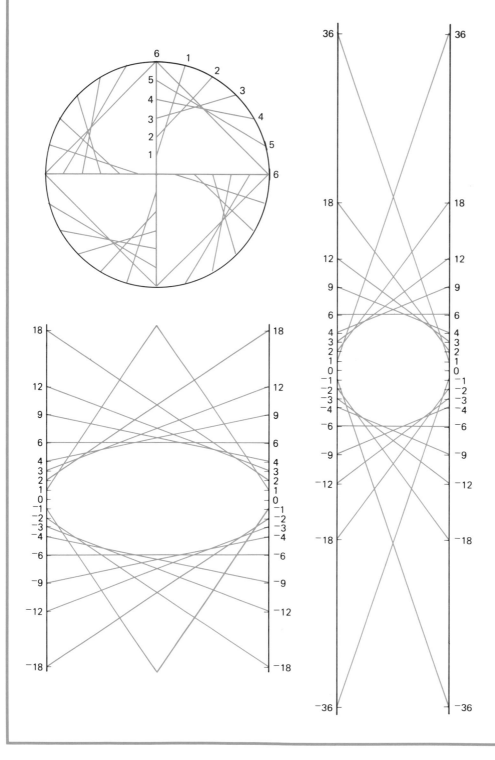

3 Designs based on the knight's tour of the chessboard

The knight's move takes him across the diagonal of a 3 × 2 rectangle. (From kt to one of the black spots.) This leads to the puzzle of finding a way to move the knight so that he covers all squares of the board without visiting any square more than once. This is called the knight's tour

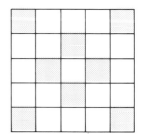

(a) Before you try to discover a knight's tour on the full chessboard, try to find a tour for a board 5 × 5.

(b) Patterns can be generated* from knight's tours by colouring in all the squares the knight visits.

Explore this idea and make interesting patterns for yourself.

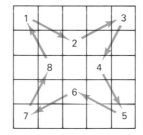

The arrows give a star pattern.

These patterns can be built into larger and more complex ones using each 5 × 5 pattern as a 'tile'.

(c) (i) Examine Euler's solution to the knight's tour.
It has one very special property. Can you find it?

(ii) Can you find your own solution to the knight's tour, starting at the centre of the board?

11	38	23	58	7	42	27	54
22	59	10	39	26	55	6	43
37	12	57	24	41	8	53	28
60	21	40	9	56	25	44	5
13	36	61	20	45	4	29	52
64	17	34	15	32	49	2	47
35	14	19	62	3	46	51	30
18	63	16	33	50	31	48	1

* Ask your teacher what this means.

Investigations and practical work

Geometry is a practical subject (the word means 'earth measurement') and the best way of understanding the principles is by drawing and measurement. However, argument is an important part of the subject. Many things—like calculating the size of the Earth, which the Greeks did—can be proved by argument that could never be proved by measurement alone. In the past, the study of geometry concentrated on the arguments and proofs, but this approach is not followed these days. Some people (including me) think that this is a shame. It is interesting to draw a triangle, measure the angles, and find out that they add up to 180° (more or less), but it is more interesting to realise that every triangle that has ever been drawn, or ever will be drawn, anywhere in the universe must have angles which add up to 180°. *

The investigations which follow will involve you in practical work but also in geometrical argument. I hope you enjoy them.

Investigation 1: Regular polygons

1.1 Drawing

Draw a careful set of regular polygons with from 3 to 10 sides. Two methods are suggested here. The sides should be at least 4 cm long.

1: d, α method

    1∅ Choose a length for d.
    2∅ Calculate α for the number of sides to be drawn.
    3∅ Draw d, turn α.
    4∅ Repeat 3∅.

Note: This is the way you would draw a regular polygon using a simple computer language called LOGO. One of your school computers may have a logo attachment. If so you should experiment on it.

2: Circle, equal arcs method

    1∅ Calculate α.
    2∅ Draw a sector with $\alpha°$.
    3∅ Step off equal arcs round the circle.
       [*Hint*: Go halfway round clockwise and
             halfway round anticlockwise.]
    4∅ Join up to produce the polygon.

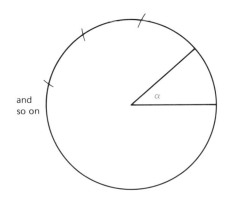

and so on

Use your set of regular polygons in the investigations which follow.

* Provided it is drawn on a flat surface of course.

1.2   Diagonals

Definition: A diagonal is a straight line which joins two vertices of a polygon but is not one of the sides.

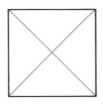

Square,
2 diagonals

Pentagon,
5 diagonals

Investigate the diagonals for all of the regular polygons you have drawn. Here are some of the questions you could start off with

● How many diagonals does each polygon have?
● Find the relationship between the number of sides and numbers of diagonals. This relationship should enable you to predict the number of diagonals:
   (i) in a 20-gon,
  (ii) in a 100-gon,
 (iii) in an *n*-gon.
● Investigate the relationships between lengths of diagonals and length of side of the polygon.

1.3   Spaces and shapes

(1) Investigate the number of spaces formed when all the diagonals of a regular polygon are drawn.
    Can you find a general relationship which would enable you to estimate the number of spaces made by a 16-sided polygon with all its diagonals?
(2) All the shapes in a regular polygon (with its diagonals) are related.

Example

The two triangles obtained from a square are $(90, 45, 45)°$ and the larger one is a $\sqrt{2}$ enlargement of the smaller one.
[$AC:AB = \sqrt{2}:1$, $AB:OA = \sqrt{2}:1$.]

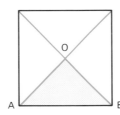

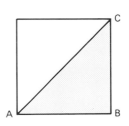

Investigate these relationships for your set of regular polygons.

1.4   Colour and design

Your regular polygons and their diagonals can lead to many beautiful designs. Enjoy yourself!

1.5 The nonagon

In a thorough study of this nonagon (9-sided regular figure) you would
want to

- count the numbers of diagonals,
- identify all the different sizes of angles,
- identify all the different types of shape,
- investigate interesting designs that can be found by colouring.

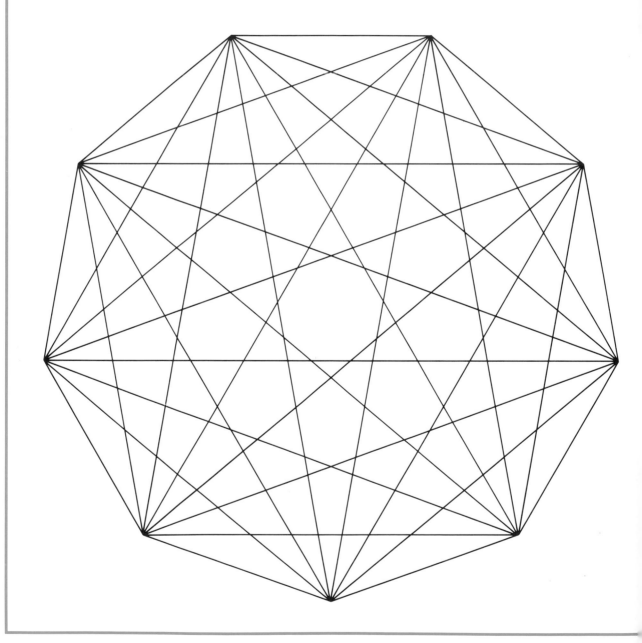

Investigation 2: Some ideas in topology

Topology is a more general form of geometry. Instead of studying lengths shapes and angles, we look at intersections, spaces and order.

Networks

Networks are used in designing roads, drains, wiring in buildings and in electronic equipment and in many other activities. A study of networks consists of studying branches, nodes (junctions) and regions (spaces).

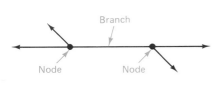

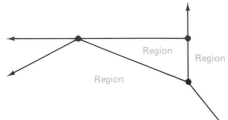

Investigations

1 Count the nodes, regions and branches on the networks drawn here. Don't forget the outside.

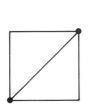  

2 Can you design a network with more nodes than branches?

3 Can you find a relationship between the number of branches, nodes and regions which will be true for any network?

4 Compare the networks drawn here with the faces, edges and vertices of a tetrahedron and cube.

Region 1

Use your results to draw networks that would relate to
  (i) a triangular prism,
 (ii) a pyramid on a square base,
(iii) an octahedron.

5 Two network problems to investigate. Both of these problems are very old.

(a) The three houses. The problem is to connect all three houses with gas, water and electricity, without any of the supply lines crossing. You can place the houses and the supplies of gas, water and electricity wherever you wish.

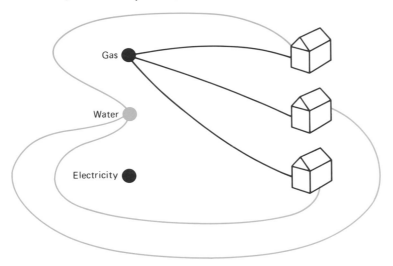

(b) The seven bridges of Königsberg. The people of Königsberg tried to find a route which would cross all seven bridges just once. Can you find it?

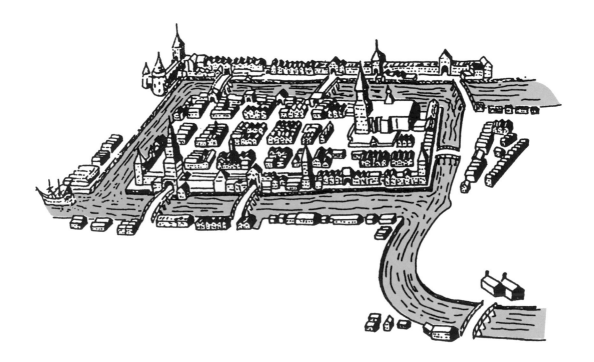

6 Some networks can be drawn in one continuous line, without going over any line a second time. They are unicursal.

Obvious

Start at a node ?

(a) Can you find a unicursal way of drawing these figures?

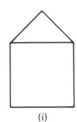

(i)

(ii)

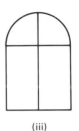

(iii)

(b) Show that these figures cannot be drawn unicursally.

(i)

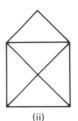

(ii)

(iii)

(c) A rule suggests that 'networks with more than two odd nodes cannot be drawn unicursally'. Investigate this rule.

(d) How can the work of (a), (b) and (c) help you to solve the Königsberg bridges problem?

Investigation 3: Circle/line intersections

You need a pair of compasses and tracing paper for this investigation.

(a) Draw a circle on ordinary paper and a pair of perpendicular lines on a sheet of tracing paper.
Move the tracing paper around and look for interesting results.
Here are some things to look for: lengths; symmetries; ratios; areas; angles.

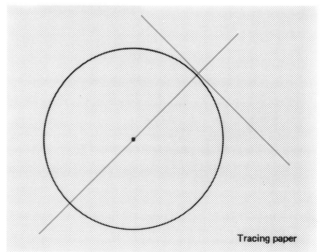

Tracing paper

(b) Repeat the investigation, but this time draw the lines at an angle of 40°. Four different situations to explore are shown below. You will be able to find other situations which give interesting results. [Try using two pairs of lines.]

Pair of tangents from a point.

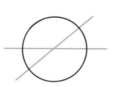

Pair of chords meeting inside the circle.

Pair of chords meeting on the circumference.

Pair of chords meeting outside the circle.

Worked answers to examination questions D

1 (a) Draw an isosceles triangle with one side 5 cm long and at least one angle of 40°. (b) Can you draw a second, different triangle from the same data?

(a)

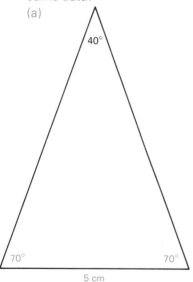

(b)

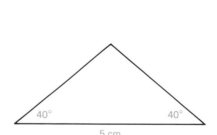

If the triangle has at least one angle of 40°, it has either one angle of 40° or two angles of 40°. The 5 cm side must be the base. There are only two triangles that fit the data.

(a) To draw this triangle you need to find the base angles:

$180° - 40° = 140°$

$140° \div 2 = 70°$.

(b) Draw the base first. Then add lines at 40° to each end of the base. The point where these lines meet will be the third vertex of the triangle.

2 O is the centre of the circle. Find an equation connecting x and y.

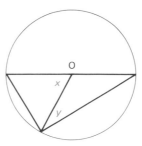

$x = 2y$

The first step is to letter the diagram so that it is easier to think about.

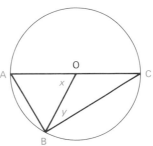

Since OB = OC (O being the centre of the circle) $\widehat{OCB} = y$.
Therefore $x = 2y$, since x is an external angle of $\triangle OBC$.
[See 'Key facts' D.2.1; point (iv).]

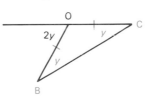

3 Calculate the values of s and t.

$s = 140°$ $t = 45°$

$s + 40° = 180°$ ... the angle on a straight line
so $s = 140°$.
$125° = t + 80°$ ... because the exterior angle is the sum of opposite
                              interior angles
so $t = 45°$.

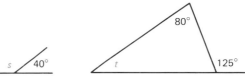

4 Find (i) The length of CH
          (ii) The size of $\widehat{BCH}$
Use the results to find BH.

(i) 5 cm   (ii) $\widehat{BCH} = 90°$ BH $= \sqrt{50} = 7.07$ cm

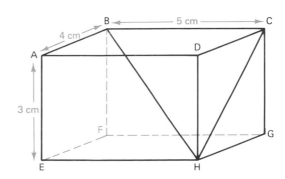

△HGC is a right angled triangle as shown.
$CH^2 = 9 + 16 = 25$
$CH = 5$ cm
[The 3, 4, 5 triangle]

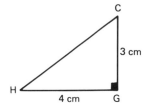

BC is perpendicular to the face DCGH of the cuboid. So $B\hat{C}H = 90°$
$BH^2 = BC^2 + CH^2$
$= 25 + 25 = 50$
$BH = \sqrt{50} = 7\cdot07$ cm

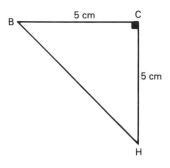

5 Draw a circle radius 4 cm. Draw
  (a) a diameter,
  (b) a chord perpendicular to the diameter, and
  (c) a tangent at the end of the chord.
It is helpful when drawing the tangent to draw a radius first.
The tangent can then be drawn at right angles to the radius.

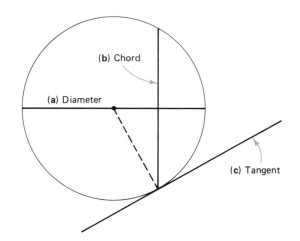

6 Calculate the value of y if △XYZ is isosceles.

$y = 58°$

$X\hat{Z}Y$ is $y°$ because the triangle is isosceles.
$64° + 2y = 180°$
$\Rightarrow \quad 2y = 116°$
$\Rightarrow \quad y = 58°$ 180 ⊟ 64 ⊜ ⊟ 2 ⊜

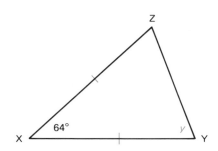

7 Which of the following is the right name for the figure PQRS?
(a) rhombus   (b) rectangle
(c) parallelogram   (d) trapezium

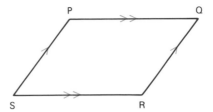

Parallelogram

Both pairs of opposite sides are parallel.

8 Draw any rectangle. Mark in   (a) the diagonals   (b) the axes of symmetry, and   (c) the centre of rotational symmetry.
Note: I have deliberately drawn a tilted
        rectangle to show that its position
        does not affect the symmetry.

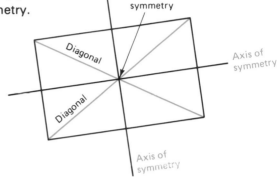

9 Copy the one figure from the three below which has rotational symmetry but no axis of symmetry.

 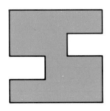

(a)   (b)   (c)

(b)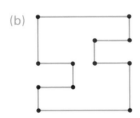

Note: When asked to copy a diagram, if possible you should put your paper over the diagram and mark the vertices with small dots. These dots can then be joined with straight lines to form the figure. No measurement is needed. Of course, if you cannot see through the paper you will have to construct the copy by careful measurement. Always use a pencil.

10 The diagram shows three telephone wires going from a pole to three different houses. Calculate *a*.

$a = 90°$

All three angles must add up to 360°,
so $a + 130° + 140° = 360°$
$\Rightarrow a = 360° - 270°$
$= 90°$ [360 − 140 − 130 =]

185

11 Write down the number of faces, edges and vertices for each of these figures.

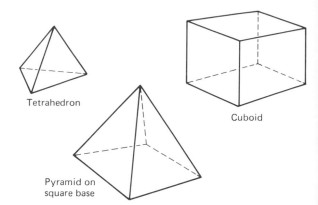

Tetrahedron

Cuboid

Pyramid on square base

Tetrahedron: 4 faces, 6 edges, 4 vertices.
Pyramid: 5 faces, 8 edges, 5 vertices.
Cuboid: 6 faces, 12 edges, 8 vertices.

You can do this question simply by careful counting. If you want to be 100% sure, then letter the vertices and list the faces, edges and vertices for each solid.

Tetrahedron

Faces	*Edges*	*Vertices*
ABD (back)	AB (sloping)	A (top)
ABC (side)	AC (sloping)	B (base)
ADC (side)	AD (sloping)	C (base)
BCD (base)	BC (base)	D (base)
	BD (base)	
	CD (base)	
Total: 4	Total: 6	Total: 4

and so on for the pyramid and cube.

- It is also interesting that Euler's formula, which is $F + V = E + 2$, clearly works for these solids.

12 TP and TQ are tangents to a circle with centre O. PT̂O is 40° as shown.
What are
(a) PT̂Q   (b) TP̂Q   (c) PX̂T?

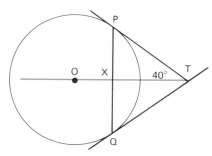

(a) 80°   (b) 50°   (c) 90°

The angles follow from the symmetry. OT is an axis of symmetry so the other angle at T is also 40°. This leaves 100° in △PTQ to share between TP̂Q and TQ̂P so both are 50°. TX̂P = TX̂Q from the symmetry, so both angles are $\frac{1}{2}$ of 180°, i.e. 90°.

13 Calculate the sizes of x, y and z.

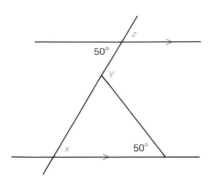

x = 50°   *y* = 100°   *z* = 50°

In fact, the easiest angle to start with is *z*.

z = 50°, vertically opposite   *x* = 50°, corresponding   *y* = 100°, exterior angle of triangle is sum of opposite interior angles

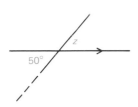 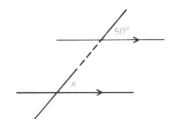 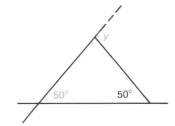

14 Calculate the values of x and y. Explain your reasoning carefully.

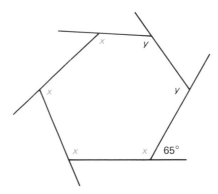

x = 115°   *y* = 130°

This problem is best solved by working with the external angles.
There will be four 65° angles totalling 260°.
The remaining 100° are shared equally by the external angles next to the *y* angles. Thus they will be 50° and *y* = 130°.
Since *x* + 65° = 180°, *x* = 115°.
These solutions depend on two facts:
 (i) The external angles of any polygon add up to 360°.
 (ii) The angle on a straight line is 180°.

15 Given that TA is a tangent to the circle at A, calculate the values of p and q.

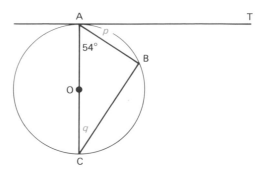

$p = 36°$ $q = 36°$

At A the tangent is perpendicular to the diameter, so $54° + p = 90°$

$$\Rightarrow \quad p = 36°$$

$A\hat{B}C = 90°$ (angle in a semicircle), so $54° + q = 90° \Rightarrow q = 36°$.

16 Measure the three angles of this triangle with your protractor. Comment on the results.

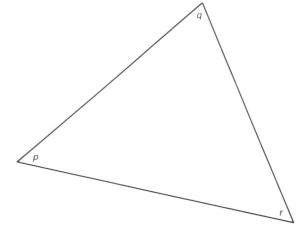

The angles are 53°, 55° and 72°.

These angles should add up to 180°. If they do not, you have not been very accurate in your measurement.

17 Draw the reflection of the coloured area in the axis.

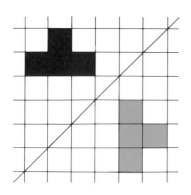

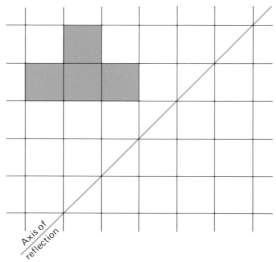

18 (a) What is the correct name for this shape?
(b) Show how it could be cut and rearranged into a parallelogram in two different ways.

(a) Isosceles trapezium.

(b) (i) This produces a parallelogram, height h:
base $= \frac{1}{2}$(top + base).

(ii) This produces a parallelogram, height $h/2$:
base = top + base.

(iii) This produces a rectangle height h:
base $= \frac{1}{2}$(top) $+ \frac{1}{2}$(base).

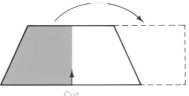

• I have given three methods. Can you find others?

19 (a) Copy this drawing of a simple house.
(b) Mark, in dotted lines, the unseen edges of the house.
(c) How many faces, edges and vertices does the house have?

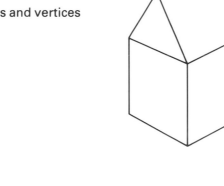

9 faces, 17 edges, 10 vertices.
Note: This result fits Euler's formula $F + V = E + 2$.

20 This shape is the net of a cube. Draw two more arrangements of six squares which will fold up into a cube.

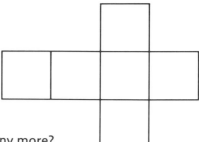

These are two possible solutions. Can you find any more?

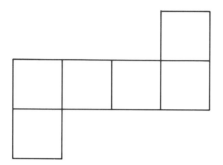

21 The only known facts about the triangles in the diagram are marked on them.
Is it possible that any pairs of triangles are congruent or similar? Give reasons for your answers.

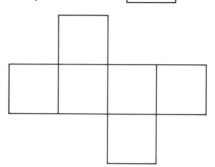

The triangles are neither congruent nor similar.

The best way to tackle this question is to consider the triangles in pairs.

△'s ABC, LMN

They cannot be congruent as the two triangles contain four different lengths of side.

At first sight they could be similar

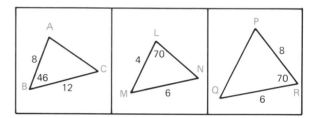

However, these triangles could not be drawn.

Reasons why △ABC is impossible as marked.

1 AC < AB, since 46° < 64° ... smaller side opposite smaller angle.

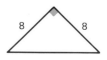

This triangle would have a base of $\sqrt{128} \simeq 11$.
Thus the angle at A would need to be greater than 90° to produce a base 12 units long, even if AC were as long as AB which it is not!

2 The sine rule for all triangles states that

$$\frac{a}{\sin A} = \frac{b}{\sin B} = \frac{c}{\sin C}$$

$$\frac{8}{\sin 64} = 8 \cdot 9$$

$$\frac{12}{\sin 70} = 12 \cdot 77$$

△'s ABC, PQR

If the triangles were congruent AC would have to be 6 units long, $\hat{P}$ would be 46° and $\hat{A}$ would be 70°. This is the impossible situation above.

For similarity it would need AC = 16 and PQ = 4. This would lead to impossible situations in both triangles, with smallest sides opposite largest angles.

△'s LMN, PQR

Congruence is impossible because if MN = QR = 6 units then $\hat{L} = \hat{N} = 70°$ and MN should be equal to ML. This is not the case.
If the triangles were to be similar with PR corresponding to LM, LN would have to be 3 units. This would mean △LMN would have an obtuse angle at L. This is not the case.
If QR corresponds to LM (see below) the lengths are as shown.

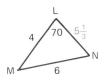

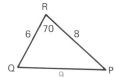

In fact $\hat{L}$ and $\hat{R}$ would have to be 78·6° for these triangles to exist. [Drawing demonstrates this quite clearly].

Note: All triangles satisfy the rule $a^2 = b^2 + c^2 - 2bc \cos A$ and this can be used to establish that the triangle with sides 6, 8, 9 and an angle of 70° cannot be drawn.

22 Triangle ABC has a right angle at C.
The lengths of the sides of △ABC are
AB = c cm
BC = a cm
and
CA = b cm.
(a) Find $\hat{A}$ and $\hat{B}$ and show that the figure consists of three similar triangles.
(b) BX = x cm. Show that (i) $cx = a^2$
(ii) $(c - x)c = b^2$. Give reasons.
(c) Use the results (i) and (ii) to prove Pythagoras' theorem for △ABC. What changes need to be made in this question to prove Pythagoras' theorem for any triangle ABC, right angled at C?

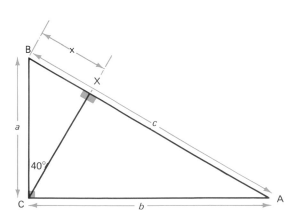

(a) $\hat{A} = 40°$; $\hat{B} = 50°$. There are three triangles in the figure. Each triangle has angles of 90°, 50° and 40° and therefore they are all similar.

(b) Since △BXC is similar to △ABC, ratios of corresponding sides are equal.

$$\frac{x \ldots \text{opp } 40° \ldots a}{a \ldots \text{opp } 90° \ldots c} \Rightarrow xc = a^2$$

△BXC ⎿ △ABC

By a similar argument, since △AXC is similar to △ABC and XA = c − x

$$\frac{c - x}{b} = \frac{b}{c} \Rightarrow c(c - x) = b^2$$

(c) From the results obtained in part (b)

$$xc = a^2$$
$$c(c - x) = b^2$$

Add $\quad xc + c^2 - cx = a^2 + b^2$

$\Rightarrow \qquad\qquad c^2 = a^2 + b^2$

This is Pythagoras theorem for △ABC.

If the 40° angle is replaced by $\theta°$ the results proved above are still true. Thus the steps form a proof of Pythagoras theorem for any right angled triangle.

23 (a) Prove that a quadrilateral whose opposite sides are equal must be a parallelogram.

(b) Prove that a parallelogram whose diagonals are equal must be a rectangle.

(a) 1∅ Data AB = DC, AD = BC
2∅ △'s ABC, CDA are congruent ... from 1∅
3∅ DĈA = CÂB (corresponding angles)

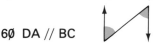

4∅ DC // AB
5∅ DÂC = BĈA (corresponding angles)

6∅ DA // BC
7∅ ABCD is a parallelogram.

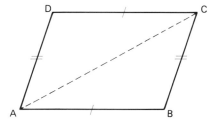

(b) 1∅ Data PQRS is a parallelogram
2∅ Data PR = QS
3∅ QP̂R = PR̂S ... from 1∅
4∅ QR̂P = SP̂R ... from 1∅
5∅ △'s PQR, PRS are congruent ...
   * two angles and a corresponding side equal.

* On the way we have proved that the opposite sides of a parallelogram are equal and that the opposite angles are equal as well.

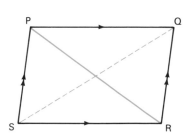

192

6Ø PQ = SR and PS = QR
7Ø △SPR and △SQR are congruent ... three sides equal
8Ø PŜR = SR̂Q ... from 7Ø

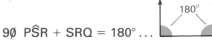

9Ø PŜR + SRQ = 180° ...
1ØØ PŜR = SR̂Q = 90° ... from 8Ø and 9Ø
11Ø PQRS is a rectangle ... from 1ØØ

Note: you might find another proof of this result.

24 The semicircle shown is cut by a line XY
(parallel to the base) which cuts the
semicircle into two equal halves.
(i) Show that $\theta = 132.35°$.
(ii) Show that this value of θ fits the
equation
$$\frac{\theta \times \pi}{180} - \sin \theta = \frac{\pi}{2}$$

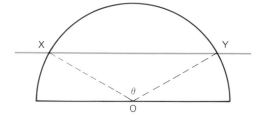

Formulae: Area of a sector $= \frac{1}{2}r^2 \left[\dfrac{\theta \times \pi}{180} \right]$

Area of a $\triangle = \frac{1}{2}ab \sin C$.

(i) This problem is the same whatever the
radius of the circle so it is sensible to choose a radius of 1 unit.

1Ø Area of sector OXY $= \frac{1}{2} \times 1 \times 1 \times \dfrac{132.35}{180} \times \pi = 1.1550$

2Ø Area of triangle OXY $= \frac{1}{2} \times 1 \times 1 \times \sin 132.35 = 0.3695$

3Ø Area of segment $= 1.155 - 0.3695 = 0.7855$ (units^2)

4Ø Area of semicircle $= \frac{1}{2}\pi r^2 = \frac{1}{2}\pi = 1.5708$

5Ø $\frac{1}{2} \times$ semicircle $= 0.5 \times 1.5708 = 0.7854$

6Ø Thus the angle 132.35° gives a segment which is half the area of
the semicircle ... from 3Ø and 5Ø

(ii) Replacing 132.35 by the general angle θ, we have
sector $-$ triangle $= \frac{1}{2} \times$ semicircle
$$\frac{1}{2}r^2 \frac{\theta \times \pi}{180} - \frac{1}{2}r^2 \sin \theta = \frac{1}{4}r^2\pi$$
$$\Rightarrow \frac{\theta \times \pi}{180} - \sin \theta = \frac{\pi}{2}.$$

Note: This problem would have been more challenging if the size of
the angle had not been given. It would then have been
necessary to solve the equation. [Try finding the angle if XY
slices off exactly one third of the semicircle]

25 XY is the perpendicular bisector of a line
segment.
  (i) P is any point on XY. Prove that
      PA = PB.
  (ii) Q is not on XY. Prove that Q must be
       nearer to one of the points A, B than to
       the other.

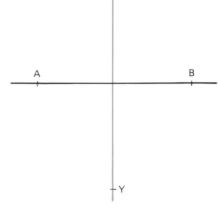

(i) 1∅ Join PA and PB.
   2∅ △'s POA and POB are congruent . . .
         AO = OB
         OP = OP
         PÔA = PÔB
   3∅ AP = PB, corresponding sides in
        congruent triangles.

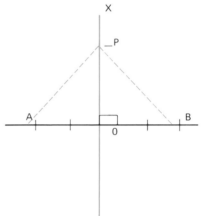

(ii) This question is more subtle than part (i). We are told
     that Q is not on the perpendicular bisector, but
     assume it is equidistant from A and B.
     1∅ Data QA = QB, AO = OB,
          XÔA = 90°.
     15 Data Q is not on OX.
     2∅ Join QA, QO, QB
     3∅ △'s AQO and OQB are congruent
          three sides equal . . . AQ = QB
                                  AO = OB
                                  OQ = OQ
     4∅ QÔA = QÔB (corresponding angles)
     5∅ QÔA = 90° . . . from 4∅
     6∅ Q is on OX.

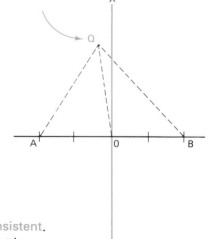

The proof shows that the two data sets 1∅ and 15 are inconsistent.
They cannot happen together. Thus if Q is not on OX it must be
nearer to one or other of A, B.

26 (a) Demonstrate how to bisect any angle using ruler and compass.

(b) Draw accurate angles of
(i) 90°   (ii) 45°   (iii) 60°   (iv) 30°   (v) 75°.
Explain the steps taken in each construction.

(a) The diagram is sufficient answer to this question but if you have time it is worth describing the construction.

Steps 1 and 2 Centre 0, draw arcs to cut OX and OY.

Steps 3 and 4 Centres, the points of intersection from 1 and 2, draw arcs 3 and 4, with equal radii, meeting at P.

Step 5 Draw OP, the required bisector.

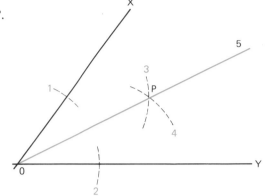

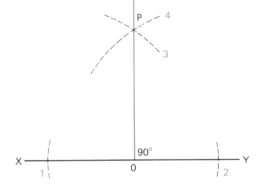

(b) (i) Step 1 Centre 0, draw arcs 1 and 2.
Step 2 Centre 1, draw arc 3.
Step 3 Centre 2, draw arc 4.
Step 4 Draw OP,
P$\hat{O}$X = P$\hat{O}$Y = 90°.
(ii) Bisect P$\hat{O}$Y to obtain 45° angle.

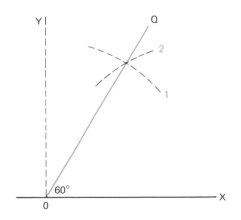

(iii) Construct any equilateral triangle starting at 0.
(iv) Bisect the 60° angle at O.
(v) Bisect Q$\hat{O}$Y, having constructed OY at 90° to OX.

27 A theorem states . . . 'The bisector of an angle of a triangle divides the opposite side in the ratio of the sides surrounding the angle'.
(a) Test this suggestion by an accurate drawing.
(b) Prove the theorem by considering the areas of the two parts of the original triangle.

(a) To answer this question draw any triangle at random. Make it a reasonable size so that you can take fairly accurate measurements, then bisect one angle.

Record the measurements
AB = 50 mm $\dfrac{AB}{AC} = \dfrac{50}{63} = 0.79$
AC = 63 mm

BD = 22 mm $\dfrac{BD}{DC} = \dfrac{22}{27.5} = 0.8$
DC = 27.5 mm

This is near enough to confirm the theorem.

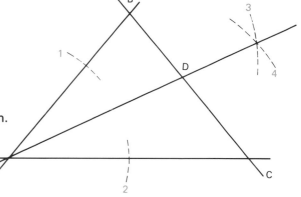

(b) 1∅ The area of △AXC $= \frac{1}{2}bx \sin \theta$
2∅ The area of △BXC $= \frac{1}{2}ax \sin \theta$

3∅ $\dfrac{△AXC}{△BXC} = \dfrac{b}{a}$

4∅ The area of △AXC $= \frac{1}{2} \times AX \times h$
5∅ The area of △BXC $= \frac{1}{2} \times BX \times h$

6∅ $\dfrac{△AXC}{△BXC} = \dfrac{AX}{BX}$ . . . from 4∅, 5∅

7∅ $\dfrac{AX}{BX} = \dfrac{b}{a} = \dfrac{AC}{CB}$ . . . from 3∅, 6∅

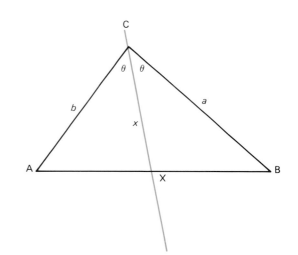

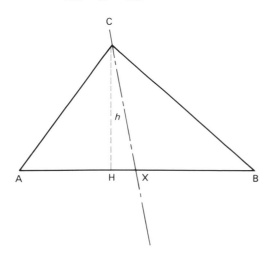

28 A point A is chosen outside a circle. Lines from A meet the circle at B, C, D and E.
(i) Given AB = AC prove AD = AE.

(ii) Investigate a similar situation with A inside the circle.

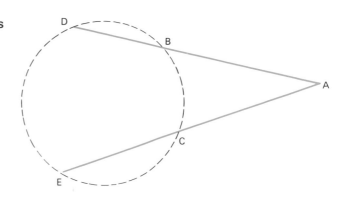

(i) Join BC and DE.
1∅ Data AB = AC
2∅ AB̂C = AĈB   from 1∅
3∅ AB̂C = CÊD
   AĈB = BD̂E   property of cyclic quadrilaterals
4∅ BD̂E = CÊD   from 3∅
5∅ AD = AE   since △ADE is isosceles.

(ii) Investigating the situation with A inside the circle leads to the same result as above.
ie. AB = AC ⇒ AD = AE.
The proof follows the same lines. BC and ED are joined and the angles in the same segment property used.

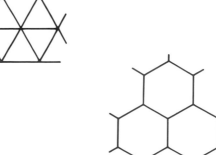

Both situations have an axis of symmetry but a full proof will gain more marks than a mere reference to symmetry.
Can you organise a proof which works for both positions of A.

29 (a) Hexagons will form a tessellation and so will equilateral triangles. Construct a tessellation using a mixture of regular hexagons and equilateral triangles.

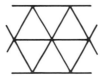

(b) Investigate ways of constructing tessellations from a mixture of squares and equilateral triangles.

(a) Since each node of the tessellation must consist of 360° there are a limited number of choices.

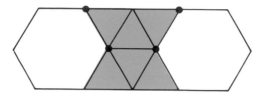

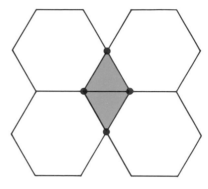

Each node contains two angles of 120° and two angles of 60°.

It is sensible to draw a 60° grid as a start to this question rather than waste time drawing individual hexagons and triangles.

Each node contains one angle of 120° and four angles of 60°.

(b) There might seem to be many alternative tessellations but each node must still have a 360° total angle. This can only be obtained from two squares and three equilateral triangles arranged as shown.

It is possible to build up the design around a regular hexagon and you have probably managed to find other alternatives.

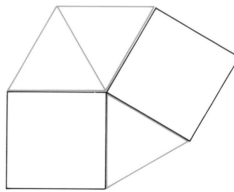

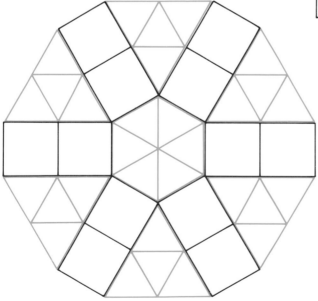

30 (a) What solid fits the following description?
- It is not a prism.
- It is not a pyramid.
- It has no vertices.
- It has one edge.
- It has one plane (flat) face and one curved face.
- The area of the curved face is double the area of the plane face.

(b) List the number and type of faces, edges and vertices of the following objects.
  (i) A sharpened hexagonal pencil.
  (ii) A rugby football.
  (iii) A glass lens (convex).

(a) The solid is a hemisphere.

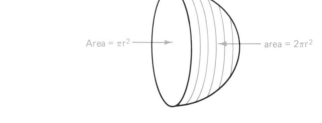
Area = πr^2 area = $2\pi r^2$

(b) (i) 13 vertices, 12 edges, 8 faces.
    (ii) 2 vertices, no edges, 1 surface.
   (iii) 1 edge, 2 faces, no vertices.

Note: These solids seem to contradict Eulers rule for solids with plane faces $F + V = E + 2$. Considering that a circle is a polygon with an infinite number of sides, and a curved surface contains an infinite number of plane surfaces, you would expect 'infinity' to cause the equation to break down.

Topic E Sets, statistics and probability

Contents

Sets: universal set $\mathcal{E}$; complement; union and intersection; the empty set $\emptyset$; subsets
Statistics: sampling; presenting sample data; misleading statistics; mean, median, and mode; grouped data; cumulative frequency, range, interquartile range; scattergrams
Probability: estimating probabilities 1; estimating probabilities 2; tree diagrams; combining probabilities

Self assessment

As you know by now, the purpose of this task is to find out if you need revision on Topic E. There is no time limit.

- Make a table in your book, like the one on page vi. You need space for 8 questions on 'sets', 12 questions on 'statistics' and 8 questions on 'probability'.
- Write down your answers to all the questions.
- When you have finished calculate your score from the answers on pp. 426–428.
- If you score more than 80% go on to Topic F self assessment (pp. 257–259).

Sets

1 The set A is {P, E, T, E, R} while set B is {K, A, N, E, R}. What letters are in
  (i) A ∩ B (ii) A ∪ B (iii) A′
  (iv) B′   (v) A′ ∩ B′?

2 Which of the following are not the empty set $\emptyset$?
  (i) A ∩ A′ (ii) B ∩ B′ (iii) $\mathcal{E}$′
  (iv) A ∪ A′ (v) B ∪ B′

3 The Venn diagram shows our class. T are the people who play tennis, S are the swimmers.
  (i) How many don't swim?
  (ii) How many swim and play tennis?
  (iii) How many don't swim or play tennis?
  (iv) How many people in the class?

4 What is the universal set from which this set is taken.
{Aston Villa, Birmingham City, Chester, Darlington, Everton}.

5 Pick out a subset of the numbers between 1 and 20 so that every member of the subset is the sum of square numbers, without repeats.

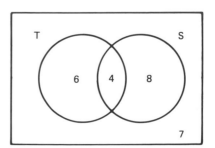

◆ **6** (a) Use a Venn diagram to show that
(A ∪ B)' = A' ∩ B' and give two
examples with A and B chosen from the
universal set of whole numbers.

(b) Explain why
$x \in A \Rightarrow x \in B$ and $A \subset B$
are two ways of describing the same
situation.

◆ **7** (a) These three diagrams represent A, B and
A ∩ B but not in order. Which is which?

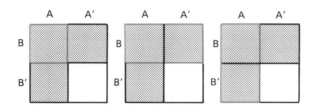

(b) Draw similar diagrams to represent
(i) A ∪ B (ii) (A ∩ B)'
(iii) A' ∪ B (iv) A ∩ B'

◆ **8** In a class of 35 children

—25 children can speak English
— 3 children can speak only Urdu
—all children speak English, Urdu or Hindi
— 5 children speak Urdu and Hindi but not
English
— 3 children speak all three languages
— 5 children speak both Urdu and English

(a) How many children speak only Hindi?
(b) What is the largest linguistic group in the
class?

Statistics

1 What are the facts that can be obtained
from the bar chart? (The bar chart is about
the numbers of accidents in which 1000
motorists were involved.)

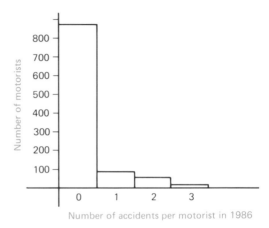

2 The graph appeared in *The Times* on
6 December 1985 under the heading
'Unemployment falls for third month in
succession'. Do you think the graph gives a
fair picture of the unemployment situation
and its changes from 1984 to 1985? Give
reasons for your answer.

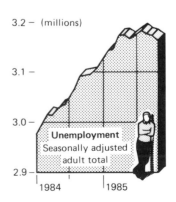

3 Copy and complete the frequency table from the data. Heights of 100 applicants to the Women's Royal Army Corps:

166	168	165	170	170	177	167	174	170	169
170	169	169	171	172	176	171	172	171	172
177	175	165	165	169	166	172	169	168	175
165	178	172	166	167	169	165	177	169	177
168	172	177	172	166	170	168	165	166	167
172	177	175	168	171	180	172	166	164	173
179	169	168	169	174	177	169	168	170	177
180	170	174	166	177	171	170	170	170	179
167	178	172	169	165	175	170	168	172	166
174	172	170	165	169	169	166	171	168	168

Height (cm)	Tally	Frequency (f)
164·0– 165·9	⦀⦀ ⦀⦀	9
166·0– 167·9		13
168·0– 169·9		
170·0– 171·9		
172·0– 173·9		
174·0– 175·9		
176·0– 177·9		
178·0– 180		

4 Write down all the data you can deduce from this pictogram showing the use of land in Moorside rural district. Comment.

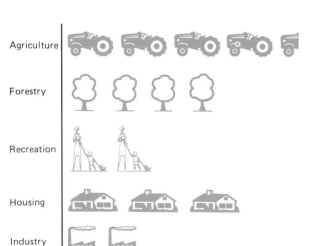

Agriculture

Forestry

Recreation

Housing

Industry

5 The number of examination passes gained by the 5th year students of a comprehensive school.

Number of examination passes	f	
	boys	girls
0	7	3
1	8	5
2	10	8
3	16	22
4	38	36
5	26	29
6	17	12
7	8	5
8	3	5
Totals		

(i) How many girls obtained five exam passes?
(ii) How many boys obtained more than five passes?
(iii) How many boys and girls are there altogether in the table?
(iv) Would you say boys or girls had better results? [Give reasons.]

203

6 What is wrong with the way the following samples were chosen?

   (i) In a survey to find out who had a telephone, 100 people were picked from the telephone directory. They were then asked 'Do you have a phone?'.

  (ii) In a survey about young people's attitudes to jobs a group of teenagers at a youth club were sampled at 2·30 p.m. on a Tuesday.

 (iii) In an attempt to find out how people would vote in local elections, all those in the reading room of the public library were asked their views.

7 Twins, Matthew and Joanna are in the same class. Their position in class and the marks they scored in their exams are given in this table.

	Matthew		Joanna	
Subject	position	marks (%)	position	marks (%)
Art	3	73	5	71
Biology	12	54	9	66
Chemistry	11	58	15	54
English	6	66	10	63
French	14	51	16	49
Geography	9	68	8	71
History	15	55	12	65
Mathematics	4	73	7	70

Find the average position and average mark for both twins. Do you notice anything odd??

8 An athlete training for an important 2000 m race ran 23 times during a month. Find the mean, mode, median and range of the data given in the table.

Time in seconds	320	321	322	323	324	325
f	4	7	3	3	2	4

(total no. of attempts: 23)

9 A mistake has been made in constructing the pie chart about the jobs people do. Can you find it?

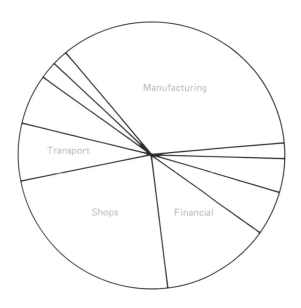

Occupation	Thousands	%
HM Forces	300	1·5
Manufacturing (factories)	7000	35
Agriculture	400	2
Mining	400	2
Building	1200	6
Transport	1400	7
Financial, professional and scientific	4800	24
Shops etc.	2700	13·5
Local government	1000	5
National government	700	3·5

10 Part of a traffic survey past the school gates between 9 a.m. and 10 a.m. on Friday 13 December 1985 is shown in the table below. How many of each vehicle went by?

Coaches	~~||||~~ ||
Lorries	~~||||~~ ~~||||~~ ~~||||~~ ~~||||~~ ||
Cars	~~||||~~ ~~||||~~ ~~||||~~ ~~||||~~ ~~||||~~ ~~||||~~ |||
Motorcycles	~~||||~~ ~~||||~~ ~~||||~~ ||
Bicycles	~~||||~~ ~~||||~~ ~~||||~~

◆**11** The table refers to serious crimes committed in 1977 (by age groups).

Age range	Crimes (1000's)	
	M	F
under 14	20·9	2·5
14 and under 17	63·9	7·8
17 and under 21	95·2	12·7
21 and over	180·8	44·9
Total	360·8	67·9

(a) Draw a diagram which shows the data and which emphasises the differences between the figures for males and females.

(b) Discuss problems in presenting these data in terms of means and medians.

(c) The 1987 data are given in the table below. What important changes have taken place over the ten years?

Age range	Crimes (1000's)	
	M	F
under 14	29·3	2·7
14 and under 17	102·2	10·2
17 and under 21	109	16
21 and over	226	38
Total	466·5	66·9

◆**12** (a) Make a scattergram for the height/weight data given below. Does this sample suggest a direct height/weight relationship? Give reasons for your answer.

Heights/weights of police recruits

Name	Age	Height (cm)	Weight (Kg)
Adams	21	180	72
Baker	23	170	76
Cohen	19	185	74
Dawa	24	177	82
Ellis	19	178	77
Fujikawa	20	183	80
Gregory	27	176	90
Hill	22	174	83
Idle	25	182	75
Jones	31	181	72

(b) Find the mean, median and interquartile range for the 5000 army recruits of the table below.

Heights of 5000 army recruits

heights	f
170–174·9 cm	1368
175–179·9 cm	1762
180–184·9 cm	1280
185–189·9 cm	390
190–194·9 cm	180
195–199·9 cm	20
Total	5000

Probability

1 Which of these do you think more likely:
  (i) throwing three sixes in a row with one die, or
  (ii) drawing two aces in a row from a full pack of cards (shuffling in between)?

2 A train is late 40 times out of 365 in a year. What is the probability that it will be late tomorrow?

3 A parachute has a 99% chance of opening. Would you jump out of an aeroplane with it? Explain your answer.

4 In 4 out of every 10 crimes committed the criminal is caught. What is the chance of not being caught? A criminal commits 5 crimes. What is his chance of not being caught (at these odds)?

5 Copy and complete the tree diagram to a third crime.

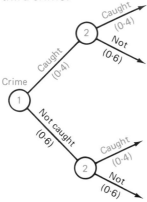

Use the diagram to estimate these probabilities:
(1) the criminal escapes all three times,
(2) the criminal is caught the third time but not on the first two.

6 There are 500 tickets in a raffle numbered from 001 to 500. A lady buys all the tickets whose digits add up to 10.
What is her chance of winning the raffle?

♦ **7** A tennis player has to win two matches to qualify for the final in a competition. Her chance against the first opponent is estimated as $\frac{5}{16}$ and her chance against the second is $\frac{2}{3}$.
What is the probability of the following events?
(a) The player qualifies.
(b) The player loses both matches.
(c) The player loses one match and wins the other.
[What would you expect to be the total of the answers to (a), (b) and (c)?]

♦ **8** (a) A card is drawn at random from a pack of cards.
What is the chance that it is an ace?
(b) The card is placed at the bottom of the pack and a second card is drawn. What is the chance that this card is an ace
(i) if the first card was an ace,
(ii) if the first card was not an ace?

Key facts E

The three topics in this set of key facts are sets, statistics and probability. They have been grouped together because statistics is all about sets of data. Probability too has a close connection with the ideas explained in the section on sets. The symbols $\in$, $\notin$, $\cap$, $\cup$, $\emptyset$ and $\mathcal{E}$ are very easy to understand. When you are used to them they can be very useful in explaining the main ideas of probability and statistics.

♦E.1 Sets

Sets are just collections of things. It is usual to give a set a capital letter for its name. There must also be a rule which tells you which things belong to a set and which do not. The sign $\in$ means 'belongs to'. $\notin$ means 'does not belong to'

Example

If P = {the set of names beginning with P}
then Peter ∈ P, Paula ∈ P, and Sandra ∉ P.

E.1.1 Universal set Ɛ

When a collection is formed there is a background set in mind. The collection is taken from this bigger set by the rule of choice.

Taking names beginning with P, the background set is the set of all names. This set is called the universal set for this example. A curly E which stands for 'everything' is always used for a universal set.

Universal sets and the sets which are part of them are easily shown in a diagram.*

* Usually called a Venn diagram, it is just common sense really.

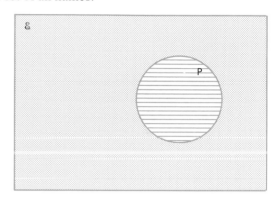

The space inside the rectangle corresponds to the universal set.

The space inside the circle corresponds to the set P.

E.1.2 Complement

We are now left with the set of things which belong to the universal set but do not belong to P. This is written P′ and is called the complement of P. In the 'names' example, Ɛ is the set of all names, P is the set of names beginning with P, P′ is the set of names that do not begin with P.

E.1.3 Union and intersection

Two sets, A and B give rise to two more sets.
1: The union of A and B . . . A ∪ B.
   This set consists of all the members of A and B.
   [Think about the USSR and the States of the Union of America (USA).]
2: The intersection of A and B . . . A ∩ B.
   This set consists of the members which are in both A and B.

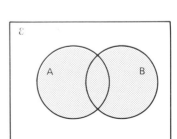

E.1.4 The empty set ∅

If A and B have no members in common then A ∩ B has no members. A set with no members is called the empty set and is written ∅.

Can you see that   (i) P ∩ P′ = ∅,
     and that (ii) A ∩ B = B ∩ A,
              (iii) A ∪ B = B ∪ A,
              (iv) A ∪ A′ = Ɛ,   whatever the sets A and B are?

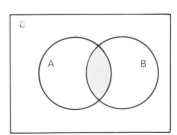

E.1.5 Subsets

If all the members of A also belong to B then A is called a subset of
B . . . A $\subset$ B.

In the diagram, you can see that the members of B are all inside A. It is not
true the other way round. There are members of A which are not members
of B.

This is another very simple idea about sets which helps clear thinking. The
idea of a subset can also be shown using $\Rightarrow$, the 'if . . . , then . . .' arrow of
implication.

If $x \in A \Rightarrow x \in B$ then A $\subset$ B.

[Can you sort this out? Give examples to show how it works.]

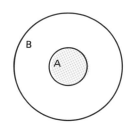

Exercise E.1

H is the set of numbers from 1 to 100.

1 List 9 numbers which belong to H,
which are also multiples of 10.   C

2 If E is the set of even numbers
belonging to H, and F is the set of
multiples of 5 which belong to H, what
are
(i) E $\cap$ F   (iii) E' $\cap$ F
(ii) E $\cup$ F   (iv) E $\cap$ F'?   C

3 If E is the set of even numbers
belonging to H, R is the set of odd
numbers belonging to H and P is the set
of prime numbers, list
(i) E $\cap$ P   (iii) P $\cap$ R'
(ii) E $\cap$ R   (iv) (E $\cup$ R)'   B

4 X $\subset$ Y and Y $\subset$ Z. Is it always true that
X $\subset$ Z whatever the elements of X, Y
and Z?
Give two examples in support of your
answer and draw a diagram.   B

5 A survey of 57 girls found that every girl
reads at least one of the magazines
'Teens' (T), 'Sixteen' (S), 'Young Love'
(YL). The survey also found that . . .
(i) 36 girls read T, 30 read S and 25
read YL,
(ii) 6 girls read all three,
(iii) the same number read T and S as
read T and YL,
(iv) half as many girls read both S and
YL as read both T and S.
Work out how many read T only, S only
and YL only.   B

6 The set X has three elements,
X = {a, b, c}.
(a) List all the possible subsets of X.
(b) List all the possible subsets of
Y = {p, q, r, s}
(c) How many possible subsets could
be obtained from a set with ten
elements?   A

7 Mark two points X and Y, 5 cm apart.
P = {points 2 cm from X}
Q = {points 3 cm from Y}
R = {points less than 2 cm from X}
S = {points more than 3 cm from Y}
(i) Draw the sets P and Q.
(ii) Find n(P $\cap$ Q).
(iii) Shade R $\cup$ S . . . $\equiv$
(iv) Shade R $\cap$ S . . . ||||.   B

8 Sets A and B are in $\mathcal{E}$. Illustrate in four
diagrams
A $\subset$ B $\Leftrightarrow$ B' $\subset$ A' $\Leftrightarrow$ A $\cap$ B' = ϕ
$\Leftrightarrow$ A' $\cup$ B = $\mathcal{E}$ A

E.2 Statistics

Statistics is the art of good guessing. The guesses are based on sets of data which have been collected by sampling. These sets of data are also called 'statistics', so the word has two meanings.

(i) The whole art of using carefully collected sets of data to solve a problem.

(ii) The sets of data themselves.

Statistics is so important in the management of a country that the UK government has a special branch called the Statistics Office. The methods of statistics are used in many important activities such as medical research, population studies, weather forecasting, business marketing, agriculture, etc.

E.2.1 Sampling

The relationship between a sample and a population is like using a torch on a very dark night. As we flash the torch about we can see samples of the countryside, a tree there, a cottage, a gate and so on, but it is not until daylight that we can see everything at once.

Bad sampling can give very misleading results. If you wanted to find out how many people had a telephone, it wouldn't be much use picking names at random from the telephone directory and ringing them up. [Why not?] A sample must be chosen in a way that is free from bias. Remember, too, that you want the sample to have the same proportions as the universal set.

Examples

1 *Left-hand/right-handed people*
 ε is the whole population.
 L is the set of left-handed people,
 R is the set of right-handed people.
 Sample ... all the people living in the city of Derby.

2 *Voting in the General Election*
 The sample is chosen from the list of electors in 12 different cities of Great Britain.
 The first two voters whose surnames begin with S are asked their voting intentions.

Can you see any bias in these methods of sampling?

Sampling without bias is called random sampling. Numbers can be used to produce a random result, such as the winners of a lottery.

Every ticket sold has a number attached. Random numbers are then found to select the winner. For example, if a million tickets were sold, numbered 000 000 to 999 999, the winner could be found by choosing a number from 0 to 9 six times to form a six-digit winning number.

[If you have a scientific calculator it may have a random number generator marked ran# . This will enable you to produce an unbiased 3-figure number every time you press it. This is equivalent to having a 999-sided die whenever you want it! Of course you can use ran# as a six-sided die. Just use the last figure and ignore numbers that end in 0, 7, 8 or 9.]

E.2.2 Presenting sample data

Data is usually collected by a 'tally' process and then entered into a table. To help get an idea of what the data implies four types of diagram may be drawn:
(i) pictogram   (ii) bar chart,   (iii) frequency graph,   (iv) pie chart.

Example

On a catering course 60 students were asked to estimate the weight of a piece of fish. The results were entered on a tally chart.

Estimate in lb	Tally	Totals
$2\frac{1}{2}$–3	|||	3
3^+–$3\frac{1}{2}$	NN		6
$3\frac{1}{2}^+$–4	NN NN ||	12
4^+–$4\frac{1}{2}$	NN NN NN |||	18
$4\frac{1}{2}^+$–5	NN NN ||	12
5^+–$5\frac{1}{2}$	NN ||||	9

If the tally marks are left out the table becomes a frequency table.

Estimate in lb	$f \leftarrow$ frequency
$2\frac{1}{2}$–3	3
3^+–$3\frac{1}{2}$	6
$3\frac{1}{2}^+$–4	12
4^+–$4\frac{1}{2}$	18
$4\frac{1}{2}^+$–5	12
5^+–$5\frac{1}{2}$	9
Total	60

Note: This is the basic set of information and no diagram can give any more information that can be obtained from the table!

The following diagrams show four different ways of making a diagram to illustrate a set of data. The choice is really up to you as to which you choose. It depends on what point you want to make to the reader.

Pictogram

I think you will agree that this type of diagram is rather childish. It is, however, often used, especially in comparing arms of different countries!
For example,

 = 1000 tanks, etc.

Estimate in lb	= 1 catering student
$2\frac{1}{2}^{+}$–3	
3^{+}–$3\frac{1}{2}$	
$3\frac{1}{2}^{+}$–4	
4^{+}–$4\frac{1}{2}$	
$4\frac{1}{2}^{+}$–5	
5^{+}–$5\frac{1}{2}$	

Pie chart

The whole set corresponds to the 360° at the centre:

60 students → 360°
3 students → 18°
6 students → 36°
12 students → 72°
18 students → 108°
9 students → 54°

[Not really suitable for this particular set of information.]

Estimate in lb

$2\frac{1}{2}^{+}$–3

3^{+}–$3\frac{1}{2}$

$3\frac{1}{2}^{+}$–4

4^{+}–$4\frac{1}{2}$

$4\frac{1}{2}^{+}$–5

5^{+}–$5\frac{1}{2}$

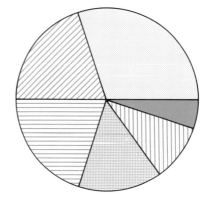

Frequency graph

A frequency graph is just like an x, y graph with frequency taking the place of the y values. Each range of values is replaced by its midpoint:

$2\frac{1}{2}^{+}$–3 → $2\frac{3}{4}$
3^{+}–$3\frac{1}{2}$ → $3\frac{1}{4}$
$3\frac{1}{2}^{+}$–4 → $3\frac{3}{4}$
4^{+}–$4\frac{1}{2}$ → $4\frac{1}{4}$
$4\frac{1}{2}^{+}$–5 → $4\frac{3}{4}$
5^{+}–$5\frac{1}{2}$ → $5\frac{1}{4}$

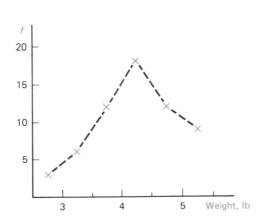

Bar chart

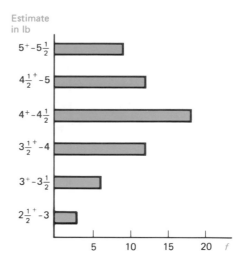

Horizontal version with thinner bars.

Examples

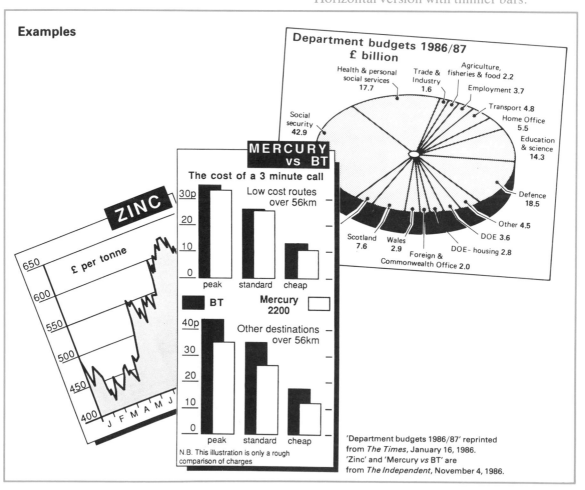

N.B. This illustration is only a rough comparison of charges

'Department budgets 1986/87' reprinted from *The Times*, January 16, 1986. 'Zinc' and 'Mercury *vs* BT' are from *The Independent*, November 4, 1986.

212

E.2.3   Misleading statistics

Some advertisements give false impressions in their diagrams. So you should always treat such diagrams with caution. The following examples show some of the ways that things can be made to look different.

Examples

1   Altering the base line. This looks as though robberies tripled from 1983 to 1986!!

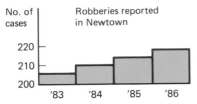

But here is the full story . . .

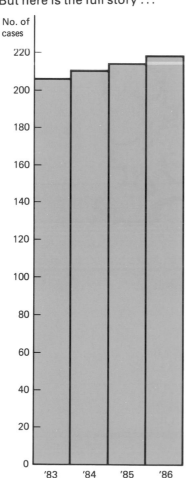

2   Altering the scale. These three graphs all represent exactly the same data. The growth rate looks quite different. This is achieved by varying the scales. If you really want to know exactly what is going on always go back to the original data!

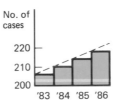

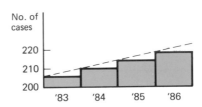

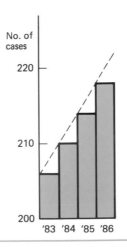

[You can see how a company could give a very different picture of the growth of its sales, just by changing the scales along the axes of the sales graph.]

Other things to watch for . . .

- Sometimes important information is left out:
  'Our company increased sales by £2·4 million.' . . . but what happened to profits?
- Sometimes a biased sample population has been asked and then their opinions quoted as though the sample was random.
  '90% of people asked approved of the new route for the bypass.'
  . . . but did any of them come from areas that would be affected by noise and pollution?

- Sometimes a survey is designed to produce (or avoid) particular answers.
  'If you smoke is it because: (a) you enjoy it?
                                (b) it soothes your nerves?
                                (c) it helps overcome shyness?'
  This question could lead to a statement that 70% of smokers smoke to soothe their nerves, but the question leaves no space for the person to add reasons of their own, or to say 'sometimes one reason and then another'.

Remember that a statement is not necessarily true just because it is printed and also that people do not need to give truthful answers to surveys if they don't like the questions.

E.2.4 Mean, median, and mode

There are three different 'averages' in use in statistics: the mean, mode and median. They each give a single value to represent a set of data.

Example

Our town team is not too good at scoring! In their last twenty matches they scored
0, 5, 1, 3, 2, 1, 4, 0, 1, 1, 2, 3, 1, 2, 1, 3, 4, 1, 0, 2 goals.
This information can be represented by three different measures.
  (i) The arithmetic mean ... total score ÷ number of games.
 (ii) The mode ... the score that happened most often.
(iii) The median ... the score that divides the data into equal halves.

Arithmetic mean (or mean for short): $\dfrac{\text{Total score}}{\text{No. of matches}} = \dfrac{37}{20} = 1.85$

Note that the mean is not one of the possible numbers of goals.

Mode: Arrange the results in a frequency table.

Goals scored	f
0	3
1	7
2	4
3	3
4	2
5	1
Total	20

In 3 matches the score was 0
In 7 matches the score was 1, etc.

The mode is clearly 1 goal. This is the score that happened most often (i.e. with the greatest frequency).

Median: Arranging the scores in order of size we have
0 0 0   1 1 1 1 1 1 1   2 2 2 2   3 3 3   4 4 5
  10 worst games   ↑   10 best games
            median value
              1.5

E.2.5 Grouped data

Collections of data are often grouped for convenience. Instead of a single value and its frequency, the frequency of a whole class of data is given. Before the mean of a set of grouped data is calculated, each class should be replaced by a single representative value. This is usually the mid-member of the class.

● Care must be taken when the class-range is not the same for each class.

Example

Adoptions of children in England and Wales by age and sex (in 1978)

Age	Males	Females
Under 6 months	505	422
6–11 months	982	907
12–23 months	253	232
2–4 years	1 099	1 009
5–9 years	2 041	1 855
10–20 years	1 379	1 337

In order to calculate the mean age of adopted children the classes are replaced by the middle value (in months) with some common sense adjustments.

3 months ... for under 6 months
9 months ... for 6–11 months
18 months ... for 12–23 months
36 months ... for 2–4 years
84 months ... for 5–9 years
168 months ... for 10–20 years ... allows for the fact that there are probably more adoptions of younger children in the age range.

The means are calculated in the following tables.

Age (months) x	Males f	xf	Age (months) x	Females f	xf
3	505	1 515	3	422	1 266
9	982	8 838	9	907	8 163
18	253	4 554	18	232	4 176
36	1 099	39 564	36	1 009	36 324
84	2 041	171 444	84	1 855	155 820
168	1 379	231 672	168	1 337	224 616
Totals →	6 259	231 672	Totals →	5 762	430 365
	Σf	Σxf		Σf	Σxf

$\dfrac{\Sigma xf}{\Sigma f}$ = mean = 73·1 months

i.e. average age for adoption is just over six years

$\dfrac{\Sigma xf}{\Sigma f}$ = mean = 74·7 months

i.e. average age for adoption is over six years

These results suggest that there is not much difference for the boys and girls. This is much harder to see if you just look at the 'raw data'.

◆ E.2.6 Cumulative frequency. Range. Interquartile range

When a set of data is put in order of size, each item can be allocated a
number. These numbers can be used to divide the total frequency into half
(median) and quarters (quartiles).
The spread of the data is measured by the range or by the interquartile range:

$$range = x_{max} - x_{min}$$

interquartile range = upper quartile − lower quartile

The ideas are best understood from an example.

Example

Examination results for 70 students.

Grade x	Frequency f	Cumulative Frequency CF
A	3	3
B	7	10
C	10	20
D	18	38
E	14	52
F	9	61
G	6	67
Unclassified	3	70 ↑
	70	← total

The CF column shows frequency 'so far'.
Thus 10 candidates scored A, B; 20 candidates scored A, B, C

The last value in the CF column must be the same as the total frequency.
The candidates could be numbered in order of results from 1 to 70.

1 A	2 A	3 A	4 B	5 B	6 B	7 B	8 B	9 B	10 B	
11 C	12 C	13 C	14 C	15 C	16 C	17 C	18 ● C	19 C	20 C	lower quartile
21 D	22 D	23 D	24 D	25 D	26 D	27 D	28 D	29 D	30 D	
31 D	32 D	33 D	34 D	35 D	36 ● D	37 D	38 D	39 E	40 E	median
41 E	42 E	43 E	44 E	45 E	46 E	47 E	48 E	49 E	50 E	
51 E	52 E	53 ● F	54 F	55 F	56 F	57 F	58 F	59 F	60 F	upper quartile
61 F	62 G	63 G	64 G	65 G	66 G	67 G	68 U	69 U	70 U	

Since there are 70 results altogether, result number 35/36 will be the median.
The median grade is D.
The quartiles which divide each half of the frequency in half again are results number 18 and number 53.
The quartile grades are C and F.

Interquartile range is thus 3 grades in this case   C͡ D͡ E͡ F

• Note the connection between the cumulative frequency of a grade and the number of the last candidate in each grade class.

The range is 7 grades   A͡ B͡ C͡ D͡ E͡ F͡ G͡ U

Graphs

The frequency graph and the cumulative frequency graph should be considered together.

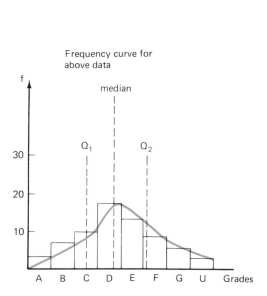

Frequency curve for above data

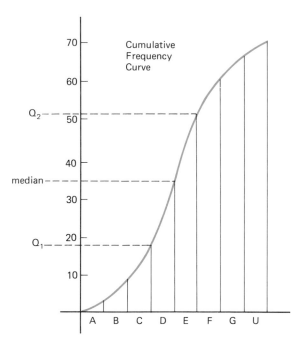

The cumulative frequency curve can easily be used to find the median and quartiles. It can be seen from the frequency graph that the area is divided into four equal parts and that this area corresponds to the frequency.

Example

The number of days before a job was obtained after leaving school [from 560 employed young people]

Number of days	f	CF
0–10	150	150
11–20	38	188
21–30	67	255
31–40	110	365
41–50	84	449
51–60	27	476
61–70	40	516
71–80	22	538
81–90	15	553
91–100	7	560
Total	560	

Total frequency is 560.
Median number 280
Quartiles numbers 140 and 420

Number 280 comes in the 31–40 class roughly $\frac{1}{4}$ along.
Or more exactly:

$$\text{median} = 30 + \frac{25}{110} \times 10 = 32\cdot27$$

Number 140 is in 0–10 class.

$$\text{Lower quartile} = 0 + \frac{140}{150} \times 10 = 9\cdot33$$

Number 420 is in the 41–50 class.

$$\text{Upper Quartile} = 40 + \frac{55}{84} \times 10 = 46\cdot55$$

Median: 32·3   Quartiles: 9·3, 46·6
Range: 100   Interquartile range: 37·3

E.2.7 Scattergrams

These are diagrams which are used to try to establish links between variables.
The example which follows shows how they can be used in a simple case.
Links between variables are important in medicine [e.g. the link between smoking and heart disease is statistical].

Example

An examination in French consists of two papers. Paper I is a written paper and paper II is an oral test.
The results for 30 candidates are given below.

Paper I	16	13	92	11	46	41	64	85	30	86	57	75	89	77	38
Paper II	77	45	70	44	17	18	54	51	50	89	43	46	40	73	56
Paper I	72	63	58	59	73	50	20	44	43	62	89	10	71	40	19
Paper II	39	21	33	44	88	78	34	15	51	78	73	47	64	70	59

These results are marked on a scattergram. Each ● corresponds to one candidate.

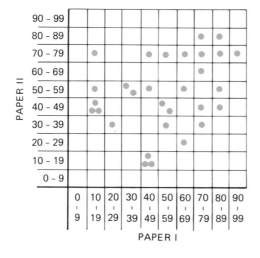

Scattergram each ● represents one candidate.

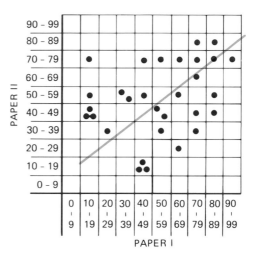

The same scattergram with an estimated LINE OF BEST FIT drawn. This line is chosen so that the total distances of all the points from the line is as low as possible.

The slope of the line of best fit gives a guide to the degree of association between the two variables.

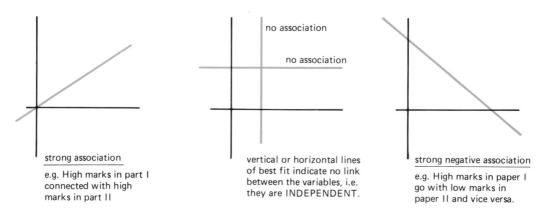

strong association

e.g. High marks in part I connected with high marks in part II

no association

no association

vertical or horizontal lines of best fit indicate no link between the variables, i.e. they are INDEPENDENT.

strong negative association

e.g. High marks in paper I go with low marks in paper II and vice versa.

Note: The association of variables is always hard to express accurately in real life situations.

Using mean values

The degree of association of the variables can become clearer if mean values are calculated and these are added to the scattergram.
Paper I : mean score 53·1
Paper II: mean score 52·233 . . .

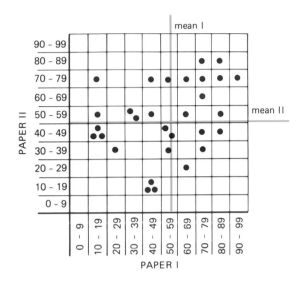

Counting the candidates . . .

9 above average in both papers
7 below average in both papers
4 above average in I and below average in II
6 above average in II and below average in I

These figures show some degree of connection between the scores on paper I and paper II but by no means 'perfect agreement'.

Exercise E.2

1 A person who offers to give blood is first asked for a sample. What does this mean? C

2 Boxes of matches are filled by machine. A sample of 60 boxes is drawn from a batch. The number of matches in each sample box is found. Make a tally chart of the data which is given below. The figures are the number of matches over 50 in each box. C

0	2	0	3	1	2	2	3	0	0	1	1
2	1	3	1	0	1	2	1	2	2	0	2
0	2	0	2	2	1	3	0	2	3	1	0
1	2	2	1	0	3	2	2	1	0	2	2
3	0	1	2	1	2	0	0	3	2	1	1

3 The number of cups of coffee sold from a coffee stall is shown in the bar chart.

(i) Which days were market days? Why?
(ii) Which day was the stall closed?
(iii) Estimate the total number of coffees sold during the whole week.

C

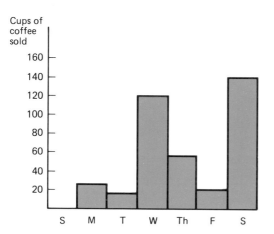

4 The pie chart shows the proportions of different cars sold in 1986 (by country of production) in Britain.
If 1 600 000 cars were sold altogether, estimate how many from each country were sold.

C

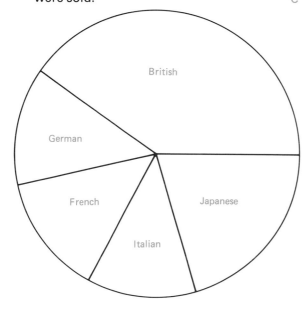

5 The table below gives the number of brothers and sisters for all the children in eight classes at Upton Junior School.

Class	Numbers of brothers/sisters							Total
	0	1	2	3	4	5	6	
1a	8	12	7	9	3	0	1	40
1b	7	11	10	6	1	2	0	37
1c	10	9	9	5	5	0	1	39
2a	6	14	10	8	0	0	0	38
2b	11	7	8	7	2	2	1	38
2c	9	13	5	10	1	0	1	39
3a	8	11	8	8	4	0	0	39
3b	7	12	2	10	3	2	1	37
Total	66	89	59	63	19	6	5	307

Calculate the mean, mode and median for each class and for the whole group of children.

B

6 The 'duration of unemployment' statistics compare England and Scotland in 1983. Find the mean, mode and median for both countries.

Weeks	England (%)	Scotland (%)
0–2	6·2	5·6
2⁺–8	14·5	14·2
8⁺–13	7·0	7·0
13⁺–26	13·6	14·0
26⁺–52	18·0	16·9
52⁺–104	20·2	19·0
104⁺	20·5	23·3

Comment on the differences between the statistics for the two countries.

B

7 A police station keeps a daily record of the number of 999 calls received. Draw a cumulative frequency graph from the data and find the median and interquartile range. Suggest how the data might be used in police manpower planning.

A

Number of calls	0–10	11–20	21–30	31–40	41–50	51–60	61–70
Number of days	62	106	102	66	40	16	4

8 The data below relate the average daily time spent watching TV to the number of examination successes achieved by 50 students. Make a scattergram of the data and draw an estimated line of best fit. Comment on your results.

A

Student	TV watched (hrs)	Exam passes	Student	TV watched (hrs)	Exam passes
Long	2·0	5	Abel	3·6	7
Ming	5·4	2	Bloggs	3·2	4
Munn	2·3	3	Brown	5·8	4
Nouse	0·0	8	Bunn	0·7	2
O'leary	6·9	2	Carpenter	6·6	5
Ovens	0·8	1	Cove	3·3	7
Pim	1·5	6	Diwa	5·7	5
Pym	2·3	4	Doon	2·7	6
Ratt	0·1	6	Dunn	5·9	8
Rilke	2·9	2	Earp	1·0	2
Roume	5·2	6	Eng	6·1	8
Rugg	3·8	6	Fenn	0·9	1
Smith	6·1	6	Fatim	2·1	7
Smith	3·5	6	Gunn	1·6	7
Sword	0·0	9	Hill	2·9	4
Synge	4·8	5	Hoy	0·5	2
Tall	5·2	5	Ing	3·2	2
Thomas	0·7	8	Isaacs	3·6	7
Trapper	4·2	7	Jing	3·4	2
Uwe	4·9	0	Jumblatt	4·1	5
Wall	3·8	2	Kane	3·7	1
West	2·5	2	Khan	0·9	5
Wonder	5·4	1	King	0·8	4
Yeo	3·2	2	Kung	3·8	5
Young	4·4	3	Love	1·6	2

You might like to follow up this set of data with some collected for your own class using 'mock' results.

E.3 Probability

Probability brings scientific thinking to guessing. Every event has a
probability ranging from
100% ... certain   to   0% ... definitely not.

Examples

1	It will rain tomorrow	... 30% (say)
2	A tossed coin will land heads up	... 50%
3	A thrown die will score a 6	... $\frac{1}{6}$ = 16·6%
4	An unborn baby is a girl	... 49·5%.

E.3.1   Estimating probabilities 1

There are two main ways of estimating probabilities. The first way is really a
simple 'counting' method.

Examples

1 I had a bet with a friend that even blindfold I could pick a vowel with a pin
from a page of a book. I checked my chance in advance by simply
counting the vowels and consonants on a page.
In 1000 letters I found 350 vowels and 650 consonants.

Probability of picking a vowel (p) = $\dfrac{350}{1000}$ = 0·35.

[*Note*: You might expect a probability of 5/26 but you would be wrong!]

2 I choose two horses from 8 in a race. The chance of picking a winner is
$\frac{2}{8}$ = 0·25 or 25%.
But this is only true if all horses are equally likely to win.
Some horses will have a better chance of winning than others (as shown
by their starting prices).
Betting on horses is a mug's game.

E.3.2   Estimating probabilities 2

The second way of estimating probability is by experiment and experience.

Example

In an experiment three dice were thrown together 1000 times. The scores were
added and recorded.

Score	f	Score	f	Score	f
3	6	9	112	15	47
4	13	10	127	16	25
5	28	11	125	17	14
6	44	12	116	18	5
7	71	13	94		
8	97	14	76	Total	1000

Total 9

These figures suggest . . .

- The probability of scoring 9 is about 11·2% . . . 0·112
- The probability of scoring 11 is about 12·5% . . . 0·125 or once every 8 throws
- The probability of scoring more than 15 is 4·4% . . . 0·044 $\dfrac{25 + 14 + 5}{1000}$

  or about once every 20 throws

and so on.

Note that the scores are not equally likely.

Make an experiment to check the above probabilities.

E.3.3   Tree diagrams

Probabilities can be worked out using a tree diagram.

Examples

1   A journey consists of a train journey to
London, a coach ride to the airport and a
flight in an aeroplane. Each part of the
journey can be early, late or on time [all
equally likely].

The diagram shows 27 different
possibilities for being late, early and on
time.

The method shows things clearly but gets
very 'crowded' after three events.

The chance of all three—train, coach and
plane—being early is $\frac{1}{27}$.

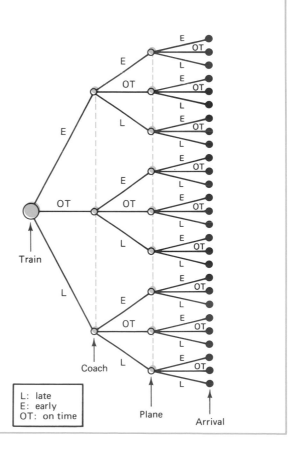

L: late
E: early
OT: on time

Train

Coach

Plane

Arrival

225

2 Chuck bought five tickets in one lottery (A) and 10 tickets in another (B). Each lottery had 100 tickets.

- His chance of winning in A is $\frac{5}{100}$ = 0.05 or 5%.
- His chance of winning in B is $\frac{10}{100}$ = 0·1 or 10%.
- His chance of winning in both in 0·005 or $\frac{1}{2}$%.

$$[0·05 \times 0·1]$$

Also

- His chance of *not* winning A is 95%.
- His chance of *not* winning B is 90%.

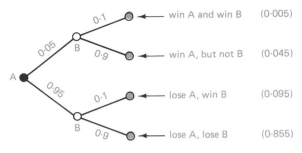

Tree diagram showing all probabilities.

E.3.4   Combining probabilities

Special language is needed in discussing combined probabilities.

Events ... E_1, E_2 ... etc.

These are happenings which can be allocated a probability value E.g. a coin is tossed and it comes down heads is an event with probability 0·5. Just tossing a coin is not an event in this sense.

Independent events ... These are events which are not connected in a way which affects their probability.

E.g. the probability that I shall catch a cold next year and the probability that I will have a car accident next year are not connected, so the two events are independent.

[*Note*: Independence is difficult to establish, for example I might have a cold on the day of the accident!]

Mutually exclusive events ... These are events which cannot happen together. A baby cannot be both boy and girl. You cannot score 5 and 6 at the same time with a die.

♦*The laws of compound probability*

(1) Two events E_1 and E_2 are independent, with probabilities p_1 and p_2. The probability that both E_1 and E_2 will happen is $p_1 \times p_2$.

(2) Two events E_1 and E_2 are mutually exclusive, with probabilities p_1 and p_2. The probability that either E_1 or E_2 will happen is $p_1 + p_2$.

Example

A couple are about to have a child. The example looks at the probabilities that the child will be male or female and will be right or left handed.

Event	Probability
The new baby is . . .	
male	0·5
female	0·5
left handed	0·3
right handed	0·7

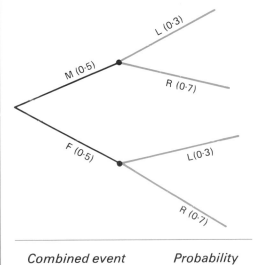

Combined event	Probability		
The new baby is . . .			
either male or female	0·5 + 0·5 = 1	mutually exclusive	
either left or right handed	0·3 + 0·7 = 1	mutually exclusive	
male, left handed	0·5 × 0·3 = 0·15	independent	4 mutually
male, right handed	0·5 × 0·7 = 0·35	independent	exclusive
female, left handed	0·5 × 0·3 = 0·15	independent	events. Total
female, right handed	0·5 × 0·7 = 0·35	independent	probability is 1

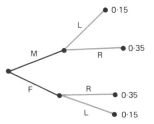

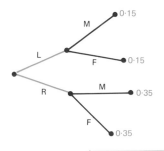

Two diagrams of the same situation.

Exercise E.3

1 In a raffle all the tickets from 0000 to 2500 were sold. 7 is my lucky number so I bought all the tickets ending in 7. What is my chance of winning the raffle?   C

2 Two dice are thrown and the total score taken. Construct a table which will give the probabilities of throwing each score between 2 and 12.
   [*Hint*: Consider 36 throws]   B

3 A football team has a 40% chance of winning against each of the next three teams to be played. What is the chance
   (a) the team will win all three matches,
   (b) the team will win two out of the three matches?   B

4 Two snooker players George and Jake play a match of three frames. George is slightly better and is estimated to have a 60% chance of winning each frame. Draw a tree diagram to show the results of three frames and estimate the chance that Jake will win the match.   B

5 A pair of numbers are chosen from the first 100. What is the chance that both are prime. [1 is not considered a prime number].   B

6 A box of chocolates contains 20 soft centres and 10 hard centred. Rosa takes two chocolates when she is offered the box (rude girl). What is the probability that one is hard and the other soft.   B/A

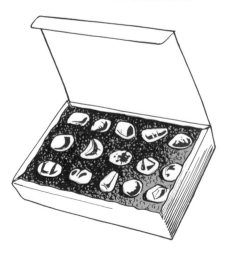

7 In the gambling game of roulette a ball is rolled on to a revolving wheel. The ball comes to rest against one of the numbers 0 . . . 32 when the wheel stops. If the ball stops at zero the bank wins.
   (a) What would be fair odds on the numbers 10–20 inclusive?
   (b) What is the probability that the ball will stop on a number containing a 1?
   (c) What is the probability that the ball will stop at a number which is both even and a multiple of 5?
   (d) Explain why it is unlikely that the bank will lose over a long period.   B

8 At my bus stop there is a bus every hour. It is due at 12 minutes past the hour but is sometimes early and sometimes late.
   I collected and noted the times of the bus over the last week.

	Early	Late
More than 10 minutes	1	3
5+–10 minutes	7	29
0 – 5 minutes	16	34

Estimate the probability
   (a) that the next bus will be early;
   (b) that I will catch the 11.12 bus if I get to the bus stop at 11.17;
   (c) that I will catch the 11.12 bus if I get to the bus stop at 11.20;
   (d) that the next three buses will all be early.
State any assumptions that are made in obtaining the estimates.   A

Examination questions E

1 ε = pupils in 5W, S = pupils who swim,
T = pupils who play tennis.
  (a) How many pupils are there altogether in 5W?
  (b) How many of the tennis players do not swim?

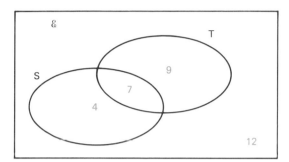

2 (a) The probability that an event will occur is 0·65. What is the probability that it will not occur?
  (b) The probability that a bus arrives early at the bus stop is $\frac{1}{10}$ and the probability that it arrives late is $\frac{2}{5}$.
    (i) What is the probability that it is on time?
    (ii) 60 buses stop at the bus stop every day. How many of these would you expect to be late?

◆3 The Venn diagram shows three sets, X, Y and Z.
  (a) Which of these statements is true?
    (i) X ∩ Y = Ø (ii) Y ∩ Z = Ø
    (iii) X ∩ Z = Ø
  (b) Which of the sets listed here corresponds to the coloured part of the diagram?
    (i) X ∩ Y ∩ Z   (ii) (X ∩ Y) ∪ (X ∩ Z)
    (iii) X ∩̇ Y' ∩ Z (iv) X' ∩ Y ∩ Z'
    (v) X ∪ Y' ∪ Z

4 A caravan site owner keeps records of the number of caravans parked each night.

	M	T	W	Th	F	Sat	Sun
Week 1	49	3	34	40	4	36	43
Week 2	29	33	54	21	14	27	44
Week 3	40	18	10	45	32	41	35
Week 4	48	25	55	34	17	26	48
Week 5	40	44	34	42	14	51	45

  (a) Tabulate the data in groups 0–9, 10–19, etc, showing the frequency of each group.
  (b) Construct a cumulative frequency graph from the data.
  (c) Use the cumulative frequency curve to find the median and interquartile range of the number of caravans.
  (d) Compare the median with the mean and the mode for the data.

5 The mean of 4, n, 8, 12 and 20 is 10·1. Calculate n.

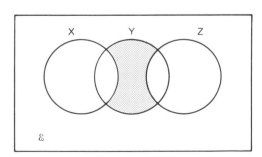

6 Students in a class were given grades A, B, C, D or E in their exams. The results are shown in the table.

Grade	A	B	C	D	E
Number of students	4	6	11	8	3

(a) Show this data in a bar chart.
(b) What was the 'average' grade?

7 A fairground game uses a coloured disc and an arrow. The arrow is spun and if it lands on a section showing a sum of money, that is paid out. The cost of a spin is 20p. If the arrow stops on a blank, nothing is paid out.

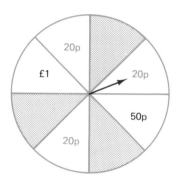

(a) What is the chance of winning on one spin of the arrow?
(b) What is the chance of losing the stake?
(c) Make a 'win/money back/lose' tree diagram for two spins of the wheel.
(d) What is the probability that a player will win the £1 prize twice in a row?

♦ **8** In a forestry experiment trees were measured five years after planting. There were originally 500 Norway spruce and 500 Scots pine in the sample and all were 30 cm high when planted.

	NS	SP
0 –1 m	12	32
1⁺–2 m	39	105
2⁺–3 m	46	85
3⁺–4 m	152	70
4⁺–5 m	106	110
5⁺–6 m	30	30
6⁺–7 m	15	8
Totals →	400	440

Use the data to find mean, median and interquartile range for each species. Which of the two species had a faster growth rate in this experiment.

9 An ice cream parlour keeps careful records of all sales. The data are given in the table below for 1 year.

	0 ‑ 10	11 ‑ 20	21 ‑ 30	31 ‑ 40	41 ‑ 50	51 ‑ 60	61 ‑ 70	71 ‑ 80	81 ‑ 90	91 ‑ 100	*Total*
					Litres						
				number of weeks in which this quantity was sold							
Lime	4	7	10	11	4	10	6	0	0	0	52
Raspberry	2	5	7	10	13	5	4	6	0	0	52
Vanila	0	0	3	15	18	12	0	3	1	0	52
Strawberry	3	4	8	4	12	11	3	3	3	1	52
Chocolate	4	2	5	14	10	11	0	6	0	0	52

Which was the most popular flavour? Give your reasons.

10 The data in the table give the average number of hours spent per day watching T.V. ... before and after marriage. The data were collected from 310 young married people all under 21 years old.

Daily hours of viewing	Before marriage	After marriage
0–1	16	28
1^+–2	35	46
2^+–3	149	156
3^+–4	86	67
4^+–5	22	8
Over 5	2	5
Total	310	310

Do the figures agree with the suggestion ... 'Married couples watch TV more than single people'.

◆ **11** The table gives the number of cigarettes smoked per day for a group of patients at a chest clinic. Calculate the mean, mode, median and IQ range for the data. Add any comments you consider relevant.

	Age	
Number of cigs. smoked per day	Under 50	Over 50
0–5	140	116
6–10	38	88
11–15	77	29
16–20	132	44
21–25	41	15
26–30	48	11
31–35	30	13
36–40	22	0
Over 40	2	4
Totals →	530	320

12 40 volunteers had their reaction time tested after drinking various quantities of alcoholic beverage. The individual data are given. The first figure gives reaction time in tenths of seconds, the coloured figure gives the number of units of alcohol drunk.

(4 2)(4 8)(8 3)(5 3)(2 5)
(9 9)(4 1)(7 7)(4 6)(1 2)
(8 9)(5 8)(4 7)(9 6)(6 4)
(3 4)(9 8)(7 7)(7 2)(4 5)
(8 9)(2 1)(4 7)(1 4)(5 3)
(4 2)(6 8)(3 3)(2 4)(5 6)
(9 6)(7 2)(4 7)(4 5)(7 8)
(5 1)(4 5)(5 4)(9 6)(2 3)

Make a table of the results and draw a scattergram. Add an estimated line of best fit.
Do your results indicate a strong connection between reaction time and quantity of alcohol?

◆ **13** The number of fatal road accidents per 100 000 is given for twelve towns, with their populations. Decide whether there is some connection between size of town and accident rate.

Town	Population (000's)	Accident rate per 100 000
Penzance	19	11·2
Bedford	74	9·1
Norwich	122	9·4
Swansea	167	10·3
Stoke on Trent	205	10·6
Cardiff	273	9·8
Coventry	317	9·9
Belfast	363	10·2
Edinburgh	419	9·9
Sheffield	477	11·1
Liverpool	510	10·7
Glasgow	762	10·9

Suggest some of the factors that could cause a connection.

14 Make a scattergram from the data given below, which relate distance from home and number of late arrivals during a year, for a group of 30 students. Which of the following hypotheses agree with the data?
(a) Distance from home does not affect the number of late arrivals.
(b) Students who live further away tend to be late more often.
(c) Students who live nearer to be late more often.

Distance \ Times late	0 | 5	6 | 10	11 | 15	16 | 20	Totals
under 1 km	3	2	1	0	6
$1^+ - 2$ km	1	2	2	1	6
$2^+ - 3$ km	1	1	3	1	6
$3^+ - 4$ km	0	2	3	2	7
$4^+ -$	1	0	2	2	5
Total	6	7	11	6	30

15 The pages of a book are numbered 1 to 320. If a page is chosen at random, what is the chance the page number will contain a zero?

16 Choose the correct statement (or statements) from (i), (ii), (iii) and (iv).
A bag contains yellow, blue, and black tokens. The probability of choosing
a yellow token is p.
a blue token is q.
a black token is r.
 (i) $p + q < 1$ (iii) $p + q + r = 1$
 (ii) $p + q + r < 1$ (iv) $pq < r$

17 An ordinary die is thrown twice and the results are entered in a table as shown below. The table is designed to show all the possible outcomes of throwing a die twice.

		FIRST THROW				
	1	**2**	**3**	**4**	**5**	**6**
S E C O N D 1	1 1	2 1	3 1	4 1		
2		2 2				
3					5 3	
T H R 4						
O 5				4 5		
W 6						

Copy and complete the table. Use the table to find:
(a) the probability that both first and second throws score the same.
(b) the probability that the first throw is better than the second.
(c) the probability that the sum of the two throws is less than 6.

◆ **18** The roads in the diagram have no signposts. A motorist wishing to go from A to D has no map so goes by guesswork at each junction.
He is twice as likely to go straight on as to turn; and where both left and right turns are available, they are equally likely. He never turns back towards A.
Calculate the probability that he misses D altogether.

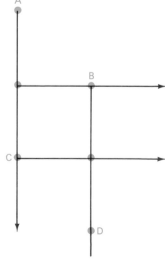

19 If you choose any four figure number at random, what is the probability that
  (i) the number has 3 as a divisor ... p_1
  (ii) the number has 7 as a divisor ... p_2
  (iii) the number has 21 as a divisor ... p_3?
What is the relationship between p_1, p_2 and p_3?

◆ **20** The guarantee on a packet of flower seeds states 'at least 75% of these seeds will germinate and grow'. A girl who is a keen gardener chooses five seeds to grow in a flower pot.
  (a) What is the probability that
    (i) none of the seeds come up
    (ii) only one of the seeds comes up
    (iii) two or more of the seeds come up?
  (b) What arguments could she use in case (i) to obtain her money back from the seed merchant?

Activities and investigations E

Competition quiz E

See p. 24, Competition quiz A, for how to play. (Answers are given on page 430.)

A's questions for B

1 A die is thrown. What is the probability that it lands with the 6 uppermost?
2 A card is chosen at random from a pack of cards. What is the probability that it is red?
3 Two cards are chosen at random from a pack. What is the probability that they are both red?
4 My bus has been late 4 times out of the last 20. What is the probability it will be on time tomorrow?
5 A racing car driver has a 30% chance of winning the Monaco Grand Prix and the same chance of winning at Le Mans. What is the chance he will win both?
6 A person who smokes at 21 has a 30% chance of getting lung cancer before 60. Out of 500 people who smoke, how many can expect lung cancer? Smoking is stupid.
7 If there is a 10% chance of being killed or wounded in a battle, how many battles can a soldier expect to fight before he has only a 50% chance of being unharmed?
8 How many different results are possible if you throw two dice? [Hint: Think of the dice as red and green.]
9 How many different scores are possible if you add the two dice?

B's questions for A

1 A card is chosen at random from a pack of cards. What is the probability that it is an ace?
2 A die is thrown. What is the chance that it scores more than 4?
3 Your chance of winning a game is 0·4. What is the chance that you won't win?
4 If 2 out of 5 people are left handed, how many left-handed children would you expect in a class of 30?
5 A runner has a 40% chance of winning the 800 m and the same chance of winning the 400 m. What is the chance he will win the 800 m and lose the 400 m?
6 A soldier reckons 10% are killed or wounded in a battle. How does he rate his chances of not being hurt? The same soldier fights two battles in a row. What are his chances of surviving unharmed?
7 A fruit machine (one-armed bandit) has eight different fruit on each wheel. How many ways can the player obtain a winning line? [All three fruit the same.]
8 There are 512 possible results for the fruit machine (8 x 8 x 8). What is a player's chance of winning first time?

233

A's questions for B (cont.)

10 How many different scores are possible if you subtract the two dice? [Smaller from larger.]
11 A coin is tossed three times. How many different results can be obtained? [Heads/tails.]
12 What is a sample?
13 What is the difference between 'a random number between 0 and 999' and 'an odd number between 0 and 999'?
14 What is a survey?
15 A die is thrown 25 times. The results are 2 ones, 3 twos, 3 threes, 5 fours, 8 fives and 5 sixes. What is the total frequency?
16 What is a bar chart?
17 In a study of lateness at school it was noticed that four children were always late *together*. Suggest reasons for this.
18 What is the mean of the numbers 1, 2, 3, 4, 5, 6, 7?
19 Eggs are graded A, B, C, D or E. In a batch there were 50 grade A, 56 grade B, 120 grade C, 200 grade D and 300 grade E. What was the median grade of egg? What was the mode size [grade]?
20 What ways are statistics and statistical diagrams used to mislead people?

B's questions for A (cont.)

9   List all the possible scores if you *multiply* the scores on two die.
10 How many different ways can 8 be scored by adding with a red and a blue die?
11 A coin is tossed and a die is thrown together. If the coin lands heads up and the die scores 5, you win. What is your chance of winning?
12 What is a random number?
13 What is 'sampling' used for?
14 What is a questionnaire?
15 What is a biased sample?
16 What is a pie chart?
17 A seed packet says that 90% of the seeds should grow when planted. How do they know?
18 What is the mode shoe size from this data:
    12 people took size 5
    14 people took size 6
    31 people took size 7
    15 people took size 8
19 What is the median size from the shoe size data?
20 How are statistics used to persuade people to buy one brand of goods rather than another?

Random number games

Random numbers

Most scientific calculators have a random number facility. If you press ran , a random number between 000 and 999 will be shown on the display.

This can be used to simulate a die. Just use the last digit. Press again if the last digit is 0, 7, 8 or 9.
Many games can be played using this facility. I can suggest three and you can invent more for yourselves.

1 *Pot luck*

   Players take it in turn to generate a random number. The highest number wins and scores a point.
   The person who scores most points in 50 goes wins the round.
   A 407 ... start
   B 629 ... B wins
   A 007 ... B wins
   B 455 ... B wins
   A 860 ... A wins etc.

2 *Round the clock*

   Players take it in turn to generate a random number.
   From 'start', if the player gets a random number which is a multiple of 2, he or she can move to 2 [A's position].
   Next a multiple of 3 will be needed, and so on until one player gets to 12.
   [B has generated multiples of 2, 3 and 4.]
   Invent variations on this game.

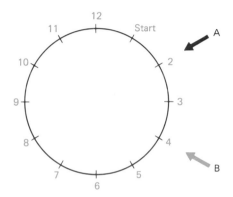

3 *Frustration*

   Players take turns to generate a random number and write it in the grid: here, A got 374, B got 245.
   The winner is the player who completes the grid. [Numbers can be written in a straight line in any direction.]

   It is possible to invent many games on the basis of this idea. The winner could be the one who writes fewest numbers in the squares. The numbers could be written in any direction, including bent lines. You can extend the grid to 5 × 5.

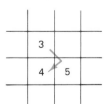

Random numbers without ran

It is thought to be possible to generate random numbers by using
sin cos tan log or inv .
First choose a number between 000 and 999, then press one of the function buttons. Use the last three figures of the decimal tail as the random number.

Investigate this method.

Random dice game

Two people throw a pair of dice in turn. The first to throw 5 or 6 wins and a new game starts.
Play the game 50 times and record the results. Do you think the person who throws first has an unfair advantage?

Random number expectations

Out of 100 random numbers generated on your calculator, how many would you expect to be
(a) *nnn*
(b) $n, n + 1, n + 2$ if you can rearrange
(c) $n, n + 1, n + 2$ if you cannot rearrange
(d) a prime number
(e) a square number
(f) a perfect cube ($n \times n \times n$)

Practical investigations

Surveys

The following surveys are ones that you can carry out within your school or community. Before you start you should consider the following points carefully.

 (i) What population you are interested in.
 (ii) What sample of people you will ask.
(iii) What style of questionnaire you will use.

Example

Open answers . . . What sports do you like?

Preselected . . . Which of the following sport(s) do you like?

($\surd$ or $\times$)
☐ Football
☐ Netball
☐ Hockey
☐ Athletics
☐ Swimming
☐ Cricket

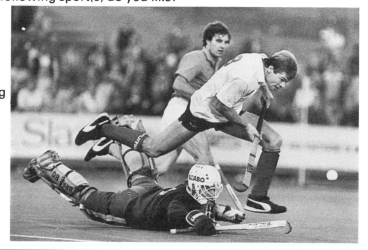

(iv) How you will record the data. Your record sheets should be prepared before the survey is started.

 (v) What questions about the population do you want to be able to answer by means of your survey.

(vi) What action (if any) should be taken as a result of your survey.

Some suggestions for projects

- A survey which would be part of a campaign against smoking in your school.
- A survey about the hours pupils spend watching TV or video films.
- A survey about part-time work by people under 16 years of age [e.g. hours of work, rates of pay, type of job, isolated or team work].
- A study of school meals: How can waiting time/queuing be reduced? Degree of satisfaction with the menu, etc.
- Careers and examinations: Choice of subjects to study related to hopes for jobs and careers.
- Recreation: A survey which shows how young people spent last Saturday night. [This could lead to a campaign for more youth facilities in your area.]
- Sizes: A survey of shoe sizes, glove sizes, shirt sizes, etc. to see if these sets of data are related. For example, do people with bigger than average feet have larger than average head circumference? . . . etc.

Practical work on probability

The whole study of probability began with games of chance. Gamblers have always wanted to know the chance of getting a particular score with two or three dice. Card players have wanted to know the chances of getting four aces or a 'run' like A K Q J 10 of one suit [a royal flush in poker].
The first guesses at the laws of probability came from experiment. Then mathematicians tried to work out a theory so that the experimental results could be explained.

Experiments with dice (2 people)

1 Throw a pair of dice 100 times and record the total score each time. Make a bar chart of the results. Can you explain why all scores are not equally likely?

2 Throw three dice a number of times and try to find the most likely score.

3   Throw five dice a number of times. Try to estimate the probability of these events:

5 of the same number	like	4	4	4	4	4
4 of the same number	like	3	3	3	3	6
high 'straight'		6	5	4	3	2
low 'straight'		5	4	3	2	1
full house [three and a pair]		5	5	5	2	2
3 of the same number		1	2	2	2	4
two pairs		3	3	4	4	5
one pair		1	4	5	6	6

4   Throw three dice 50 times and record the number of sixes which appear in each throw.

Number of sixes	Tally	f
0	√	
1	√ √	
2	√	
3		
Total		50

How many of each result (0, 1, 2 or 3 sixes) would you expect if you threw the dice 1 000 times?
[This could be investigated if 20 people throw three dice 50 times and pool their results.]

5   Throw a single die 60 times and record the results in a long line . . .
5 4 3 1 1 6 2 3 6 . . . etc. Divide these results into groups of three and count the number of 6's in each group.

    5 4 3 | 1 1 6 | 2 3 6   . . .   and so on.

      0   1   1

(a) Do you find the same pattern of results for this as for throwing sets of three dice?

(b) Do you think the pattern of results for 6's is the same as you would expect for any other number? Investigate!

Experiments with spinners

A polygon spinner can be made by making a polygon in card and pushing a sharpened match through the centre.

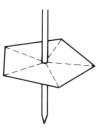

1   Make a spinner from a regular pentagon. Is it equally likely to come to rest on any one of the five sides? Check by experiment.

2   Make a spinner from a regular octagon. Check whether you have made it perfectly by spinning it 80 times and recording on which edge it comes to rest. What do you expect if the octagon is perfect?

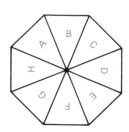

3   Make an irregular hexagon. Find its 'centre' and spin it 100 times. Do the results correspond to the irregularities?
[Does a score which corresponds to a longer edge come up more often than a score corresponding to a shorter edge?]

4 Make a set of spinners which can simulate a fruit machine with three wheels and five different fruits.
Comment on the results of your experiments with the spinners in this case.

5 Devise experiments which would test the rules of compound probability. (See key facts E.3.4.)

Worked answers to examination questions E

1 $\mathcal{E}$ = pupils in 5W; S = pupils who swim;
T = pupils who play tennis.
  (a) How many pupils are there altogether in 5W?
  (b) How many of the tennis players do not swim?

  (a) 32   (b) 9

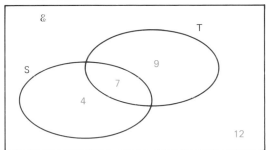

These questions just discover whether or not you understand a Venn diagram.
The total in the class is $4 + 7 + 9 + 12 = 32$.
There are 16 tennis players altogether (inside T). Of these 16, 7 swim and 9 do not swim.

2 (a) The probability that an event will occur is 0·65. What is the probability that it will not occur?
  (b) The probability that a bus arrives early at the bus stop is $\frac{1}{10}$ and the probability that it arrives late is $\frac{2}{5}$.
    (i) What is the probability that it arrives on time?
    (ii) 60 buses stop at the bus stop every day. How many of these would you expect to be late?

Early	On	Late
10%	time	40%

  (a) 0·35   (b) (i) $\frac{1}{2}$ or 50%   (ii) 24

  (a) The event either will occur or it won't. The probabilities must add up to 1 (or 100%): $1 - 0·65 = 0·35$.
  (b) (i) There are three possibilities. The bus arrives early, late or on time.
      The total probability is 1 (or 100%). The probability that the bus is on time is therefore $1 - (\frac{2}{5} + \frac{1}{10}) = 0·5$ (or 50%).
    (ii) $\frac{2}{5}$ of the buses could be expected to arrive late: $\frac{2}{5} \times 60 = 24$.

  Note: It is not certain that 24 buses will arrive late, just probable that roughly 24 will be late.

3 The Venn diagram shows three sets, X, Y and Z.

(a) Which of these statements is true?
   (i) $X \cap Y = \emptyset$ (ii) $Y \cap Z = \emptyset$
   (iii) $X \cap Z = \emptyset$

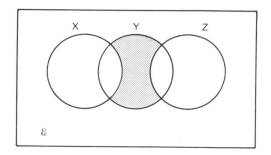

(b) Which of the sets listed here corresponds to the coloured part of the diagram?
   (i) $X \cap Y \cap Z$ (ii) $(X \cap Y) \cup (X \cap Z)$
   (iii) $X \cap Y' \cap Z$ (iv) $X' \cap Y \cap Z'$
   (v) $X \cup Y' \cup Z$

(a) $X \cap Z = \emptyset$ (b) $X' \cap Y \cap Z'$

(a) From the diagram it is clear that there are no points in both X and Z. Thus $Z \cap X = \emptyset$... $\emptyset$ being the empty set.

(b) From the diagram, the coloured area consists of points in Y and not in X and not in Z.
This is the set $X' \cap Y \cap Z'$.

Out of interest I have coloured these diagrams to correspond to the other four sets. You will note that (v) is the complement of (iv).

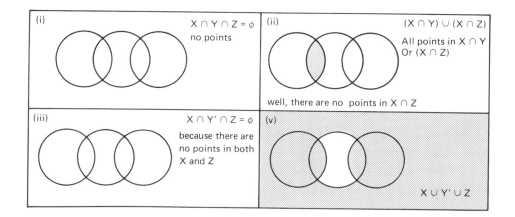

4 A caravan site owner keeps records of the number of caravans parked each night.

	M	T	W	Th	F	Sat	Sun
Week 1	49	3	34	40	4	36	43
Week 2	29	33	54	21	14	27	44
Week 3	40	18	10	45	32	41	35
Week 4	48	25	55	34	17	26	48
Week 5	40	44	34	42	14	51	45

(a) Tabulate the data in groups 0–9, 10–19, etc., showing the frequency of each group.
(b) Construct a cumulative frequency graph from the data.
(c) Use the cumulative frequency curve to find the median and interquartile range of the number of caravans.
(d) Compare the median with the mean and the mode for the data.

(a)

Number of caravans	f	cf
0–9	2	2
10–19	5	7
20–29	5	12
30–39	7	19
40–49	13	32
50–59	3	35
Total	35	

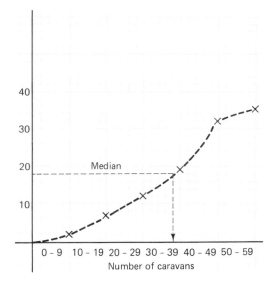

(c) Since the total frequency is 35 (nights), the median will correspond to night number 18 in order of size.

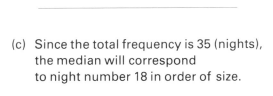

1	2	3	4	5	6	7	8	9	10	11	12	13	14	15	16	17

18	19	20	21	22	23	24	25	26	27	28	29	30	31	32	33	34	35

From the graph the median is 38 caravans.

(d) The mean is 34. [Found by adding all the figures for each night and dividing by 35.]
The mode (group) is 40–49.

5 The mean of 4, n, 8, 12 and 20 is 10·1. Calculate n.

$n = 6·5$

As 10·1 is the mean of the five numbers, $\dfrac{4 + n + 8 + 12 + 20}{5} = 10·1$

$\Rightarrow \dfrac{44 + n}{5} = 10·1$

$\Rightarrow 44 + n = 50·5$

$\Rightarrow n = 6·5$

6 Students in a class were given grades A, B, C, D or E in their exams. Their results are shown in the table.

Grade	A	B	C	D	E
No. of students	4	6	11	8	3

(a) Show this data in a bar chart.
(b) What was the 'average' grade?

(a)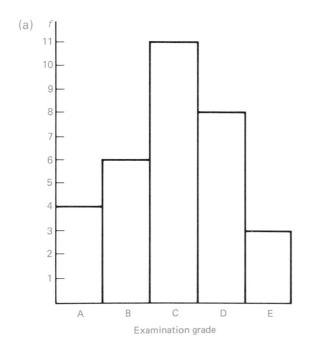

Examination grade

Only the mode and median can be used as averages because we do not have numerical values for A, B, C, D and E. The mode is C. The median (16th, 17th in order) is also C.

(b) C

7 A fairground game uses a coloured disc and an arrow. The arrow is spun and if it lands on a section showing a sum of money, that is paid out. One spin costs 20p. If the arrow stops on a blank, nothing is paid out.

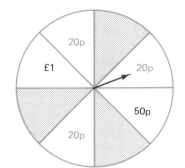

(a) What is the chance of winning on one spin of the arrow?
(b) What is the chance of losing the stake?
(c) Make a 'win/money back/lose' tree diagram for two spins of the wheel.
(d) What is the probability that a player will win the £1 prize twice in a row?

(a) $\frac{1}{4}$ or 25%   (b) $\frac{3}{8}$ or $37\frac{1}{2}$%   (c)   (d) $\frac{1}{64}$

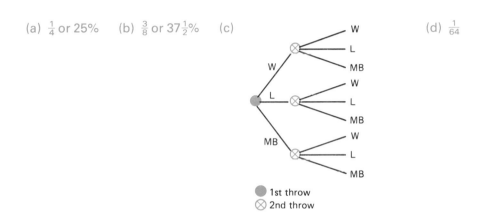

(a) There are 8 equal sections. Two of these give a win for the player. Chance of winning $= \frac{2}{8} = 0.25$ or 25%.

(b) The stake is lost on 3 out of the 8 sections. Chance of losing stake $= \frac{3}{8}$.

(c) The tree diagram shows the nine different possibilities for winning, losing or getting money back.
Note: The probabilities are
W $\frac{2}{8}$; L $\frac{3}{8}$; MB $\frac{3}{8}$. This gives probabilities
WW $\frac{4}{64}$; LL $\frac{9}{64}$; WL $\frac{6}{64}$, etc. and you can work out probabilities for all nine different results.

(d) The chance of winning £1 is $\frac{1}{8}$ so the chance of winning it twice in a row is $\frac{1}{8} \times \frac{1}{8} = \frac{1}{64}$.

8 In a forestry experiment trees were measured five years after planting. There were originally 500 Norway spruce and 500 Scots pine in the sample and all were 30 cm high when planted.

Use the data to find mean, median and interquartile range for each species. Which of the two species had a faster growth rate in this experiment.

	NS	SP
0 –1 m	12	32
1^+–2 m	39	105
2^+–3 m	46	85
3^+–4 m	152	70
4^+–5 m	106	110
5^+–6 m	30	30
6^+–7 m	15	8
Totals →	400	440

Means: NS 3·63 m   Medians: NS 3·7 m   IQ range: NS 1·5 m
            SP 3·05 m   SP 3·0 m   SP 2·6 m

In this experiment, although more Scots pine survived, the Norway spruce grew better with less variation in height.
Replace the classes by mid-class values to obtain two frequency tables. These tables are then used to calculate means and cumulative frequency for each species.

NS x	f	xf	CF
0·5	12	6·0	12
1·5	39	58·5	51
2·5	46	115·0	97
3·5	152	532·0	249
4·5	106	477·0	355
5·5	30	165·0	385
6·5	15	97·5	400
Total	400	1451·0	

SP x	f	xf	CF
0·5	32	16·0	32
1·5	105	157·5	137
2·5	85	212·5	222
3·5	70	245·0	292
4·5	110	495·0	402
5·5	30	165·0	432
6·5	8	52·0	440
Total	440	1343·0	

Mean: 1451 ÷ 400 = 3·63 m
Median: 200th tree is the 103rd tree in the 3–4 m class.
$$3 + \frac{103}{152} = 3.677 \approx 3.7 \text{ m}$$
Lower quartile: No. 100 … 3 m
Upper quartile: No. 300 … 4·5 m
                        (halfway through 4–5 m class)
IQ range = 1·5 m

Mean: 1343 ÷ 440 = 3·05 m
Median: 220th tree. This is 83rd tree in the 2–3 m class.
$$2 + \frac{83}{85} = 2.98 \text{ m} \approx 3.0 \text{ m}$$
Lower quartile: No. 110 … $1 + \frac{78}{105} = 1.74$ m
Upper quartile: No. 330 … $4 + \frac{38}{110} = 4.35$ m
IQ range = 2·6 m

9 An ice cream parlour keeps careful records of all sales. The data are given in the table below for 1 year.

	0–10	11–20	21–30	31–40	41–50	51–60	61–70	71–80	81–90	91–100	Total
Lime	4	7	10	11	4	10	6	0	0	0	52
Raspberry	2	5	7	10	13	5	4	6	0	0	52
Vanilla	0	0	3	15	18	12	0	3	1	0	52
Strawberry	3	4	8	4	12	11	3	3	3	1	52
Chocolate	4	2	5	14	10	11	0	6	0	0	52

Litres (column headers); *number of weeks in which this quantity was sold*

Which was the most popular flavour?
Give your reasons.

Vanilla is the most popular flavour.

Replace the classes by mid-values and expand the table to show quantities sold. There is no need to calculate the mean quantity per week as the total quantity will enable you to answer the question. Think about the best technique for filling up the table. The smoother the method, the smaller risk of error.

Litres / Flavour	0–10 (5)	10⁺–20 (15)	20⁺–30 (25)	30⁺–40 (35)	40⁺–50 (45)	50⁺–60 (55)	60⁺–70 (65)	70⁺–80 (75)	80⁺–90 (85)	90⁺–100 (95)	Totals
Lime	4 / 20	7 / 105	10 / 250	11 / 385	4 / 180	10 / 550	6 / 390	0 / 0	0 / 0	0 / 0	52 / 1880
Raspberry	2 / 10	5 / 75	7 / 175	10 / 350	13 / 585	5 / 275	4 / 260	6 / 450	0 / 0	0 / 0	52 / 2180
Vanilla	0 / 0	0 / 0	3 / 75	15 / 525	18 / 810	12 / 660	0 / 0	3 / 225	1 / 85	0 / 0	52 / 2380
Strawberry	3 / 15	4 / 60	8 / 200	4 / 140	12 / 540	11 / 605	3 / 195	3 / 225	3 / 255	1 / 95	52 / 2330
Chocolate	4 / 20	2 / 30	5 / 125	14 / 490	10 / 450	11 / 605	0 / 0	6 / 450	0 / 0	0 / 0	52 / 2170

10   The data in the table give the average number of hours spent per day watching T.V. ... before and after marriage. The data were collected from 310 young married people all under 21 years old. Do the figures agree with the suggestion ... 'Married couples watch TV more than single people'.

No.   The data suggest the opposite.

Daily hours of viewing	Before marriage	After marriage
0–1	16	28
1^+–2	35	46
2^+–3	149	156
3^+–4	86	67
4^+–5	22	8
Over 5	2	5
Total	310	310

The table is simply extended to give the total viewing hours. The mean may also be calculated but the question can be answered from the totals.

Daily hours of viewing	x	Before marriage	Total hours	After marriage	Total hours
0–1	0·5	16	8·0	28	14·0
1^+–2	1·5	35	52·5	46	69·0
2^+–3	2·5	149	372·5	156	390·0
3^+–4	3·5	86	301·0	67	234·5
4^+–5	4·5	22	99·0	8	36·0
Over 5	5·5	2	11·0	5	27·5
Totals		310	844·0	310	771·0

Means: before marriage ... 2·72 hours.
          after marriage ... 2·49 hours.

Note: the 'over 5' class is represented by the variable 5·5

11   The table gives the number of cigarettes smoked per day for a group of patients at a chest clinic. Calculate the mean, mode, median and IQ range for the data. Add any comments you consider relevant.

	Under 50	Over 50
Mean	15·66 cigs	10·86
Mode	0–5 cigs	0–5
Median	16 cigs	8 cigs
IQ range	17 cigs	13 cigs

	Age	
Number of cigs. smoked per day	Under 50	Over 50
0–5	140	116
6–10	38	88
11–15	77	29
16–20	132	44
21–25	41	15
26–30	48	11
31–35	30	13
36–40	22	0
Over 40	2	4
Totals →	530	320

The data for under 50 and over 50 years of age should be separated to avoid confusion. The tables are then extended to allow means and quartiles to be calculated. If careful tables are prepared they do not need explanation.

Under 50

	x	f	xf	CF
0–5	3	140	420	140
6–10	8	38	304	178
11–15	13	77	1001	255
16–20	18	132	2376	387
21–25	23	41	943	428
26–30	28	48	1344	476
31–35	33	30	990	506
36–40	38	22	836	528
over 40	43	2	86	530
Totals →		530	8300	

Mean 15·66 cigs
Mode 0–5 class
Median ... no. 265 ... 16 cigs
Upper Q ... no. 397 ... 22 cigs
Lower Q ... no. 132 ... 5 cigs
IQ range 17 cigs

Over 50

	x	f	xf	CF
0–5	3	116	348	116
6–10	8	88	704	204
11–15	13	29	377	233
16–20	18	44	792	277
21–25	23	15	345	292
26–30	28	11	308	303
31–35	33	13	429	316
36–40	38	0	0	316
over 40	43	4	172	320
Totals →		320	3475	

Mean 10·86
Mode 0–5 class
Median ... no. 160 ... 8
Upper Q ... no. 240 ... 17
Lower Q ... no 80 ... 4
IQ range ... 13 cigs

Notes: (i) It would not be enough just to compare totals, i.e. *xf*, as there are more under 50's than over 50's.
(ii) The 0–5 class is represented by 3 cigarettes even though 3 is not the central value of this class. This will not make much difference to the results.
(iii) The last figure in CF should be the same as the sum of frequencies.
(iv) The lower figure for over 50's could be because pensioners are included and they cannot afford to smoke so heavily.

12 40 volunteers had their reaction time tested after drinking various quantities of alcoholic beverage. The individual data are given.
The first figure gives reaction time in tenths of seconds, the coloured figure gives the number of units of alcohol drunk.

(4　2)(4　8)(8　3)(5　3)(2　5)
(9　9)(4　1)(7　7)(4　6)(1　2)
(8　9)(5　8)(4　7)(9　6)(6　4)
(3　4)(9　8)(7　7)(7　2)(4　5)
(8　9)(2　1)(4　7)(1　4)(5　3)
(4　2)(6　8)(3　3)(2　4)(5　6)
(9　6)(7　2)(4　7)(4　5)(7　8)
(5　1)(4　5)(5　4)(9　6)(2　3)

Make a table of the results and draw a scattergram. Add an estimated line of best fit.
Do your results indicate a strong connection between reaction time and quantity of alcohol?

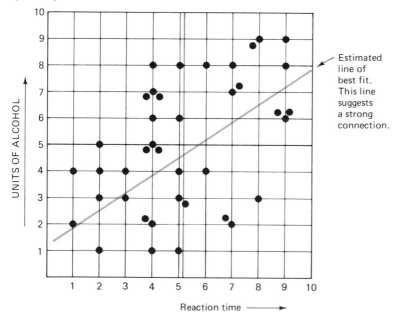

Mean reaction time = 206 ÷ 40
　　　　　　　　　= 5·15 secs
Mean units of alcohol = 200 ÷ 40
　　　　　　　　　　　= 5 units

Note: The graphs of the means show 11 negative correlations and 25 positive correlations.

13 The number of fatal road accidents per 100 000 is given for twelve towns, with their populations. Decide whether there is some connection between size of town and accident rate.

Suggest some of the factors that could cause a connection.

Town	Population (000's)	Accident rate per 100 000
Penzance	19	11·2
Bedford	74	9·1
Norwich	122	9·4
Swansea	167	10·3
Stoke on Trent	205	10·6
Cardiff	273	9·8
Coventry	317	9·9
Belfast	363	10·2
Edinburgh	419	9·9
Sheffield	477	11·1
Liverpool	510	10·7
Glasgow	762	10·9

The means are 309 000 (population) and 10·26 per 100 000 accident rate. Thus there are six examples of positive correlation (above average with above average, and below average with below average) and six examples of negative correlation. This suggests that the data are not connected.

Town	Population	Accident rate	
Penzance	−	+	disagree
Bedford	−	−	agree
Norwich	−	−	agree
Swansea	−	+	disagree
Stoke	−	+	disagree
Cardiff	−	−	agree
Coventry	+	−	disagree
Belfast	+	−	disagree
Edinburgh	+	−	disagree
Sheffield	+	+	agree
Liverpool	+	+	agree
Glasgow	+	+	agree

+ above average
− below average

Connections could be caused by factors such as "big cities tend to have more poor people who do not have cars". But this tendency does not have the support of this set of figures.

14 Make a scattergram from the data given below, which relate distance from home and number of late arrivals during a year, for a group of 30 students. Which of the following hypotheses agree with the data?
(a) Distance from home does not affect the number of late arrivals.
(b) Students who live further away tend to be late more often.
(c) Students who live nearer tend to be late more often.

Times late \ Distance	0 | 5	6 | 10	11 | 15	16 | 20	Totals
under 1 km	3	2	1	0	6
$1^+ - 2$ km	1	2	2	1	6
$2^+ - 3$ km	1	1	3	1	6
$3^+ - 4$ km	0	2	3	2	7
$4^+ -$	1	0	2	2	5
Total	6	7	11	6	30

	0–5	6–10	11–15	16–20
< 1 km				
< 2 km				
< 3 km				
< 4 km				
> 4 km				

The points appear to be evenly spread across the table and it is not possible to estimate a line of best fit by eye.
This suggests that hypothesis (a) agrees with the data.

Note: The data is almost a scattergram itself.

15 The pages of a book are numbered 1 to 320. If a page is chosen at random, what is the chance the page number will contain a zero?

$$\frac{59}{320} = 18 \cdot 4\%$$

This problem can be done by listing as the numbers are small.

10, 20, 30, 40, 50, 60, 70, 80, 90, 100	10
101–109, 201–209, 301–309	27
110, 120, 130, 140, 150, 160, 170, 180, 190, 200	10
210, 220, 230, 240, 250, 260, 270, 280, 290, 300	10
310, 320	2
	59

16 Choose the correct statement (or statements) from (i), (ii), (iii) and (iv).
A bag contains yellow, blue, and black tokens. The probability of choosing
a yellow token is p
a blue token is q
a black token is r

(i) $p + q < 1$ (iii) $p + q + r = 1$
(ii) $p + q + r < 1$ (iv) $pq < r$

(i) $p + q < 1$ and   (iii) $p + q + r = 1$ are correct

If a token is chosen it must be one of yellow, blue or black, and these
are mutually exclusive.
Hence, probability of choosing yellow, blue or black is 1 and equal to
$p + q + r$.
Since r cannot be negative, $p + q + r = 1 \Rightarrow p + q < 1$.

Note: (iv) looks appealing, but p, q and r depend on the numbers of
tokens in the bag. It is certainly true that $pq < p$ and $pq < q$ but
it is only possibly true that $pq < r$.

17 An ordinary die is thrown twice and the
results entered in a table, as shown
opposite.
The table is designed to show all the
possible outcomes of throwing a die twice.
Copy and complete the table. Use your table
to find
(a) the probability that both first and
second throws score the same.
(b) the probability that the first throw is
better than the second.
(c) the probability that the sum of the two
throws is less than 6.

FIRST THROW

SECOND THROW	1	2	3	4	5	6
1	1 1	2 1	3 1	4 1		
2		2 2				
3					5 3	
4						
5				4 5		
6						

FIRST THROW

SECOND THROW	1	2	3	4	5	6
1	1 1	2 1	3 1	4 1	5 1	6 1
2	1 2	2 2	3 2	4 2	5 2	6 2
3	1 3	2 3	3 3	4 3	5 3	6 3
4	1 4	2 4	3 4	4 4	5 4	6 4
5	1 5	2 5	3 5	4 5	5 5	6 5
6	1 6	2 6	3 6	4 6	5 6	6 6

(a) $\frac{6}{36} = \frac{1}{6}$ (b) $\frac{15}{36} = \frac{5}{12}$ (c) $\frac{10}{36} = \frac{5}{18}$

The patterns of this table are obvious. There are 36 possible results altogether.

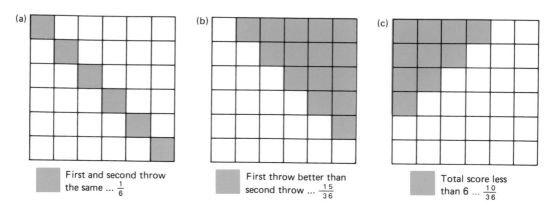

(a)

First and second throw the same ... $\frac{1}{6}$

(b)

First throw better than second throw ... $\frac{15}{36}$

(c)

Total score less than 6 ... $\frac{10}{36}$

The answers to these questions are found by simple counting.

18 The roads in the diagram have no signposts. A motorist wishing to go from A to D has no map so goes by guesswork at each junction.

He is twice as likely to go straight on as to turn; and where both left and right turns are available, they are equally likely. He never turns back towards A.

Calculate the probability that he misses D altogether.

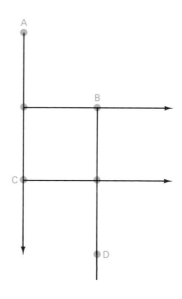

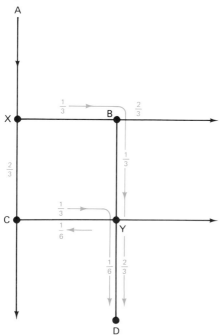

The chance he misses D is $\frac{8}{9}$

The best approach to this question is to find his chance of passing through D. The route map becomes a tree diagram.

He can go AXCYD or AXBYD

The probabilities are

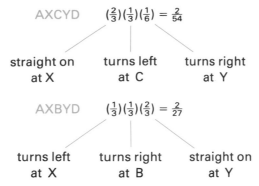

AXCYD $\quad (\frac{2}{3})(\frac{1}{3})(\frac{1}{6}) = \frac{2}{54}$

straight on   turns left   turns right
at X   at C   at Y

AXBYD $\quad (\frac{1}{3})(\frac{1}{3})(\frac{2}{3}) = \frac{2}{27}$

turns left   turns right   straight on
at X   at B   at Y

Chance of getting to D is thus
$\frac{2}{54} + \frac{2}{27} = \frac{3}{27} = \frac{1}{9}$
Chance of missing D is thus
$1 - \frac{1}{9} = \frac{8}{9}$

19 If you choose any four figure number at random, what is the
probability that
  (i) the number has 3 as a divisor ... p_1
  (ii) the number has 7 as a divisor ... p_2
  (iii) the number has 21 as a divisor ... p_3?
What is the relationship between p_1, p_2 and p_3?

$$p_1 = \tfrac{1}{3} \quad p_2 = \frac{1286}{9000}, \quad p_3 = \frac{429}{9000}; \quad p_1 + p_2 - p_3 = \frac{3857}{9000}$$

Explanation:
Multiples of 3 ... the lowest is 1002
                 the highest is 9999
$(9999 - 1002) \div 3 = 2999$.
Thus there are 2999 multiples of 3 as well as 1002. This gives 3000
altogether ...
$$p_1 = \frac{3000}{9000}$$

Multiples of 7 ... lowest is 1001
               highest is 9996
$(9996 - 1001) \div 7 = 1285$
$$p_2 = \frac{1286}{9000}$$

Multiples of 21 ... lowest 1008
                highest 9996
$(9996 - 1008) \div 21 = 428$
$$p_3 = \frac{429}{9000}$$

To find the relationship it helps to draw a venn diagram.

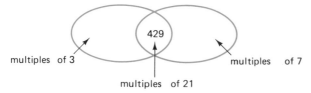

multiples of 3   multiples of 7

multiples of 21

Since there are 1286 multiples of 7 and 429 of these are multiples of 21, there are $1286 - 429 = 857$ multiples of 7 but not 21. Similarly there are $3000 - 429 = 2571$ multiples of 3 but not 21. Total of all multiples of 3, 7 or 21 is 3857.

Thus

$$\left(\frac{3000}{9000} - \frac{429}{9000}\right) + \frac{429}{9000} + \left(\frac{1286}{9000} - \frac{429}{9000}\right) = \frac{3857}{9000}$$

$$\underset{p_1}{\uparrow} - \underset{p_3}{\uparrow} + \underset{p_3}{\uparrow} + \underset{p_2}{\uparrow} - \underset{p_3}{\uparrow}$$

i.e. $p_1 + p_2 - p_3 = \dfrac{3857}{9000}$

The relationship $p_1 p_2 = p_3$ is almost but not quite true!!

20 The guarantee on a packet of flower seeds states 'at least 75% of these seeds will germinate and grow'. A girl who is a keen gardener chooses five seeds to grow in a flower pot.
  (a) What is the probability that
      (i) none of the seeds come up
      (ii) only one of the seeds comes up
      (iii) two or more of the seeds come up?
  (b) What arguments could she use in case (i) to obtain her money back from the seed merchant?

  (a) (i) $(0.25)^5$ (ii) $5 \times (0.75) \times (0.25)^4$ (iii) $\frac{63}{64}$
  (b) The chance of no seeds coming up is less than 1 in a 1000 if the guarantee is honest.

  (i) The guarantee gives a probability of 0.75 that the seed will grow, hence the probability that it will not grow is 0.25 ... for each seed. Thus the probability for the five independent failures is
      $(0.25) \times (0.25) \times (0.25) \times (0.25) \times (0.25) = (0.25)^5$
  (ii) If only one seed grows, it could happen in 5 different mutually exclusive ways. The probability for each way is
      $(0.75) \times (0.25) \times (0.25) \times (0.25) \times (0.25)$
      This gives a total probability of
      $5 \times (0.75) \times (0.25)^4$
  (iii) This result is the only alternative to (i) and (ii); so the probability of (iii) is
      $1 - [\text{probability (i)} + \text{probability (ii)}]$
      i.e. $1 - [(0.25)^5 + 15 \times (0.25)^5]$
        $= 1 - [16 \times (\frac{1}{4})^5]$ ... writing 0.25 as $\frac{1}{4}$
        $= 1 - (\frac{1}{4})^3 = 1 - \frac{1}{64} = \frac{63}{64}$

Topic F **Algebra and graphs**

Contents

Letters for numbers; collecting up terms; brackets and factors; formulae; changing formulae; linear equations; simultaneous equations; quadratic equations; graphs of functions; using graphs; gradient, maxima and minima; functions; compound functions and inverse functions; indices and surds; inequalities

Self assessment

The purpose of this task is to find out whether or not you need revision on algebra and graphs. If not you can go straight on to the next topic. There is no time limit.

- Make a table in your book (see page vi). You need space for 30 questions.
- Write down your answers to all the following questions.
- When you have finished calculate your score from the answers on page 431.
- If your score is more than 80% go on to Topic G self assessment (pp. 315–317).

1 $2a^2 - 3a^2 + 4a^2$ can be simplified to
 A $6a^2$ B $5a$ C $3a^2$ D $3a$

2 If $x = 2$ and $y = 1$, then the value of $2xy + x^2$ is
 A 6   B 10   C 4   D 8

3 If $x = 4$ then the value of $x^2 - 2x - 3$ is
 A 5   B 15   C $^-3$ D 0

4 The result of multiplying $2xy$ by x^2y^2 is
 A $2xy^2$ B x^3y^3 C $2x^3y^3$ D $4x^2y^2$

5 $\dfrac{x + y}{4} + \dfrac{y}{2}$ is the same as

 A $\dfrac{x + y}{2}$ B $\dfrac{y}{2}$

 C $\dfrac{x + 3y}{4}$ D $\dfrac{x + 2y}{2}$

6 $2x(x - 2)$ when multiplied out becomes
 A $2x^2 + 4$ B $2x^2 - 4x$ C $x^2 - 2x$
 D $2x^2 - 4$

7 The factors of $x^2 - 5x - 6$ are
 A $(x + 1), (x - 6)$ B $(x - 2), (x - 3)$
 C $(x - 1), (x + 6)$ D $(x - 2), (x + 3)$

8 The factors of $4x^2 - y^2$ are
 A $(2x - y), (2x - y)$ B $(x - 2y), (x + 2y)$
 C $(2x + y), (2x - y)$ D $(x - y), (4x - y)$

9 The correct expansion for $(a - b)^2$ is
 A $a^2 - b^2$ B $a^2 - b^2 + 2ab$
 C $a^2 + b^2 - 2ab$ D $a^2 + b^2 - ab$

10 Given that $S = \frac{1}{2}gt^2$, when $g = 981$ and $t = 0 \cdot 2$ the value of S is
 A $9623 \cdot 61$ B $9 \cdot 81$ C $196 \cdot 2$ D $19 \cdot 62$

11 When the formula $v = u + at$ is changed round to find t, it becomes

 A $t = \dfrac{v - u}{a}$ B $t = \dfrac{v + u}{a}$

 C $t = \dfrac{v}{u} - a$ D $t = \dfrac{v}{u} + a$

12 If $2x + 1 = 3 - x$ then x is

A 2   B $\frac{1}{2}$ C $\frac{2}{3}$ D 3

◆13 The solution to the pair of simultaneous

equations $\left.\begin{array}{l} 3x + 2y = 16 \\ 2x - y = 6 \end{array}\right\}$ is

A $x = 5, y = 4$ B $x = 4, y = 2$
C $x = 2, y = 4$ D $x = 2, y = 5$

14 The equation $x(x - 1) = 0$ has two solutions. One is $x = 1$, the other is

A $x = {}^{-}1$ B $x = 2$ C $x = 0$ D $x = \frac{1}{2}$

◆15 The solution to the quadratic equation $x^2 - 3x - 4 = 0$ is

A $x = {}^{-}4$ or 1   B $x = 4$ or $^{-}1$
C $x = 1$ or 4   D $x = {}^{-}1$ or $^{-}4$

16 The equation of the coloured line is

A $2x - y = 1$
B $x - y = 2$
C $x + y = 2$
D $y = x + 2$

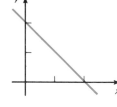

17 This is the graph of $y = x^2$. The y-coordinate of the point P is

A 9   B 4   C 3   D $^{-}9$

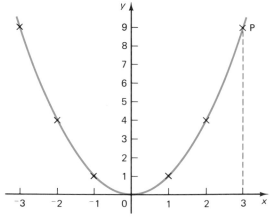

18 The graph shows the two functions $y = x^2$ and $y = 2x$.

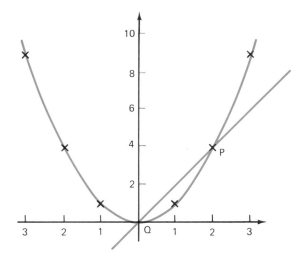

The points marked P, Q are the solutions of

A $x^2 + 2x = 0$ B $x^2 = 2x$
C $y = x^2 + 2$ D $y = x + 2$

19 If you drew the graph of $y = \dfrac{2}{x}$ the point with coordinates $(4, \frac{1}{2})$ would be

A exactly on the graph
B nearly on the graph
C well above the graph
D well below the graph

20 f: $x \rightarrow (x - 2)$ is another way of writing

A f$(x - 2)$ B f$(x) = x - 2$
C (f)$x = 2$ D f(-2)

21 If the input into f: $x \rightarrow 2x^2$ is 4, the output will be

A 8   B 16   C 24   D 32

22 The mapping shows f: $x \to 2x - 1$. The domain of the function in the diagram is the set
A $(1, 3, 5, 7)$ B $(1, 4, 9, 16)$
C $(1, 2, 3, 4)$ D $(2, 4, 6, 8)$

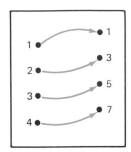

◆**23** The inverse of the function f: $x \to x^2$ is
A $x \to {}^-x^2$ B $x \to \dfrac{1}{x^2}$

C $x \to \dfrac{1}{x}$ D $x \to \sqrt{x}$

◆**24** f: $x \to 2x + 1$
g: $x \to x^2$ } so fg: $x \to$
A $x^2(2x + 1)$ B $x^2 + 1$
C $(2x + 1)^2$ D $2x^2 + 1$

25 The correct rule of indices for the division of powers is
A $a^m \div a^n = a^{m/n}$ B $a^m \div a^n = a^{m-n}$
C $a^m \div a^n = a^{m+n}$ D $a^m \div a^n = a^{mn}$

26 The value of $(100)^{-\frac{1}{2}}$ is
A 10   B $100\frac{1}{2}$ C $99\frac{1}{2}$ D 0·1

27 There is a space in the statement $a > b \Rightarrow b \dots a$. The missing sign is
A $>$ B $<$ C $\geqslant$ D $\leqslant$

28 The coloured part of the number line corresponds to
A $1 < x < 2$ B $1 > x > {}^-1$
C $^-1 < x < 2$ D $^-1 > x > {}^-2$

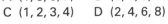

◆**29** The unshaded part of the graph corresponds
A $x + y < 4$ B $x + y > 4$
   $y < 1$ $y < 1$
   $x > {}^-1$ $x > {}^-1$
C $x + y < 4$ D $x + y > 4$
   $y > 1$ $y > 1$
   $x > {}^-1$ $x > {}^-1$

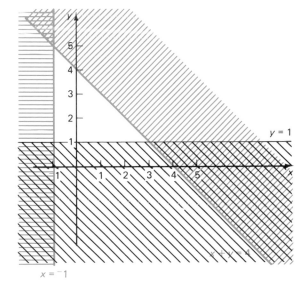

◆**30** In the graph in question 29, the point $(0, 0)$ does not lie in the unshaded area. This is because
A $(0, 0)$ does not satisfy $x + y < 0$
B $(0, 0)$ does not satisfy $x > {}^-1$
C $(0, 0)$ does not satisfy $y > 1$
D $(0, 0)$ does not satisfy $x + y < 4$

Key facts F

F.1 Letters for numbers

Letters can be used to represent numbers, especially in formulae. The letters
must obey the usual rules for numbers listed here.

  (i) $a + b = b + a$
  (ii) $a - b = -(b - a)$
  (iii) $ab = ba$
  (iv) $a \div b = 1 \div (b \div a)$
  (v) $a + (b + c) = (a + b) + c$
  (vi) $a(bc) = (ab)c$
  (vii) $a(b + c) = ab + ac$
  (viii) $a(b - c) = ab - ac$
  (ix) $a + {}^{-}a = 0$
  (x) $a \times 0 = 0$
  (xi) $a \times 1 = a$

but (xii) $a \div 0$ cannot be done [it's naughty!!!]

Check each of the rules in the case $a = 2, b = 3, c = 5$.
Remember . . . a^2 is $a \times a$ but $2a$ is $a + a = 2 \times a$.
All the algebra which follows is a direct result of the above rules for
numbers . . . so there is nothing mysterious about algebra??

Exercise F.1

1 Choose numbers for a, b and c and
demonstrate that $a + (b + c) =$
$(a + b) + c$ and $a(bc) = (ab)c$.   C

2 Choose numbers for p, q and r and
demonstrate that
  (i) $(p - q) - r \neq p - (q - r)$ and
  (ii) $(p \div q) \div r \neq p \div (q \div r)$.   C

3 Find m and n given that
  (i) $a \times m = a$ for every value of a.
  (ii) $a \times n = n$ for every value of a.   B

4 Show how the rule $a(b + c) = ab + ac$
is used in the multiplication of 7×16.   B

5 The solution of the equation
$x^2 - 3x = 4$ is given below. State the
basic rule of numbers which justifies
each line of the solution.
1∅ $x^2 - 3x = 4$
2∅ $\Rightarrow x^2 - 3x - 4 = 0$
3∅ $\Rightarrow (x - 4)(x + 1) = 0$

4∅ $\Rightarrow x - 4 = 0$ or $x + 1 = 0$
5∅ $\Rightarrow x = 4$ or $x = {}^{-}1$ B

6 One of the following expansions is *not*
correct.
  (i) $a \div (b + c) = (a \div b) + (a \div c)$
  (ii) $(a + b) \div c = (a \div b) + (a \div c)$
  Decide which is correct and give two
  counter examples for the incorrect
  expression.   B

7 A rational number is p/q where both p
and q are integers. Investigate the
twelve rules of numbers given in F.1
when a, b and c are rational numbers.
[Do all the rules hold good?]   A

8 The numbers 0, 1, 2, 3 represent the
four points of the compass and also
clockwise turns of 0°, 90°, 180° and 270°.
Thus 3 + 3 means start pointing West
and turn through 270°. You can see that
3 + 3 = 2 in this system.

Investigate the system and find all the 'number' rules. Can you find any rules which are not true for ordinary numbers.

A

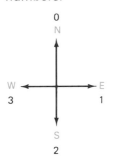

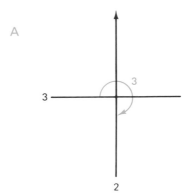

F.2 Collecting up terms

Algebra expressions can be simplified by collecting up terms.
Never ... add different letters.
Never ... add different powers.
Fractions are simplified using equivalence and cancelling.

Examples

1   $2x^2 + 2x - 3x - x^2 \rightarrow x^2 - x$

2   $\dfrac{6x}{5} - \dfrac{4x + 3y}{3} \rightarrow \dfrac{18x}{15} - \dfrac{5(4x + 3y)}{15}$

$$\rightarrow \dfrac{18x - 20x - 15y}{15}$$

$$\rightarrow \dfrac{{}^-2x - 15y}{15}$$

3   $\dfrac{a^3b^2}{b^3a^2} \rightarrow \dfrac{a(a^2b^2)}{b(a^2b^2)} \rightarrow \dfrac{a}{b}$

Exercise F.2

1   Simplify $2x^2 + 3x(y - x)$.   C
2   Simplify $x^2 + xy^2 + 2x^2 - 3xy^2$.   C
3   Simplify $3x^2y - 3x^2(x + y)$.   B
4   Simplify $a^2(b^2 + c^2) + a^2(b^2 - c^2)$.   B

5   Simplify $\dfrac{x + 5}{3} - \dfrac{2x - 1}{4}$.   A

6   Simplify $\dfrac{1}{(x + 1)(x + 2)} - \dfrac{1}{x + 2}$.   A

F.3 Brackets and factors

All work with brackets uses rule (vii) in Section F.1 above. This is known as the distributive law of numbers.
Always remember that the number outside the bracket multiplies everything inside.

Examples

1   $2(x + y) = 2x + 2y$ 2 $x(x + y - 3) = x^2 + xy - 3x$

The reverse process, $ab + ac \rightarrow a(b + c)$ is called factorising. [In its simplest form it changes sum of products into product of sums.] a is the common factor.

Examples

1   Factorise $2x^2 - xy \ldots x(2x - y)$ x is the only common factor.
2   Factorise $2a^2b + 6ab^2 \ldots 2ab(a + 3b)$ $2ab$ is common to both terms.

- Three special cases are worth learning.
  (i) $(a + b)^2 = a^2 + 2ab + b^2$
  (ii) $a^2 - b^2 = (a - b)(a + b)$
  (iii) $a^2 + b^2$ does not factorise

Note: The letters used in the above cases represent all numbers, positive, negative and fractional. [So don't be put off if you see your favourite piece of algebra wearing different clothes!]

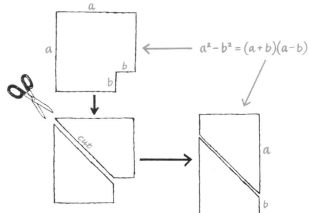

$a^2 - b^2 = (a+b)(a-b)$

- Expressions such as $x^2 + 3x + 2$ can be factorised in three steps.
  1∅ $x^2 + 3x + 2 = x^2 + x + 2x + 2$
  2∅ $= x(x + 1) + 2(x + 1)$
  3∅ $= (x + 1)(x + 2)$.
- The two factorisations of cubic expressions are worth remembering.
  (i) $a^3 - b^3 = (a - b)(a^2 + ab + b^2)$
  (ii) $a^3 + b^3 = (a + b)(a^2 - ab + b^2)$
- If $(x - a)$ is a factor of $f(x)$, then $f(a)$ must be zero.
  [Investigate this, choosing different values for a and different polynomials for $f(x)$]

Exercise F.3

1   Factorise $a^2 + 2ab^2$ C
2   Factorise $p^2 - 4p + 3$ C
3   Factorise $x^2 - 4y^2$ C
4   Factorise $2x^2 - xy - y^2$ C
5   Factorise $3a^2 - 4ab + b^2$ B

6   Factorise $4x^2 - \dfrac{1}{y^2}$ A
7   Factorise $x^3 - 5x^2 - 14x$ A
8   Factorise $8x^3 + 27y^3$ A

F.4   Formulae

A formula is a store of data. The data can be obtained by putting in the values of the variables, as in the following example.

Example

The formula $V = \pi r^2 h$ gives the volume of a cylinder if you know
(i) the radius of the base   and   (ii) the height.
V, r and h are variables, π is a constant.
If $r = 2$ cm and $h = 5$ cm, then $V = \pi \times 4 \times 5 = 62 \cdot 8$ cm.

The formula $V = \pi r^2 h$ gives rise to the table below, but the table only gives
a few out of the millions of possible values. The formula works for all values
of r and h.

Cubic unit values of the volume of a cylinder for different values of r and h
(taking $\pi = 3 \cdot 14$)

r \ h	1	2	3	4	5	6	7	8	9	10
1	3·14	6·28	9·42	12·56	15·7	18·84	21·98	25·12	28·26	31·4
2	12·56	25·12	37·68	50·24	62·8	75·36	87·92	100·48	113·04	125·6
3	28·26	56·52	84·78	113·04	141·3	169·56	197·82	226·08	254·34	282·6
4	50·24	100·48	150·72	200·96	251·2	301·44	351·68	401·92	452·16	502·4
5	78·5	157	235·5	314	392·5	471	549·5	628	706·5	785
6	113·04	226·08	339·12	452·16	565·2	678·24	791·28	904·32	1017·36	1130·4

Exercise F.4

1 Given $s = 10$ and $t = 12$ find the value
of $\frac{1}{2}st^2$.   C

2 Find y when x is 4 given that
$y = 2x^2 + 1$.   C

3 The cost of electricity (£) is found from
the formula
$$C = 0 \cdot 06n + 15$$
where n is the number of units used.
What is the cost if 180 units have been
used?   C

4 The increase in length of some metal
rails is given by the formula
Increase $= 0 \cdot 0009 \times t \times$ length
where t is the temperature change in
degrees Celsius.

Find the increase in 1 km of rail when
the temperature rises 10°C.   C

5 The area of a triangle is given by the
formula $A = \frac{1}{2}bh$.
Calculate A when $b = 5$ cm and
$h = 4$ cm.   C

6 The area of a flat ring is
given by the formula
$A = \pi(R - r)(R + r)$.
Calculate the area if
$R = 6$ cm and $r = 5$ cm.   C

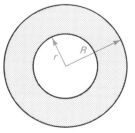

7 The formula for the energy (measured in kilowatts) used by an electrical heater is $E_{kW} = \dfrac{V \times A}{1000}$. Calculate E if $V = 240$ volts and $A = 5$ amps.　　　B

8 Income tax is calculated from the formula Tax $= 0\cdot27\,(G - A)$, where G is gross income and A is the sum of allowances. Calculate the tax if $G = £9600$ and $A = £3600$.　　　B

F.5　Changing formulae

Sometimes a formula is in the wrong order for use. It can be changed round using the rules of algebra.

Example

Formula　wanted　known
$V = \pi r^2 h$　　r　　V, h ... $V = 100$ cm³, $h = 5$ cm

Method 1
The r is gradually isolated.

$V = \pi r^2 h \Rightarrow \dfrac{V}{h} = \pi r^2 \qquad \Rightarrow \dfrac{V}{h\pi} = r^2 \qquad \Rightarrow \sqrt{\dfrac{V}{h\pi}} = r$

Step 1: divide by h;　　Step 2: divide by π;　　Step 3: take square root ... $= r$

100 ÷ 5 =　　　÷ π =　　　√　　　2·52

We have found the radius of a cylinder whose volume is 100 cm³ and whose height is 5 cm. [See worked examples of exam questions.]

Method 2
This method inverses the changes that were made to r to get V.

$$r \xrightarrow{(\ )^2} r^2 \xrightarrow{\times h} r^2 h \xrightarrow{\times \pi} \pi r^2 h = V$$

$$r = \sqrt{\dfrac{V}{\pi h}} \xleftarrow{\sqrt{\ }} \dfrac{V}{\pi h} \xleftarrow{\div h} \dfrac{V}{\pi} \xleftarrow{\div \pi} V$$

[cylinder diagram: $v = 100$ cm³, 5 cm]

Notes:　(i)　It is often easier to work on the formula than to work on the measurements of the problem first.

(ii)　Checking back to the table in Section F.4, which gives values for V, r and h, we find that if $h = 5$, then $V = 62\cdot8$ cm³ when $r = 2$, and $V = 141\cdot3$ cm³, when $r = 3$. So for $V = 100$ we would expect r to be about $2\cdot5$ cm.

Exercise F.5

1 The perimeter of a rectangle is given by the formula $p = 2(a + b)$. Change the formula so that b can be found if p and a are known.　　　C

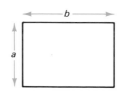

P264
ExF5
Q1→

cylinder is $\pi r^2 h$, where
~~~d~~~ h is the height.
~~~ormula~~~ so that h can be
~~~/~~~ and r are known.
~~~formula~~~ to find the
~~~linder~~~ whose volume
is 500 cm~~~³~~~ and whose radius is
15 cm.

B

3 Given that $t = \sqrt{\dfrac{2s}{g}}$ find
(i) a formula for g in terms of t and s,
(ii) a formula for s in terms of g and t.

4 The famous energy formula $e = mc^2$ is
the formula of nuclear power.
(i) Change the formula to obtain
c and m.
(ii) Find c if $e = 9 \times 10^{11}$ units of
energy and $m = 10$ units of mass.

A

5 The stopping distance in feet of a car
travelling at v miles per hour is given
by the formula
$d = 0\cdot055\, v^2 + 1\cdot1\, v$.
It takes a car 75 ft to come to a halt.
Estimate v.

A

6 The number of diagonals that can be
drawn in a polygon with n sides is given
by the formula
$$d = \frac{n^2 - 3n}{2}$$
(i) Show that a polygon with
20 diagonals will have 8 sides.
(ii) Show that a polygon with exactly
128 diagonals cannot be drawn.

A

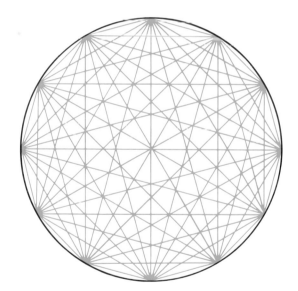

F.6 Linear equations

The simplest form of equations have just one letter. To solve them, treat
them like formulae and get the letter on its own using the rules of algebra.
● In any equation, both sides may be multiplied by the same number without
upsetting the balance.
● Similarly, the same number may be added to both sides without upsetting
the balance.

Examples

1 $3x + 5 = 9 - x$

$\Rightarrow 4x + 5 = 9$ adding x to both sides

$\Rightarrow 4x\quad\ = 4$ adding $^-5$ to both sides

$\Rightarrow\ x\quad\ = 1$ dividing both sides by 4

Always check a solution by putting the value back in the original equation and making sure that the left-hand side (LHS) has the same value as the right-hand side (RHS).

Check: LHS $= 3x + 5 = (3 \times 1) + 5 = 8$ ⟵
RHS $= 9 - x = 9 - 1 = 8$ ⟵   the same value

2 $\dfrac{x}{3} + \dfrac{x-4}{5} = 4$

Because fractions occur, multiply both sides of the equation by 3×5.

$\dfrac{x}{3} + \dfrac{x-4}{5} = 4 \Rightarrow \dfrac{15x}{3} + \dfrac{15(x-4)}{5} = 60 \quad \times 15$

$\Rightarrow 5x + 3(x - 4)\quad = 60$ cancelling

$\Rightarrow 5x + 3x - 12\quad = 60$ multiplying out brackets

$\Rightarrow 8x - 12\qquad\quad = 60$ gather up x's

$\Rightarrow 8x\qquad\qquad\ \ = 72$ adding 12

$\Rightarrow x\qquad\qquad\quad = 9$ dividing by 8

Check: LHS $= \dfrac{x}{3} + \dfrac{x-4}{5} = \dfrac{9}{3} + \dfrac{9-4}{5} = 3 + 1 = 4$ ⟵

RHS $= 4$ ⟵   the same value

Exercise F.6

1 Solve the equation $3x - 5 = 19$. C
2 Solve the equation $2x + 5x - x = 18$. C
3 Solve $4(x - 2) = 12$ C
4 Solve $2x + 1 = 10 - x$ C
5 Solve $3(x + 1) = 2(2x - 1)$ C

6 Solve $7m + 15 = 3(m + 2) + 1$ C
7 Solve the equation $\frac{1}{2}x + 3 = 2x - 12$. C
8 Solve the equation $\dfrac{y}{4} - \dfrac{2y}{5} + 3 = 0$. B

◆F.7 Simultaneous equations

An equation such as $x + y = 10$ has many solutions: for example $(1, 9)$, $(2, 8) \ldots$ etc. However, if x and y satisfy two equations, it is usually possible to find the one and only value of x and of y using the rules of algebra. [It is like an 'address'. One equation gives the road while the other equation tells you the number of the house!]

Another way of looking at a pair of simultaneous equations is as a pair of straight lines, as in the following example.

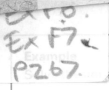
ExF.8.
Ex F7.
P267.

ations $x + y = 10$
$\qquad 2x - y = 2$

Since adding the equations will eliminate y, the simplest method is to add the left-hand sides and the right-hand sides.

$\quad x + y = 10$
$\quad 2x - y = 2$
$\Rightarrow \quad 3x = 12$
$\Rightarrow \quad x = 4$ and $y = 6$

Check that these results work for both equations
$\qquad x + y = 10$
$\quad$ LHS $= 4 + 6 = 10 \qquad$ RHS $= 10$
$\qquad 2x - y = 2$
LHS $= 2(4) - 6 = 2 \qquad$ RHS $= 2$

[See Unit H for another method of solution (by vectors).]

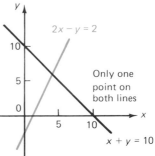
Only one point on both lines

If it is not possible to eliminate x or y straight away, a little adjustment is needed. Try to get the same number of x's or y's in both the equations. [If one lot is positive and the other is negative it is even better.]

Example

$2x + 5y = 11$
$\ x + 4y = \ 7$

The equations are solved by eliminating x first and then eliminating y.

Method 1:

$\times 1 \quad 2x + 5y = 11 \rightarrow 2x + 5y = 11$
$\times 2 \quad x + 4y = \ 7 \rightarrow 2x + 8y = 14$

$\qquad$ Subtract $\quad {}^-3y = {}^-3$
$\qquad \Rightarrow \qquad y = 1$
$\qquad \Rightarrow \qquad x = 3$

Method 2:

$\times 4 \quad 2x + 5y = 11 \rightarrow 8x + 20y = 44$
$\times 5 \quad x + 4y = \ 7 \rightarrow 5x + 20y = 35$

$\qquad$ Subtract $\qquad 3x = 9$
$\qquad \Rightarrow \qquad x = 3$
$\qquad \Rightarrow \qquad y = 1$

Exercise F.7

1. Solve the equations $x + y = 17$
$\qquad\qquad\qquad\qquad x - y = \ 9$

2. The graph gives the solution to a pair of simultaneous equations. What are the equations?

C

B

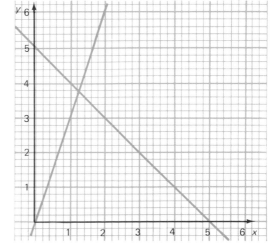

3 Solve the equations $2p + 3q = 13$
$$3p = 2q \qquad \text{B}$$

4 Draw graphs which will enable you to solve the pair of solutions
$$x + y = 4$$
$$2x - y = 5 \qquad \text{B}$$

5 Solve the simultaneous equations
$$3x + 5y = 6$$
$$6x - 2y = 48$$

Why would you suggest that an algebraic method is easier than a geometric (graphical) method in this case? B

6 Solve the simultaneous equations
$$\left.\begin{array}{r} x^2 - y^2 = 20 \\ x - y = 10 \end{array}\right\}$$
[*Hint*: $x^2 - y^2 = (x - y)(x + y)$] A

◆F.8 Quadratic equations

Quadratic equations like $x^2 + 3x + 2 = 0$ cannot be solved by 'rearrangement'. (Try it?) They are solved by changing the equation from a sum of mixed powers of x into a product of two linear factors. We use the following basic rule of numbers:
$$ab = 0 \Rightarrow a = 0 \quad \text{or} \quad b = 0$$

Example

Solve $x^2 + 3x + 2 = 0$

We look for two factors $(x + a)$ and $(x + b)$ so that
$(x + a)(x + b) = x^2 + 3x + 2$.
Since $(x + a)(x + b) = x^2 + (a + b)x + ab$ we need two numbers
 (i) whose sum is 3,
(ii) whose product is 2.
This suggests $a = 1$ and $b = 2$ (or the other way round).
The solution of the equation proceeds like this:
$$x^2 + 3x + 2 = 0 \Rightarrow (x + 1)(x + 2) = 0$$
$$\Rightarrow x + 1 = 0 \text{ or } x + 2 = 0$$
$$\Rightarrow x = {}^{-}1 \text{ or } {}^{-}2.$$

Note: The sum of the solutions is $^{-}3$ and the product is $^{+}2$. In general, the sum of the solutions of $x^2 + px + q = 0$ will be ^{-}p, while the product will be q.

F.8.1 Solution by formula

The general quadratic equation $ax^2 + bx + c = 0$ can be solved using the formula
$$x = \frac{-b \pm \sqrt{b^2 - 4ac}}{2a}, \qquad \text{provided } b^2 > 4ac,$$
so that you are not asked to evaluate the square root of a negative number.
This formula is worth learning even though it will be given in the examination.

Examples

1 Solve the equation $2x^2 + 3x - 1 = 0$.

In this case $a = 2, b = 3, c = {}^-1$.

$$x = \frac{{}^-b \pm \sqrt{b^2 - 4ac}}{2a} \Rightarrow x = \frac{{}^-3 \pm \sqrt{9 + 8}}{4}$$

The values of x are $\dfrac{{}^-3 + \sqrt{17}}{4}$ and $\dfrac{{}^-3 - \sqrt{17}}{4}$

i.e. $x = 0{\cdot}28$ or $^-1{\cdot}78$, correct to two decimal places.

To check, make sure that (i) the sum of the roots is $-\dfrac{b}{a}$

(ii) the product of the roots is $\dfrac{c}{a}$

In this case $0{\cdot}28 + {}^-1{\cdot}78 = {}^-1{\cdot}5 = {}^-\frac{3}{2}$

$\qquad\qquad 0{\cdot}28 \times {}^-1{\cdot}78 = {}^-0{\cdot}4984 \rightarrow {}^-0{\cdot}5 = {}^-\frac{1}{2}$

2 Solve the equation $x^2 + x + 1 = 0$.

In this case $a = 1, b = 1, c = 1$.

$$x = \frac{-1 \pm \sqrt{1 - 4}}{2} = \frac{-1 \pm \sqrt{{}^-3}}{2}$$

Thus x cannot be evaluated ... (try it!!)

The expression $\sqrt{b^2 - 4ac}$ is known as the discriminant of the quadratic.

- If $b^2 - 4ac$ is a perfect square the quadratic will factorise.
- If $b^2 > 4ac$ the equation has two real roots.
- If $b^2 < 4ac$ the equation has no real roots.
- If $b^2 = 4ac$ the quadratic is a perfect square and the equation has only the one solution.

Exercise F.8

1 Solve the quadratic equation $(x + 4)(x - 6) = 0$.   C

2 Solve the quadratic equation $x^2 - 3x + 2 = 0$.   C

3 Solve the quadratic equation $2x^2 - 3x - 10 = 0$.   B

4 Solve the equation $\dfrac{2}{x} = 3 - x$.   A

5 Use the formula to solve the quadratic equation $x^2 + x - 1 = 0$.   A

6 Show that factorising and solution by formula give the same solutions for the quadratic equation $6x^2 + x - 2 = 0$.   A

7 Explain why it is useless to search for solutions to the equation $x^2 + 3x + 4 = 0$.   A

8 The equation $3x^2 + 5x + 2 = 0$ has two solutions. Show that the sum of the solutions must be $-\frac{5}{3}$ and the product must be $\frac{2}{3}$.   A

F.9 Graphs of functions

A graph is a picture of a relationship between numbers. You need to understand that . . .

- an equation produces pairs of values of x and y [usually written as a table];
- each pair of values gives a point (x, y);
- all these points lie on a straight or curved line;
- this line is the graph of the relationship [and the relationship is the equation of the graph].

Note: Don't get mixed up between the terms relationship and equation. The equation is simply a short way of describing the relationship.

There are a number of well-known graphs. The following are four simple examples.

Examples

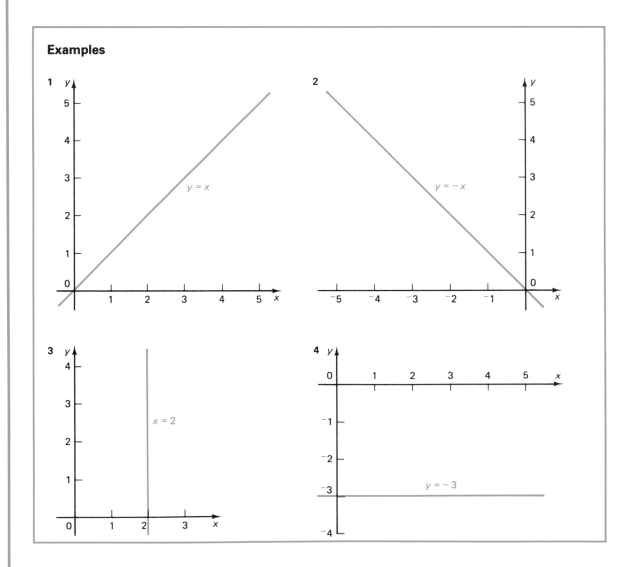

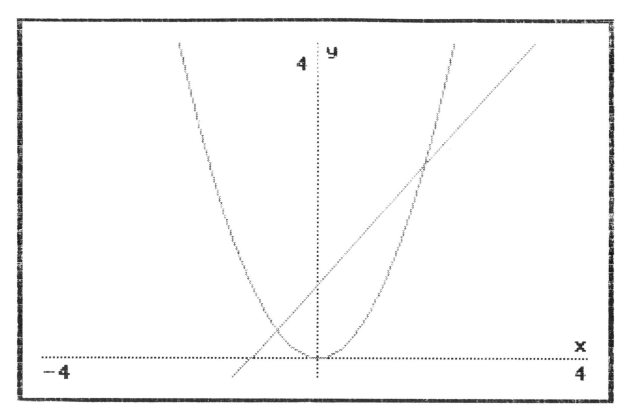

A computer-generated plot of the graphs $y = x + 1$ and $y = x^2$.

Examples

In each of these examples, pairs of values are tabulated and plotted. The whole graph is then drawn and labelled. The graphs are:

1 $y = 2x + 3$ **2** $x + y = 5$ **3** $y = x^2$ **4** $y = \dfrac{1}{x}$ **5** $y = 2x^2 - 3$

1 $y = 2x + 3$

x	0	1	2	3	4
y	3	5	7	9	11

(0, 3)
(1, 5)
(2, 7)
(3, 9)
(4, 11)

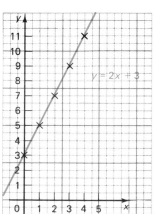

Note: Since this graph is a straight line, two points would be enough to draw it, e.g. (0, 3) and (4, 11).

271

2 $x + y = 5$

x	$^-2$	$^-1$	0	1	2	3	4	5
y	7	6	5	4	3	2	1	0

($^-2$, 7)
($^-1$, 6)
(0, 5)
(1, 4)
(2, 3)
(3, 2)
(4, 1)
(5, 0)

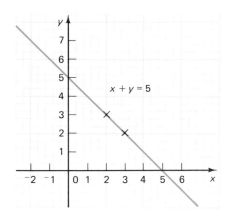

Notes: (i) The line continues into the negative part of the graph.

(ii) The graph slopes down from left to right. This is because the y values get smaller as the x values increase.

3 $y = x^2$

x	$^-3$	$^-2$	$^-1$	0	1	2	3
y	9	4	1	0	1	4	9

($^-3$, 9)
($^-2$, 4)
($^-1$, 1)
(0, 0)
(1, 1)
(2, 4)
(3, 9)

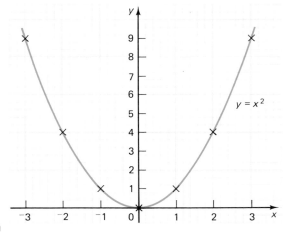

Notes: (i) This equation has a curved graph so more than two points are needed before the graph is drawn.

(ii) I have used a different scale for x and y. This 'opens out' the curve and makes its sides less steep.

(iii) No part of the graph comes below the x-axis.

(iv) When drawing curves like this, make sure the bottom (or top) is rounded—not curved or flat.

4 $y = \dfrac{1}{x}$

x	0	1	2	3	4	5
y	*	1	0·5	0·33	0·25	0·2

*There is no value of y corresponding to $x = 0$. Extra values of y are needed between $x = 0$ and $x = 1$.

x	0·2	0·4	0·6	0·8
y	5	2·5	1·66	1·25

(0·2, 5)
(0·4, 2·5)
(0·6, 1·66)
(0·8, 1·25)
(1, 1)
(2, 0·5)
(3, 0·33)
(4, 0·25)
(5, 0·2)

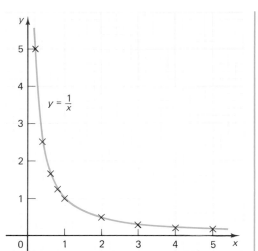

5 $y = 2x^2 - 3$

x	⁻3	⁻2	⁻1	0	1	2	3
x^2	9	4	1	0	1	4	9
$2x^2$	18	8	2	0	2	8	18
$y = 2x^2 - 3$	15	5	⁻1	⁻3	⁻1	5	15

(⁻3, 15)
(⁻2, 5)
(⁻1, ⁻1)
(0, ⁻3)
(1, ⁻1)
(2, 5)
(3, 15)

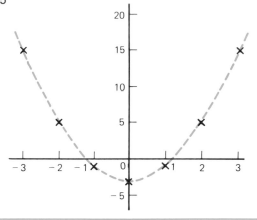

Exercise F.9

1 Draw on the same axes the graphs of $y = x$, $y = -x$, $x + y = 5$, $x - y = 5$ from $x = ⁻3$ to $⁺3$. B

2 Draw graphs of $y = 2x$ and $y = 3x - 4$ on the same axes. Show the point corresponding to the solution of the equation $3x - 4 = 2x$. B

3 Draw graphs of the functions $y = \dfrac{2}{x}$ and $y = x + 1$ from $x = ⁻4$ to $x = ⁺4$. Use the graph to obtain approximate solutions of the equation $x^2 + x - 2 = 0$. Compare the solutions with those obtained using the formula. A

4 Using scales of 1 cm per unit on the x axis and 5 mm per unit on the y axis, draw graphs of the functions
  (i) $y = x^2$
  (ii) $y = x^2 - 3$
  (iii) $y = x^2 + x + 1$
  What do you notice about the three graphs? A

5 Draw the graph of the function $f(x) = x^2 + 5x - 24$ from $x = ^-10$ to $^+10$.

Use the graph to solve the equations
  (i) $x^2 + 5x - 24 = 0$
  (ii) $x^2 - 4x - 22 = 0$ A

6 By choosing values of x, show that the points which satisfy the equation $x^2 + y^2 = 3$ all lie on a circle. Find the radius and centre of this circle and the coordinates of the points where it meets the parabola $y = x^2$. A

F.10 Using graphs

Graphs are mathematical tools which give pictures of relationships. They can be drawn from tables of values. Each pair of values corresponds to a point on the graph. The values can be found from a formula.

Example

The graph shows the connection between degrees Fahrenheit and degrees Celsius when measuring temperature.
The graph has been drawn from the table of values

C	0	10	20	30	40
F	32	50	68	86	104

The values themselves were calculated from the formula
$F = (\frac{9}{5} \times C) + 32$.
The graph can be used to estimate other values.
$(80°F \rightarrow 26°C)$

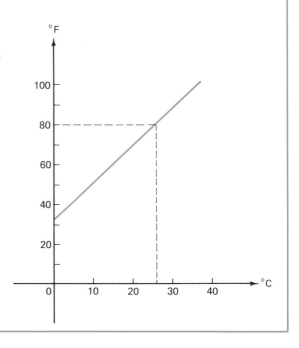

Each graph is a store of information. If the relationship is linear, only two points are needed to draw the graph. All other values can then be read from the graph.
This is especially useful when $(0,0)$ is one of the pairs of values.

Example

Conversion: hectares ↔ acres
100 hectares = 247 acres
It is easy to see that, for example,
    120 acres $\hat{=}$ 48 hectares
    70 hectares $\hat{=}$ 170 acres

The graph can be easily adapted (by changing the units on the scales) to convert between 0–10 hectares and 0–24·7 acres or even between 0–1 hectare and 0–2·47 acres.

All values obtained from the graph can, of course, be obtained directly from the formula

$$A_{\text{hectares}} = \frac{100}{247} \times A_{\text{acres}}$$

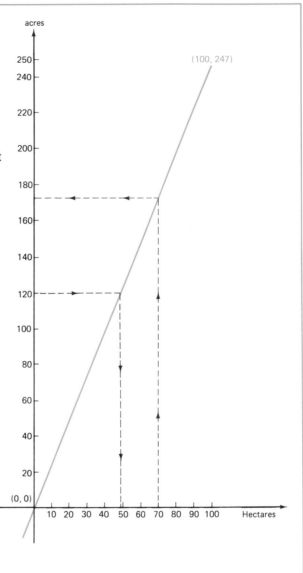

Exercise F.10

1 Make a conversion graph that can be used to change D. Marks to pounds, based on £1 → 2·4 DM. Use the graph to find the value in pounds of 75 DM.   C

2 Draw a graph to show the following data.

Daily quantity of food (g)	250	500	750	1000	1250
Weight of dog (kg)	5	10	15	20	25

What weight of food would be needed for a dog weighing 40 kg?   C

3 The table below gives the amount of wool needed to knit jumpers of different sizes.

Size	32	34	36	38
Weight of wool (g)	450	480	510	540

Draw a graph of the data. Estimate the largest jumper that could be knitted from 600 g of wool.

C

4 Make a graph which would enable you to estimate your weekly pay in a job that pays £2·50 per hour for the first 36 hours and £4·50 per hour for overtime. C

5 The formula $d = 5t^2$ gives the distance fallen in metres after t seconds of fall. Draw a graph which shows the distance fallen during the first 5 seconds. C

6 A parachutist jumps from an aircraft flying at 1000 m. She falls freely for 12 seconds and then opens her parachute (see question 5). From then on she falls at 4 metres per second. Use the axes shown to draw a graph of her fall. How long does she take to reach the ground? B

altitude
(metres)

1000

800

600

400

200

0   10   20   30   40   50   60   70   80   90

time (seconds)

◆F.11   Gradient, maxima and minima

F.11.1   The gradient of a straight line

This is found by choosing any two points on it.

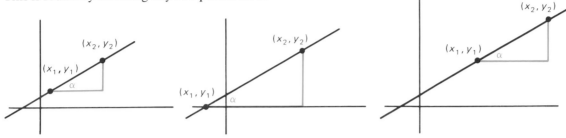

In each case the gradient is the same.

$$\frac{y_2 - y_1}{x_2 - x_1} = \tan \alpha.$$

Clearly the gradient is the same at every point on a straight line.

F.11.2   The gradient of a curve

This is different at different points.
The gradient is taken to be the gradient of the tangent at the point.
Thus the gradient of the curve at Q is much greater than the gradient at P.

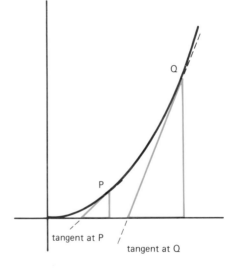

F.11.3   Gradient at maximum or minimum

When a curve turns, its gradient will be zero at maximum or minimum points.

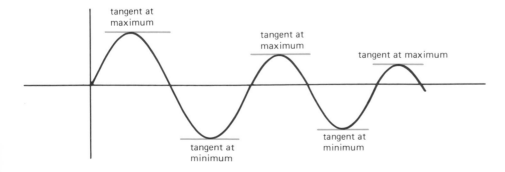

F.11.4 Negative gradient

If the y values of a graph are decreasing while x is increasing the curve has negative gradient

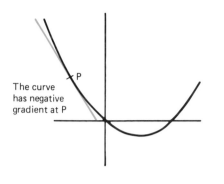

The curve has negative gradient at P

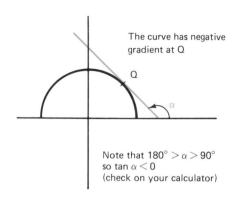

The curve has negative gradient at Q

Note that $180° > \alpha > 90°$
so $\tan \alpha < 0$
(check on your calculator)

- At a maximum the gradient changes from positive to negative.
- At a minimum the gradient changes from negative to positive.
- On a continuous curve there will be a maximum between every two minima, and a minimum between every two maxima. [Try and draw one where this is not true!]

F.11.5 Applications of gradient

Gradient measures rate of change rather than actual size. Some important examples are

$$\ldots \text{velocity} = \frac{\text{distance}}{\text{time}}$$

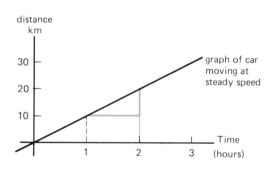

graph of car moving at steady speed

The gradient of the line gives the distance travelled in 1 hour (i.e. the speed).

$$\ldots \text{acceleration} = \frac{\text{change in speed}}{\text{time}}$$

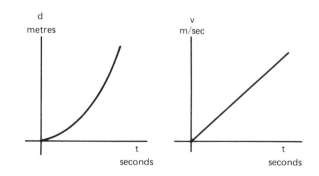

278

Falling body The first graph shows the distance fallen by a freely falling body. The velocity (gradient) changes with time.
The second graph shows that the velocity changes in a linear way. Its gradient is constant. This gradient is the acceleration.

$$\ldots \text{inflation} = \frac{\text{change in the retail price index}}{\text{time}}$$

According to this graph the rate of inflation for 1993 is about 3%.

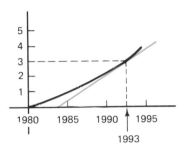

Collect other examples of application of gradient.

Exercise F.11

1 (i) The straight line in the graph passes through (0, 1) and (3, 3). Calculate the gradient of the line.

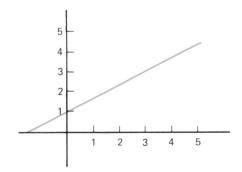

(ii) Sketch a straight line with a gradient 2.
(iii) Sketch a straight line with gradient ⁻0·5.
(iv) Two straight lines have the same gradient. Which of these statements are true?
   (a) The lines pass through the same points.
   (b) If a point is on one line it is not on the other.
   (c) The lines are parallel.   B

2 The graph shows part of the curve
$y = \sqrt{4 - x^2}$
Estimate the gradient of the curve at points P, Q and R.   A

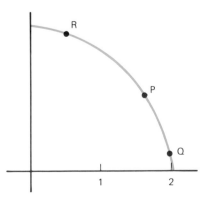

279

3 The graph shows part of the function
$y = \cos x$.

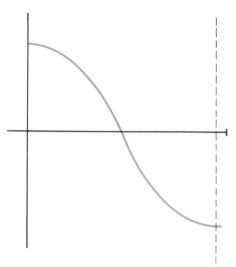

Estimate the gradient at a number of
points on the graph to test the
suggestion that the gradient of
$y = \cos x$ is $^-\sin x$ everywhere
on the curve.
[See Key Facts G for more information
about graphs of sin x and cos x.]   A

4 The graph shows the function
$y = \sin 3x$ for values of x between 0°
and 120°.

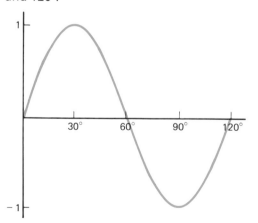

(i) What are the maximum and
minimum values of the function for
this range of x.
(ii) For what values of x is the gradient
of the curve 0·5.   A

5 Rectangles are drawn with perimeter
40 cm long. Draw a graph which shows
the areas of the rectangles, for different
lengths of base. Use your graph to find
the maximum possible area for one of
these rectangles.   A

6 The following table gives the heights
reached by a rocket, t seconds after
firing. Use the data to draw a graph and
estimate
  (i) the maximum height reached by
    the rocket,
 (ii) the gradient of the graph at $t = 2\cdot5$
    and $t = 6\cdot5$.
(iii) What practical information is given
    by the two gradients you have
    found in (ii)?   A

t (sec)	0	1	2	3	4	5	6	7	8	9	10
h (m)	0	54	98	132	157	172	176	172	157	132	98

F.12 Functions

Mathematics is about ideas. One of the most important is the idea of function. It is functions which bring algebra to life, but it is hard to describe exactly what they are. However, we can see functions at work when we make tables of values, draw mapping diagrams, solve equations and draw graphs.

Examples

The function which changes $x \rightarrow 2x + 3$ can be shown in six different ways:

1 a table of values:

x	$y = 2x + 3$
1	5
2	7
3	9
4	11
.	.
.	.
.	.

2 an equation: $y = 2x + 3$
or $f(x) = 2x + 3$

3 a graph:

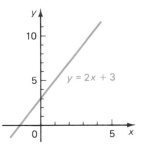

4 A mapping between two sets:

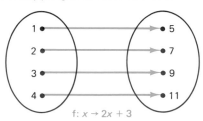

f: $x \rightarrow 2x + 3$

The first set is called the domain of the function.
The second set is called the range of the function.

5 a mapping from one number line to another:
[What would happen if you continued the arrows backwards in this case?]

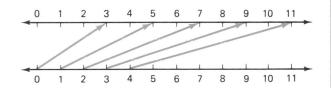

6 a function 'machine' which changes any number into its double +3:

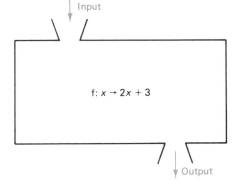

f: $x \rightarrow 2x + 3$

It is important for you to realise that all the above examples are different views of the same thing.

You can see what a function does by considering different values of x.

Examples

1   If $f(x) = 2x$, then $f(3) = 6$.   2   If $f(x) = x^2$, then $f(4) = 16$.
3   If $f(x) = x^2 + 2x$, then $f(6) = 36 + 12 = 48$.

Exercise F.12

1   Copy and complete the function table up to $x = 5$, for the function $x \to 2x - 5$.   C

x	0	1	2	3	4	5
$f(x)$	$^-5$	$^-3$				

2   Make a table of values for the function $x \to x^2/2$ from $x = {}^-2$ to $x = {}^+3$.   C

3   Which of the given mappings corresponds to the diagram?
A $x \to x + 1$ B $x \to x - 1$
C $x \to 2x + 1$ D $x \to x + 3$ C

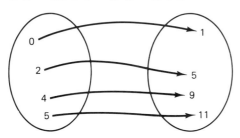

4   The output of a function machine which maps $x \to x^2 + 1$ is 17. What was the input?   C

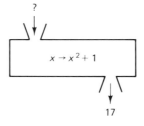

◆F. 13   Compound functions and inverse functions

Functions can be combined. The output of the first is used as the input of the second. This can be shown clearly as a pair of function 'machines'.
This idea is easy to understand if you think of the functions as processors.

$f_2(f_1(x))$ can be written as $f_2 f_1(x)$ or $f_2 \cdot f_1(x)$ *

[You might think of f_1 as a potato peeler and f_2 as an oven. Then $f_1 f_2$(potato) would mean 'take a potato, bake it and then peel it'. $f_2 f_1$(potato) would mean 'take a potato, peel it and then bake it'. The results would be different.]

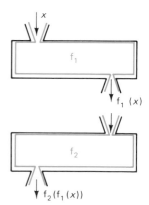

* Instead of using f_1, f_2, etc. in combined function expressions, your exam board may use f, g, etc. So $f_1(f_2(x))$ will be written $f(g(x))$. As you can see, either way is easy to remember: '1 before 2', 'f before g' (in the alphabet).

Example

$f_1: x \rightarrow 2x + 3$
$f_2: x \rightarrow x^2$

If x has the value 2, then

$$f_1(2) = 7 \qquad f_2(f_1(2)) = 49$$
$$f_2(2) = 4 \qquad f_1(f_2(2)) = 11$$

Make sure you understand where these numbers come from. Note that f_1f_2 and f_2f_1 do not give the same result.

If f_1 and f_2 are inverse functions, the compound functions f_1f_2 and f_2f_1 will both map x onto itself.

Examples Inverse functions

1 $x \rightarrow x^2$ ... so $3 \xrightarrow{x^2} 9 \xrightarrow{\sqrt{x}} 3$

2 $x \rightarrow \sqrt{x}$ ... so $3 \xrightarrow{\sqrt{x}} 1 \cdot 732 \ldots \xrightarrow{x^2} 3$

There are many other pairs of inverse functions on your calculator. How many can you find?

The function buttons $\boxed{+/-}$ and $\boxed{1/x}$ are their own inverses as can be seen from the following examples.

Examples

1 $4 \xrightarrow{1/x} 0 \cdot 25 \xrightarrow{1/x} 4$ **2** $3 \cdot 6 \xrightarrow{-x} {}^- 3 \cdot 6 \xrightarrow{-x} 3 \cdot 6$

Exercise F.13

Given $f_1: x \rightarrow 2x$, $f_2: x \rightarrow x + 4$, and that $f_1(x)$ is the output of f_1 for input x ...

1 what is the value of $f_1f_2(3)$?   B

2 what is the value of $f_2f_1(3)$?   B

3 what function is the inverse of f_1?   B

4 what function is the inverse of f_2?   B

5 A function is defined as
$f(x) = x^2 + 5x - 24$.
(a) Evaluate $f(^-2)$ and $f(^-3)$.
(b) Find values of x for which $f(x) = 0$
and for which $f(x) = 24$.   A

6 The function $g(x)$ is the inverse of the function $x \rightarrow \sin x$. Explain why this inverse function cannot be found by choosing any value of x and pressing $\boxed{\text{inv}}$ $\boxed{\text{sin}}$.   A

F.14 Indices and surds

F.14.1 Indices

The power $a^m = 1 \times a \times a \times a \ldots m$ times.
Thus $a^4 = 1 \times a \times a \times a \times a$.
This simple definition leads to the following rules of indices.

Rules	Examples
(i) $a^m \times a^n = a^{m+n}$	$2^3 \times 2^4 = 2^7$
(ii) $a^m \div a^n = a^{m-n}$	$3^5 \div 3^3 = 3^2$
(iii) $(a^m)^n = a^{mn}$	$(4^2)^3 = 4^6$
(iv) $a^0 = 1$	$5^0 = 1$
(v) $a^{-1} = \dfrac{1}{a}$ since $a^{-1} \times a = 1$	$2^{-1} = \frac{1}{2}$
(vi) $a^{\frac{1}{2}} = \sqrt{a}$ since $a^{\frac{1}{2}} \times a^{\frac{1}{2}} = a$	$(36)^{\frac{1}{2}} = \sqrt{36} = 6$
(vii) $a^{m/n} = \sqrt[n]{a^m}$	$8^{\frac{2}{3}} = \sqrt[3]{64} = 4$
	$8^{\frac{2}{3}} = (8^{\frac{1}{3}})^2 = 2^2 = 4$

Note: The $\boxed{x^y}$ and $\boxed{x^{1/y}}$ buttons on your calculator will calculate the values of powers whatever the value of the index.

Examples

1 Find $(1.08)^5$ [the value of £1 after 5 years at 8% compound interest]:
1·08 $\boxed{x^y}$ 5 $\boxed{=}$ 1·469 328

2 Find the cube root of 1728: 1728 $\boxed{x^{1/y}}$ 3 $\boxed{=}$ 12

The calculator can be used to confirm all the rules listed above.

F.14.2 Surds

'Surds' is another name for square roots. There are simple rules to follow.

Rules of surds	Examples
(i) $\sqrt{a} \times \sqrt{b} = \sqrt{ab}$	$\sqrt{3} \times \sqrt{2} = \sqrt{6}$
(ii) $\sqrt{a} \div \sqrt{b} = \sqrt{a \div b}$	$\sqrt{10} \div \sqrt{5} = \sqrt{2}$

Note that $\sqrt{a + b} \neq \sqrt{a} + \sqrt{b}$.
[These rules can be confirmed by choosing numbers for a and b and working out $\sqrt{a} \times \sqrt{b}$ and $\sqrt{ab}$ on the calculator.]

These rules can be used to simplify surds.

Examples

1 $\sqrt{98} = \sqrt{49 \times 2} = \sqrt{49} \times \sqrt{2} = 7\sqrt{2}$

2 $\sqrt{\dfrac{4}{9}} = \dfrac{\sqrt{4}}{\sqrt{9}} = \dfrac{2}{3}$

Exercises F.14

1. What is the value of 8^{-2}?   C

2. What is the value of $(0.1)^{-1}$?   C

3. What is the value of $(64)^{\frac{1}{3}}$?   C

4. What is the value of $\sqrt{45}$?
   Show why $3\sqrt{5}$ and $\sqrt{45}$ have the same value.   B

5. Show how you would find the value of $\sqrt{90}$ without using the $\sqrt{}$ function on your calculator.   A

6. Show that $\dfrac{a+b}{2} > \sqrt{ab}$ for three different values of a and b.

   [*Note*: $\sqrt{ab}$ is called the geometric mean of a and b.]   A

F.15   Inequalities

F.15.1   > and <

Relationships involving 'greater than', $>$, or 'less than', $<$, lead to sets of solutions instead of just one solution. For example, the question 'Who is taller than 5 ft 6 in in this class [of 30]?' could have anything up to 30 people in its solution set.

The solutions are found by using the simple rules summarised below.

(i) $a > b \Rightarrow a \pm c > b \pm c$
   You can add or subtract the same number on both sides without upsetting the inequality

(ii) $a > b \Rightarrow a \times n > b \times n$
   provided n is a positive number

(iii) $a > b, b > c \Rightarrow a > c$

(iv) $\left.\begin{array}{l} a > b \\ c > d \end{array}\right\} \Rightarrow \left\{\begin{array}{c} a + c > b + d \\ ac > bd \end{array}\right.$

Note: All the rules work equally well for $<$.

Diagrams can be drawn using scales to show the inequality.

a is heavier than b $(a+c)$ is heavier than $(b+c)$

Rule (i)

You should make your own diagrams for the other three rules.

Number inequalities show up clearly on a number line.
$^-7 < {}^-4$ and $^-4 > {}^-7$
$^-4 < 4$ and $4 > {}^-4$
$4 < 6$ and $6 > 4$

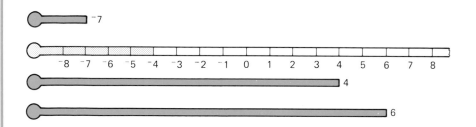

Example

Solve the inequation $2x + 3 > 8$.

$2x + 3 > 8 \Rightarrow 2x > 5$
$ \Rightarrow \ x > 2\cdot5$

F.15.2   Graphs

Inequations in both x and y can be shown by shading out an area on a graph.
Two examples are given below.

Examples

1 $x + 2y > 4$

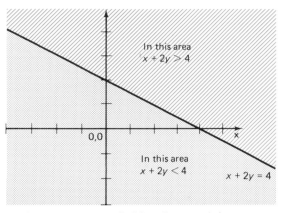

You can see that the line $x + 2y = 4$ divides the graph into two areas.
▨ $x + 2y > 4$ above the line; ☐ $x + 2y < 4$ below the line.
If you are not sure which is which, look at the point (0, 0). Putting $x = 0$
and $y = 0$, $x + 2y$ becomes 0, so this point is in the $x + 2y < 4$ area,
since 0 is obviously less than 4.

2 Show the region on a graph which satisfies all the inequalities $x > 0$, $y < 3$, $y > x - 1$ and $x + y < 7$.
Begin by drawing the lines $x = 0$, $y = 3$, $y = x - 1$ and $x + y = 7$.
In this example, it is sensible to shade out the areas which do not satisfy the inequalities. The clear space then satisfies all of the inequalities.

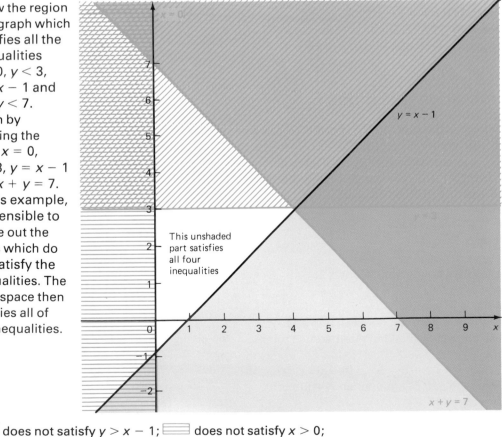

This unshaded part satisfies all four inequalities

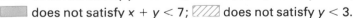

☐ does not satisfy $y > x - 1$; ▤ does not satisfy $x > 0$;
■ does not satisfy $x + y < 7$; ▨ does not satisfy $y < 3$.

F.15.3 ≥ and ≤

The expression $x > 2$ tells you that x must be more than 2. The expression
$x \geq 2$ says that x must be more than 2 or exactly equal to 2.
These two situations are shown on the number lines below.

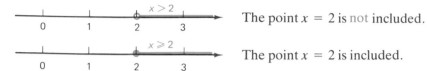

The point $x = 2$ is not included.

The point $x = 2$ is included.

Exercise F.15

1 Mark the numbers ⁻3, ⁻1·7, 2, 3·5 and 0 on a number line. Use your number line to put > or < correctly into these statements.
  (i) ⁻1·7 ... ⁻3   (ii) ⁻3 ... 2
  (iii) 3·5 ... 0   (iv) 0 ... ⁻1·7   C

2 Draw a diagram that would show $a < b \Rightarrow 2a < 2b$.   C

3 Draw the line $y = 2x + 1$ on a graph from $x = ⁻3$ to $⁺2$. Shade in the area of the graph corresponding to $y < 2x + 1$.   C

4 On the same axes, draw graphs of
  (i) $x = 3$,   (ii) $y = ⁻2$ (iii) $x + y = 2$.
  Shade in areas corresponding to $x > 3$, $y < ⁻2$ and $x + y < 2$. What relationships are satisfied by all points in the remaining unshaded area?   B

5 Show on a number line the points which satisfy the inequality $x^2 + 2x \geq 8$.
  [*Hint*: consider $x^2 + 2x - 8 \geq 0$]   A

Examination questions F

The following questions are typical of the questions you can expect. Worked out answers are given on pages 297–313. The questions have been divided into two sections because there are a large number of different ideas in this topic. I suggest that you attempt Section 1 first, and check your answers. The second section can then be tackled.

Section 1

1 A formula connecting W and x is
  $W = x^3 + 2x$.
  What is W when $x = 3$?

2 I think of a number, double it and add 12. The answer is 20. What number did I think of?

3 Solve: (a) $4x - 3 = 5$;   (b) $2(6 + 3x) = 18$

◆ 4 Solve the pair of simultaneous equations
  $3x + 2y = 16$
  $4x - y = 14$

5 Copy and complete the table of values for $y = x^2 - 2x - 3$.

x	⁻2	⁻1	0	1	2	3	4
x^2		1			4		
$⁻2x$		2			⁻4		
$⁻3$		⁻3			⁻3		
y		0			⁻3		

(a) Draw a graph whose equation is $y = x^2 - 2x - 3$ for values of x from ⁻2 to 4.

(b) (i) What is y when $x = 2·5$?

(ii) What is x when $y = 3$?

$$\left[x = \frac{-b \pm \sqrt{b^2 - 4ac}}{2a} \right]$$

(c) What is the equation of the axis of symmetry?

(d) Find the value of the positive root of $x^2 - 2x - 3 = 0$.

6 (a) When $p = a + b + c$, b is

$p + a + c$, $p - a + c$, $a + c - p$,

$p - a - c$ or none of these.

(b) If $y = mx + c$, then x is

$y - c - m$ $\dfrac{y - c}{m}$ $\dfrac{y}{m} - c$ $y + c + m$

or none of these.

(c) When $A = \pi(a + b)$, the value of a may be written as

$\dfrac{A - b}{\pi}$ $\dfrac{A}{\pi} - b$ $\dfrac{A - \pi}{b}$ $\dfrac{\pi b}{A}$

or none of these

(d) If f is made the subject of $\dfrac{1}{u} + \dfrac{1}{v} = \dfrac{1}{f}$ we have

$f = v + u$ $f = \dfrac{uv}{u + v}$

$f = \dfrac{2}{u + v}$ $f = \dfrac{u + v}{2}$

7 $y = k^x$. Find
(a) y if $k = 5$ and $x = 2$.
(b) x if $y = 64$ and $k = 4$.
(c) k if $y = 32$ and $x = 5$.

8 Insert brackets to make the following true:
(a) $14 - 11 - 7 = 10$ (b) $14 - 7 - 11 = 18$.

9 If $x * y$ means $2x + y$, calculate
(a) $2 * 3$ (b) $5 * 1$ (c) $2 * (3 * 4)$

10 Write in simplest form:

(a) $\dfrac{4(2x + 3)}{4} + \dfrac{2(6 - x)}{4}$

(b) $2(x^2 + 4) - x(2x + 3)$.

11 Simplify $5x + 2y + 3x + 4y$.

12 Factorise $ab - 3a + b - 3$.

♦ 13 Solve the simultaneous equations

$5x + 4y = 5$

$2x + 3y = 9$

♦ 14 Solve $2d^2 + 6d - 5 = 0$, giving answers to 2 significant figures

$$\left[\text{The equation } ax^2 + bx + c = 0 \text{ has solutions } x = \frac{-b \pm \sqrt{b^2 - 4ac}}{2a} \right]$$

15 $\dfrac{a}{b} + \dfrac{b}{a}$ equals one of the following:

A $\dfrac{ab}{ab}$ B $\dfrac{a + b}{a + b}$ C $\dfrac{a + b}{ab}$ D $\dfrac{a^2 + b^2}{ab}$

♦ 16 If $r = 2q - 5$ and $q = 3p + 2$ express r in terms of p.

17 If $R = \dfrac{5EZ}{7}$, what does

(a) $7R$ equal?   (b) E equal?

18 Factorise   (a) $x^2 - 16y^2$ (b) $x^2 - x - 6$.

19 Look at the following statements.

$1^3 = 1^2$

$1^3 + 2^3 = (1 + 2)^2$

Do you agree that they are true? If the pattern continues so that

$1^3 + 2^3 + 3^3 + 4^3 + 5^3 = a^2$

find the value of a.

20 The points $(10, 5)$; $(12, 6)$; and $(4, 2)$ lie on the straight line $y = kx$. What is k?

Worked answers to this section are to be found on pages 297–305.

Section 2

21 Find the solution of the equation

$5x - 9 = 4x$.

22 Write an inequation to represent the number line shown below.

♦ 23 Solve the pair of equations $2m + n = 5$

$6m - 2n = {}^-15$

♦ 24 Solve the equations $x + 3y = 7$

$x - y = 3$

25 Simplify $x^{10} \div x^4$.

26 Simplify $\dfrac{25x^2yz}{100xyz^3}$.

27 The diagram shows the two graphs $y = 2x$ and $x + y = 9$. R represents the point where they meet.
   (a) What are the coordinates of any point on $y = 2x$?
   (b) Write down the coordinates of P and Q.
   (c) Solve the simultaneous equations
$$\left.\begin{array}{r} y = 2x \\ x + y = 9 \end{array}\right\}$$
to find the coordinates of R.

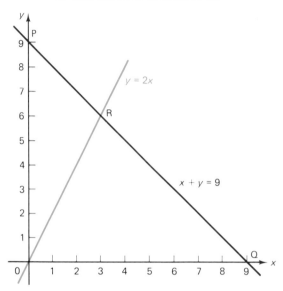

◆ 28 Find the value of $\sqrt[3]{\dfrac{3V}{4\pi}}$ where $V = 58 \cdot 93$ and $\pi = 3 \cdot 14$.

29 Given $F = 1 \cdot 8C + 32$, find C in terms of F.

30 $V = \dfrac{\pi r^2 h}{2}$
   (a) Taking $\pi = 3 \cdot 1$, find V if $r = 3$ and $h = 20$.
   (b) Find r, given that $V = 8\pi$ and $h = 2r$.
   (c) Rearrange the formula to find r in terms of h and V.

31 What are the factors of $x^2 + 10x - 24$? Use your answer to solve the equation $x^2 + 10x - 24 = 0$.

32 If $(x - 2)(x + 3) = x^2 + ax - 6$, what is the value of a?

33 Work out the value of $(3 + \sqrt{2})(3 - \sqrt{2})$.

34 Solve the equation $x^2 + 4x = 0$.

35 The mappings f: $x \rightarrow 2x$ and g: $x \rightarrow x + 2$ are combined to form a single mapping fg. Find the result of mapping the number 3 by fg.

36 If f: $x \rightarrow x^2 - 2x + 1$
   [i.e. $f(x) = x^2 - 2x + 1$],
   what is the value of
   (a) $f(10)$ (b) $f(3)$?

37 (a) Which of the numbers 9, 11, 16, 10 or 14 should be written in the small square?
   (b) Which of the mappings given below corresponds to the diagram?
$$x \rightarrow x^2, \quad x \rightarrow 4x - 3,$$
$$x \rightarrow 3x - 2 \quad x \rightarrow 2x - 1,$$
   or $x \rightarrow 2x^2 - 1$?

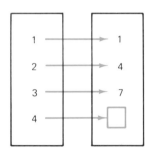

38 f is the mapping $x \rightarrow 4x$.
   (a) Which of the ordered pairs $(0, 4)$; $(2, 8)$; $(^-1, ^-4)$; $(\frac{1}{2}, 2)$; $(5, 20)$ does not belong to the mapping?
   (b) Which of the following mappings is the inverse of f?
$$x \rightarrow \tfrac{1}{4}; \quad x \rightarrow x - 4; \quad x \rightarrow \frac{x}{4};$$
$$x \rightarrow {}^-4x; \quad x \rightarrow \frac{1}{4x}.$$

◆ 39 Given that $f(x) = 3x^2 + 2$ and $x > 0$,
   (a) find the value of $f(2)$.
   (b) find the values of x for which $f(x) = 11$.
   (c) find the inverse of the function f: $x \rightarrow 3x^2 + 2$. If this is f^{-1}, show that $f^{-1}(14) = 2$.

40 The graph of the line $y = mx + c$ passes through A $(4, 0)$ and B $(0, 6)$.
   (a) Find the value of c and m.
   (b) Find the coordinates of a point on the line and on $y = x$.

Activities and investigations F

Formulae race [for two players]

Purpose of activity

This game will make you much faster at substituting values in formulae. It will also help you to understand the most efficient way of doing this. Make sure you agree with the scores claimed by your partner.

Equipment needed

Any calculator, a die, and pencil and paper for scoring.

How to play

Each player starts off with a list of the numbers 1, 2, 3, 4, 5, 6, 7, 8, 9, and ⁻1, ⁻2, ⁻3, ⁻4, ⁻5, ⁻6.
The first player throws the die to select one of the formulae given below:

1: $v = u + at$ [a formula about speed and acceleration]
2: $C = 2\pi r$ [the circumference of a circle; $\pi = 3.1416\ldots$]
3: $V = abc$ [the volume of a cuboid]
4: $A = \frac{1}{2}(a + b)h$ [the area of a trapezium]
5: $V = \frac{1}{3}\pi r^2 h$ [the volume of a cone]
6: $a = \sqrt{b^2 + c^2}$ [the length of the hypotenuse of a triangle]

If she throws a 6 the formula is $a = \sqrt{b^2 + c^2}$. She now selects two numbers from her list to substitute in the formula and scores the result. If she chooses 7 for b and 8 for c, she crosses them off her number list and her score is
$$a = \sqrt{7^2 + 8^2} = \sqrt{49 + 64} = \sqrt{113} = 10.63.$$
The second player then throws a die, selects a formula, chooses numbers to substitute, and calculates his score.
The winner is the player with the highest score. The game ends when both players have run out of numbers.
If you enjoyed the game try another one with the following formulae:

1: $v^2 = u^2 - 2gs$ 2: $I = \dfrac{PRT}{100}$ 3: $V = 2\pi r(r + h)$

4: $T = 2\pi\sqrt{\dfrac{l}{g}}$ 5: $\dfrac{1}{f} = \dfrac{1}{v} + \dfrac{1}{u}$ 6: $x = \dfrac{-b \pm \sqrt{b^2 - 4ac}}{2a}$

Notes: (i) If your calculator has a 'random number' function you can use that instead of throwing a die.
      (ii) Formulae usually have a real meaning. The formulae above relate to:
           1: The speed of an object thrown vertically in the air with speed '*u*'.

2: The simple interest [money earned] I on £P at interest rate $R\%$ for T years.

3: The surface area of a cylinder.

4: The time of swing of a pendulum.

5: The focal length of a lens and the distances of object and image [photography].

6: The solutions of the quadratic equation $ax^2 + bx + c = 0$.

Puzzles, games and investigations ... for two

These puzzles, games and investigations will help you to practise your algebra and enjoy it too!

They will improve your techniques and also your understanding.

1 Secret agents

The secret agents whose pictures are shown have code numbers which make each 'sum' correct.

Find the code number of each agent.

2 Pictures of algebra

This diagram is a picture of the relationship
$(a + b)(c + d) = ac + ad + bc + bd$.

Make sure you understand why.

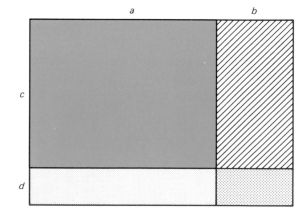

Each of the following diagrams shows a relationship. Discuss with your partner what the relationships must be.

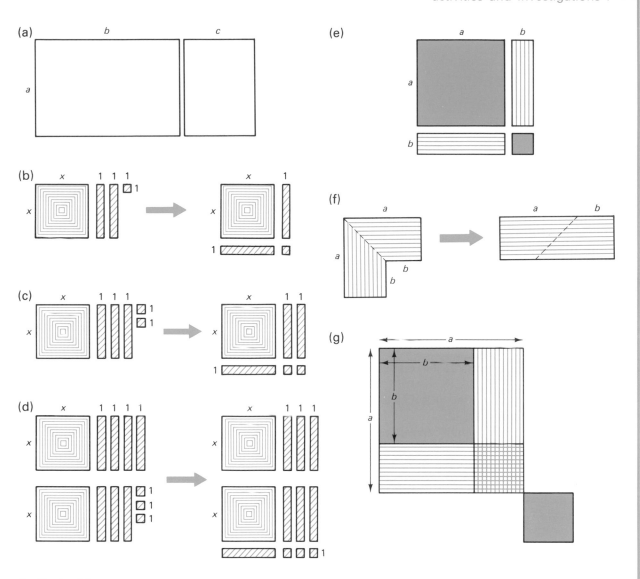

3 Factor bingo

This is a game for four or more people which will quickly make you an expert at factorising.

(a) Make a set of factor cards. Each one should give 8 factors chosen at random from this list of factors.

List of factors

$x - 1$	$x + 1$
$x - 2$	$x + 2$
$x - 3$	$x + 3$
$x - 4$	$x + 4$
$x - 5$	$x + 5$
$x - 6$	$x + 6$

A typical factor card

$x - 3$	$x + 5$	$x - 1$	$x + 2$
$x - 4$	$x + 3$	$x - 2$	$x + 1$

Two quadratic cards

$$x^2 + 3x + 2$$

$$x^2 - 25$$

(b) Make a set of quadratic cards where the quadratic is made up by multiplying two factors from the list. There should be 78 different quadratic cards in a set. Why?

How to play

(i) Each player is given a factor card and 8 counters or coins. The quadratic cards are placed face down on the table.

(ii) The first player turns up the top quadratic card for 30 seconds and then puts it face down in a separate pile.

(iii) Any player with a factor of the quadratic on his factor card covers that factor with a counter.

(iv) The next player turns up the next quadratic card for 30 seconds, and so on, until

(v) one player has covered all the factors on his or her card. This player then says 'factor bingo'.

(vi) The player's card is then checked carefully against the used quadratic cards by the others.

If all the factors are correct the player wins the round and scores 10 points. If the factors are not all contained in the quadratic cards that have been turned up the player loses 5 points and the game goes on until one of the players wins.

This game should be played in silence to help concentration.

4   Differences: an investigation

Patterns in numbers can be investigated by means of differences.

Example

The table of values for $y = 2x + 3$ is calculated:

x	0	1	2	3	4	5	6	...
y	3	5	7	9	11	13	15	...

1st differences: 2 2 2 2   2   2
2nd differences: 0 0 0   0   0

The first differences are all equal to 2. The second differences are zero.

- Explore the first and second differences for the following functions:
  (a) $y = 3x + 2$ (b) $y = 5x - 4$
  (c) $y = x^2 + 1$ (d) $y = x^2 + 3x + 5$
  ... What happens to the differences further down the line, say from
      $x = 101$ to 110 in all the functions?
  ... What happens to the differences if x is negative?
- Explore the difference patterns for the function $y = x^3$.
- Explore the difference pattern for the Fibonacci sequence:
  1 1 2 3 5 8 13 ...
  where each number is formed by adding together the two previous ones.
- Explore the difference patterns for any other functions of your own
  choice.
  ($2^x, 3^x, \ldots, u^x$ are recommended)

5   Peculiar algebras

Introduction

If the letters of algebra represent 'other things' which are not necessarily
numbers, the rules of the algebra may be different from the ones you are
used to. An investigation of such an algebra would consist of trying to find
the 'ground rules' of the system.

For example, given a meaning for $*$ and $=$, is it true that $a * b = b * a$.
Does it follow that $\{a * b = a * c\} \Rightarrow b = c$.

Investigation A.   Boolean algebra

Letters $a, b, c \ldots$ etc can only be 0 or 1 with the special rule $1 + 1 = 1$ added
to the usual properties of numbers. [There is no 2].
The Boolean 'addition' and 'multiplication' tables are given below.

+	0	1
0	0	1
1	1	1

$*$	0	1
0	0	0
1	0	1

Boolean algebra is the algebra of logic where
$*$ → both ... and ...
$+$ → either ... or ...
0 → FALSE
1 → TRUE

and also the algebra of sets where $* → \cap$
$+ → \cup$
$0 → \notin$
$1 → \in$

The algebra has important applications in
electronics as it corresponds to switches in
series and parallel.

Two switches in series. The
electricity only flows if both
switches are on.

Two switches in parallel. The
electricity flows if one of the
switches is on.

*Investigation B.   Mod n Algebra**

The elements in this algebra are 'remainders'. In mod 7 algebra the remainders are 0, 1, 2, 3, 4, 5, 6 and two numbers are taken to be the same if they give the same remainder when divided by 7.
e.g. 9 and 16 are equivalent to 2.

$+\rightarrow$ addition . . . . $2 + 5 = 7 = 0$
$*\rightarrow$ multiplication . . . $3 \times 5 = 15 = 1$
$=\rightarrow$ Gives the same remainder . . . this is usually written $a \equiv b \pmod{n}$
shorthand for 'a gives the same
remainder as b when divided by n'

Mod 12 clock

- You will find that mod 7 and mod 6 algebras have some very important differences.
- You should compare mod 2 algebra with Boolean algebra.

This algebra is the algebra of all things with repeating cycles, e.g. days of the week, phases of the moon, motion of the planets, repeated designs, repeated molecular formations in crystals, etc, etc.

6   Cubic expansions

There are four algebraic expansions involving cubes.

$(x + y)^3 = x^3 + y^3 + 3xy^2 + 3x^2y$
$(x - y)^3 = x^3 - y^3 + 3xy^2 - 3x^2y$
$x^3 + y^3 = (x + y)(x^2 - xy + y^2)$
$x^3 - y^3 = (x - y)(x^2 + xy + y^2)$.

- Satisfy yourself that all four expansions are correct for all values of x and y.
- Make solid models which will demonstrate the relationships. (see investigation F2.)

*not to be confused with 'modern' algebra!

7 Diverses, triverses and polyverses

You saw how inverse functions recover a number which has been changed by a function

$$n \xrightarrow{f} f(n) \xrightarrow{inv\,f} n$$

With a diverse the number is recovered after two applications

$$n \xrightarrow{f} f(n) \xrightarrow{diverse\,f} m \xrightarrow{diverse\,f} n$$

While a triverse requires three applications.

INVESTIGATE!   HAVE FUN!

. . .

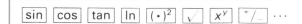

. . .

Worked answers to examination questions F

Section 1

1 A formula connecting W and x is $W = x^3 + 2x$. What is W when $x = 3$?

$W = 33$

$W = x^3 + 2x$

If $x = 3$ then $W = 3^3 + 2 \times 3$ $3^3 = 3 \times 3 \times 3 = 27$

$\qquad\qquad\qquad = 27 + 6 = 33$

Simple substitution in the formula.

2 I think of a number, double it and add 12. The answer is 20. What number did I think of?

$n = 4$

There are two ways of tackling this problem.

(i) *Working backwards*

The result is 20. The last thing that was done was to add 12. The number before must have been 8. This was the result of doubling the number before, which must have been 4:

Diagram: $20 \xrightarrow{-12} 8 \xrightarrow{\div 2} 4$

(ii) *Using an equation*

$\qquad n \xrightarrow{\times 2} 2n \xrightarrow{+12} 2n + 12$ Let n be the number . . . n

$\qquad\qquad\qquad\qquad\qquad\qquad$ Double it . . . $2n$

$\qquad\qquad\qquad\qquad\qquad\qquad$ Add 12 . . . $2n + 12$

$\qquad$ Equation $2n + 12 = 20$ $2n + 12 = 20$

$\qquad\qquad\qquad\qquad\qquad\quad \Rightarrow \quad 2n = 8$

$\qquad\qquad\qquad\qquad\qquad\quad \Rightarrow \quad\ \ n = 4$

Note: The steps used in solving the equation are the same as the steps used in working backwards.

3 Solve (a) $4x - 3 = 5$ (b) $2(6 + 3x) = 18$

(a) $x = 2$ (b) $x = 1$

(a) $4x - 3 = 5$

$\underline{+ 3 = +3}$ add 3 to both sides

$4x \quad = 8$

$x \quad = 2$ dividing both sides by 4

Note: It is always worth checking that the solution fits the problem by matching LHS and RHS of the original equation.

$\text{LHS} = 4(2) - 3 = 8 - 3 = 5$

$\qquad \qquad \uparrow$

$\qquad \quad x = 2$

$\text{RHS} = 5$

(b) $2(6 + 3x) = 18$

$6 + 3x = 9 \quad (\div 2)$

$3x = 3 \quad (-6)$

$x = 1 \quad (\div 3)$

Check: $\text{LHS} = 2(6 + 3) = 2 \times 9 = 18$

$\text{RHS} = 18$

Note: The problem can be solved by working backwards:

$x \xrightarrow{\times 3} 3x \xrightarrow{+6} 3x + 6 \xrightarrow{\times 2} 2(6 + 3x)$

$1 \xleftarrow{\div 3} 3 \xleftarrow{-6} 9 \xleftarrow{\div 2} 18$

4 Solve the pair of simultaneous equations $3x + 2y = 16$

$\qquad\qquad\qquad\qquad\qquad\qquad\qquad\qquad\qquad 4x - y = 14$

$x = 4, y = 2$

$\begin{array}{l} 3x + 2y = 16 \\ 4x - y = 14 \end{array} \xrightarrow{\times 2} \begin{array}{l} 3x + 2y = 16 \\ \underline{8x - 2y = 28} \end{array}$

Add: $11x \quad = 44$

$x \quad = 4$

$16 - y = 14$

$y = 2$

Steps: (i) Decide which equation to change so that x or y can be eliminated.

(ii) Eliminate y.

(iii) Solve for x.

(iv) Replace x in one equation to solve for y.

(v) Check in other equation.

Check: $3x + 2y = 16$

$\text{LHS} = 3(4) + 2(2) = 12 + 4 = 16$

$\text{RHS} = 16$

Note: It is sometimes quite easy to 'spot' the right values for x and y. It is an acceptable method to 'spot' the answers and then prove

you are right by a check on both equations. On the whole it is
more reliable to use the elimination method given.

5 Copy and complete the table of values for $y = x^2 - 2x - 3$.
[For values of x from $^-2$ to 4.]

x	$^-2$	$^-1$	0	1	2	3	4
x^2		1		4			
$-2x$		2		$^-4$			
-3		$^-3$		$^-3$			
y		0		$^-3$			

(a) Draw a graph whose equation is $y = x^2 - 2x - 3$ for values of x
from $^-2$ to 4.
(b) (i) What is y when $x = 2 \cdot 5$?   (ii) What is x when $y = 3$?
(c) Draw in the axis of symmetry. What is its equation?
(d) Find the value of the positive root of $x^2 - 2x - 3 = 0$.

Complete the table by horizontal patterns.
The 'y-line' is formed by adding the three
numbers above it.
Note the symmetry of the y-line.

x	$^-2$	$^-1$	0	1	2	3	4
x^2	4	1	0	1	4	9	16
$-2x$	4	2	0	$^-2$	$^-4$	$^-6$	$^-8$
-3	$^-3$	$^-3$	$^-3$	$^-3$	$^-3$	$^-3$	$^-3$
y	5	0	$^-3$	$^-4$	$^-3$	0	5

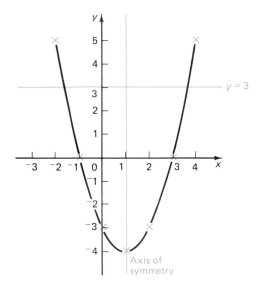

Axis of
symmetry

(b) (i) $y = ^-1 \cdot 75$ (ii) $x = ^-1 \cdot 645 \ldots$ or $3 \cdot 645 \ldots$
(c) The equation of the line of symmetry is $x = 1$.
(d) The positive root of $x^2 - 2x - 3 = 0$ is $x = 3$.

(b) (ii) You will need to use the formula $x = \dfrac{-b \pm \sqrt{b^2 - 4ac}}{2a}$.

[If you had tried to factorize first you would have found it impossible!]
For this equation, $a = 1, b = {}^-2, c = {}^-6$.

So $x = \dfrac{-({}^-2) \pm \sqrt{({}^-2)^2 - 4 \times 1 \times {}^-6}}{2 \times 1}$

$\quad = 1 \pm \dfrac{\sqrt{4 + 24}}{2}$

$\quad = {}^-1\cdot645 \ldots$ or $3\cdot645 \ldots$ (where the graph intersects $y = 3$)

(d) The positive root of the equation is the value of x where the graph crosses the x axis.

6 (a) When $p = a + b + c$, b is

$\quad p + a + c \qquad p - a + c \qquad a + c - p \qquad p - a - c \qquad$ or none of these.

(b) If $y = mx + c$; then x is

$\quad y - c + m \qquad \dfrac{y - c}{m} \qquad \dfrac{y}{m} - c \qquad y + c + m \qquad$ or none of these.

(c) When $A = \pi(a + b)$, the value of a may be written as

$\quad \dfrac{A - b}{\pi} \qquad \dfrac{A}{\pi} - b \qquad \dfrac{A - \pi}{b} \qquad \dfrac{\pi b}{A} \qquad$ or none of these.

(d) If f is made the subject of $\dfrac{1}{u} + \dfrac{1}{v} = \dfrac{1}{f}$, we have

$\quad f = v + u, \qquad f = \dfrac{uv}{u + v}, \qquad f = \dfrac{2}{u + v}, \qquad f = \dfrac{u + v}{2}$

(a) $p - a - c$ (b) $\dfrac{y - c}{m}$ (c) $\dfrac{A}{\pi} - b$ (d) $f = \dfrac{uv}{u + v}$

Stick to the rule of adding the same thing to both sides.

(a) $\quad p = a + b + c$
$\quad \Rightarrow p - a - c = a + b + c - a - c$
$\quad \Rightarrow p - a - c = b$

(b) You can argue this question in reverse. The equation states that if you take x and
  (i) multiply by m
  (ii) then add c
you will y.

$x \xrightarrow{\times m} mx \xrightarrow{+c} mx + c$

In reverse this becomes
  (i) start with y y
  (ii) subtract c $y - c$

  (iii) divide by m $\dfrac{y - c}{m}$

$\dfrac{y - c}{m} \xleftarrow{\div m} y - c \xleftarrow{-c} y$

and you will get x.

So $\quad y = mx + c$
$\quad \Rightarrow y - c = mx$
$\quad \Rightarrow \dfrac{y - c}{m} = x.$

(c) $A = \pi(a + b)$

$\Rightarrow \dfrac{A}{\pi} = (a + b) \quad (\div \pi)$

$\Rightarrow \dfrac{A}{\pi} - b = a \quad (-b)$

(d) Part (d) uses the rules of fractions.*

$\dfrac{1}{u} + \dfrac{1}{v} = \dfrac{v}{uv} + \dfrac{u}{uv} = \dfrac{v + u}{uv}$

So $\dfrac{1}{f} = \dfrac{u + v}{uv} \Rightarrow f = \dfrac{uv}{u + v}$

All the above questions can be checked by using easy values.

(a) $p = a + b + c$ ... put $a = 1, b = 2, c = 3$ then $p = 6$. Clearly $b = 6 - 3 - 1$. The other choices will not give a correct result for b.

(b) $y = mx + c$ ... put $m = 1, x = 2, c = 3$,

then $y = 5$ and $x = \dfrac{5 - 3}{1} = 2$.

Similarly for (c) and (d). Try it.

Remember that all multiple choice questions in algebra can be solved by using special values, **because** the wrong answer will not work.

Going back to (a), $p = a + b + c$: choosing $a = 1, b = 2, c = 3$, gives $p = 6$.

Now work out the values of all the alternatives.

$p + a + c = 6 + 1 + 3 = 10$ ... not equal to b.

$p - a + c = 6 - 1 + 3 = 8$ ... not equal to b.

$a + c - p = 1 + 3 - 6 = {}^-2$ ... not equal to b.

$p - a - c = 6 - 1 - 3 = 2$ ... **equal to** b.

So $p - a - c$ is the right choice of answer.

7 $y = k^x$. Find

(a) y if $k = 5$ and $x = 2$.   (b) x if $y = 64$ and $k = 4$.

(c) k if $y = 32$ and $x = 5$.

(a) 25   (b) 3   (c) 2

Substituting the values in $y = k^x$;   Use your calculator to check:

(a) If $k = 5$ and $x = 2, y = 5^2 = 25$.   (a) 5 $\boxed{x^y}$ 2 $\boxed{=}$ 25

(b) If $y = 64$ and $k = 4, 64 = 4^x \Rightarrow x = 3$.   (b) 4 $\boxed{x^y}$ 3 $\boxed{=}$ 64

(c) If $y = 32$ and $x = 5, 32 = k^5 \Rightarrow k = 2$.   (c) 2 $\boxed{x^y}$ 5 $\boxed{=}$ 32

8 Insert brackets to make the following true:

(a) $14 - 11 - 7 = 10$ (b) $14 - 7 - 11 = 18$

(a) $14 - (11 - 7)$ (b) $14 - (7 - 11)$

(a) $14 - (11 - 7) = 14 - 4 = 10$ (b) $14 - (7 - 11) = 14 - {}^-4 - 18$

* This is a useful rule:
for example, $\frac{1}{2} + \frac{1}{3} = \frac{5}{6}$ or $\frac{1}{4} + \frac{1}{2} = \frac{6}{8}$

9 If $x * y$ means $2x + y$, calculate   (a) $2 * 3$ (b) $5 * 1$ (c) $2 * (3 * 4)$

(a) 7   (b) 11   (c) $2 * (3 * 4) = 14$

(a) $2 * 3 = (2 \times 2) + 3 = 7$ (b) $5 * 1 = (2 \times 5) + 1 = 11$

(c) Start inside the bracket first: $3 * 4 = (2 \times 3) + 4 = 6 + 4$

$$= 10,$$

$$\text{then } 2 * 10 = (2 \times 2) + 10$$

$$= 14.$$

10   Write in simplest form

(a) $\dfrac{4(2x + 3)}{4} + \dfrac{2(6 - x)}{4}$ (b) $2(x^2 + 4) - x(2x + 3)$

(a) $\dfrac{3x + 12}{2}$ (b) $8 - 3x$

(a) $\dfrac{4(2x + 3)}{4} + \dfrac{2(6 - x)}{4} \rightarrow \dfrac{4(2x + 3) + 2(6 - x)}{4}$ combine fractions

$$\rightarrow \dfrac{8x + 12 + 12 - 2x}{4}$$ multiply out brackets

$$\rightarrow \dfrac{6x + 24}{4}$$ collect terms

$$\rightarrow \dfrac{3x + 12}{2}$$ cancel by 2

(b) $2(x^2 + 4) - x(2x + 3) \rightarrow 2x^2 + 8 - 2x^2 - 3x$ multiply out brackets

$$\rightarrow 8 - 3x$$ collect terms

11   Simplify $5x + 2y + 3x + 4y$.

$8x + 6y$

Just collect up the x's and y's.

12   Factorise $ab - 3a + b - 3$.

$(a + 1)(b - 3)$

$ab - 3a + b - 3 \rightarrow a(b - 3) + 1(b - 3)$

$$\rightarrow (a + 1)(b - 3)$$

Or you might change the order: $ab + b - 3a - 3 \rightarrow b(a + 1) - 3(a + 1)$

$$\rightarrow (b - 3)(a + 1)$$

Practice makes perfect. See p. 262 for practice exercises.

13   Solve the simultaneous equations $5x + 4y = 5$

$$2x + 3y = 9$$

$x = {}^-3, y = 5$

$5x + 4y = 5 \xrightarrow{\times 3} 15x + 12y = 15$

$2x + 3y = 9 \xrightarrow{\times 4} 8x + 12y = 36$

$$\text{subtract} \ldots 7x = {}^-21$$

$$x = {}^-3$$

Using $5x + 4y = 5$ $^-15 + 4y = 5$

$\Rightarrow \quad 4y = 20$

$\Rightarrow \quad y = 5$

Check: $2x + 3y = 9$

         LHS $= 2(^-3) + 3(5) = 9$

         RHS $= 9$

14   Solve $2d^2 + 6d - 5 = 0$, giving answers to 2 significant figures.

$$\left[\text{The equation } ax^2 + bx + c = 0 \text{ has solutions } x = \frac{-b \pm \sqrt{b^2 - 4ac}}{2a} \right]$$

$0 \cdot 68, \ ^-3 \cdot 68$

If you practise applying the formula $x = \dfrac{-b \pm \sqrt{b^2 - 4ac}}{2a}$,

you can become efficient in its use.

The form of the equation $2d^2 + 6d - 5 = 0$ means that in the formula, $x = d$, $a = 2$, $b = 6$ and $c = ^-5$.

$$d = \frac{^-6 \pm \sqrt{36 - (4 \times 2 \times ^-5)}}{4}$$

This gives the roots as $\dfrac{-6 + \sqrt{76}}{4}$ and $\dfrac{-6 - \sqrt{76}}{4}$

1st root 76 $\boxed{\sqrt{}}$ $\boxed{-}$ 6 $\boxed{=}$ $\boxed{\div}$ 4 $\boxed{=}$ $0 \cdot 679 \ldots$

2nd root 76 $\boxed{\sqrt{}}$ $\boxed{+/-}$ $\boxed{-}$ 6 $\boxed{=}$ $\boxed{\div}$ 4 $\boxed{=}$ $^-3 \cdot 679 \ldots$

Note: The sum of the roots is $^-3$ and the product of the roots is $^-2 \cdot 5$.

$$\left[\text{i.e. sum of roots} = \frac{-b}{a}, \text{ product of roots} = \frac{c}{a} \right]$$

This gives a very thorough check of your answer.

15 $\dfrac{a}{b} + \dfrac{b}{a}$ equals one of the following:

A $\dfrac{ab}{ab}$ B $\dfrac{a + b}{a + b}$ C $\dfrac{a + b}{ab}$ D $\dfrac{a^2 + b^2}{ab}$

$\dfrac{a^2 + b^2}{ab}$

Since four choices are given, this problem can be solved simply by choosing values for a and b.

For example, if $a = 2$ and $b = 4$: $\dfrac{a}{b} + \dfrac{b}{a} = \dfrac{2}{4} + \dfrac{4}{2} = 2\frac{1}{2}$ or $2 \cdot 5$.

(a) $\dfrac{ab}{ab} = \dfrac{8}{8} = 1$ no   (b) $\dfrac{a + b}{a + b} = \dfrac{6}{6} = 1$ no

(c) $\dfrac{a + b}{ab} = \dfrac{6}{8}$ no   (d) $\dfrac{a^2 + b^2}{ab} = \dfrac{4 + 16}{8} = \dfrac{20}{8} = 2 \cdot 5$ yes

Using rules of fractions:
$$\frac{a}{b} + \frac{b}{a} = \frac{a^2}{ab} + \frac{b^2}{ab}$$
$$= \frac{a^2 + b^2}{ab}.$$

16 If $r = 2q - 5$ and $q = 3p + 2$ express r in terms of p.

$r = 6p - 1$

$\left.\begin{array}{l} r = 2q - 5 \\ q = 3p + 2 \end{array}\right\} \Rightarrow r = 2\underbrace{(3p + 2)}_{q} - 5$

$\qquad = 6p + 4 - 5$
$\qquad = 6p - 1.$

Check this result by choosing a value for p.
Choosing $p = 2$,
$$q = 6 + 2 = 8$$
$$r = 16 - 5 = 11$$
and $6p - 1 = 12 - 1 = 11$.
So $r = 6p - 1$ is correct.

17 If $R = \dfrac{5EZ}{7}$, what does (a) $7R$ equal? (b) E equal?

(a) $5EZ$ (b) $\dfrac{7R}{5Z}$

This is simply a 'rearranged formula' problem in which the first step is given as part (a).

$R = \dfrac{5EZ}{7} \Rightarrow 7R = 5EZ \qquad$ both sides $\times$ 7

$\qquad\qquad \Rightarrow \dfrac{7R}{5Z} = E \qquad$ both sides $\div$ 5Z

Check using values: $E = 3, Z = 7$ (say), then
$$R = \frac{5EZ}{7} = \frac{5 \times 3 \times 7}{7} = 15$$
$7R = 7 \times 15 = 105 \leftarrow$
$5EZ = 5 \times 3 \times 7 = 105 \leftarrow$ $\qquad$ demonstrates $7R = 5EZ$
$\dfrac{7R}{5Z} = \dfrac{105}{5 \times 7} = 3 = E \leftarrow$ $\qquad$ demonstrates $E = \dfrac{7R}{5Z}$

18 Factorise (a) $x^2 - 16y^2$ (b) $x^2 - x - 6$.

(a) $(x - 4y)(x + 4y)$ (b) $(x - 3)(x + 2)$

(a) This is the difference of two squares. You should know that
$a^2 - b^2 = (a - b)(a + b)$. In this case $a = x, b = 4y$.
(b) There are many ways of finding the two factors.
We are looking for a and b so that

$$x^2 - x - 6 = (x + a)(x + b)$$
$$= x^2 + (a + b)x + ab.$$
If this is to fit, $a + b = {}^-1$, $ab = {}^-6$.
We can list some possible values of a, b which multiply to $^-6$:

a	b	ab	$a + b$
6	$^-1$	$^-6$	5
3	$^-2$	$^-6$	1
2	$^-3$	$^-6$	$^-1$
1	$^-6$	$^-6$	$^-5$

The only values which give the right result for both ab and $a + b$
are $a = 2$, $b = {}^-3$.
So $x^2 - x - 6 = (x + 2)(x - 3)$.
Check, putting $x = 10$:
$$x^2 - x - 6 \rightarrow 100 - 10 - 6 = 84$$
$$(x + 2)(x - 3) \rightarrow 12 \times 7 \qquad = 84$$
Factorising is a useful skill. There are practice questions on
page 262.

19 Look at the following statements. $1^3 = 1^2$; $1^3 + 2^3 = (1 + 2)^2$. Do you
agree that they are true? If the pattern continues so that
$1^3 + 2^3 + 3^3 + 4^3 + 5^3 = a^2$ find the value of a.

$a = 15$

If the pattern continues: $1^3 + 2^3 + 3^3 + 4^3 + 5^3 = (1 + 2 + 3 + 4 + 5)^2$,
so $a = 1 + 2 + 3 + 4 + 5 = 15$.
Check: $15^2 = 225$
$$1^3 + 2^3 + 3^3 + 4^3 + 5^3 = 1 + 8 + 27 + 64 + 125$$
$$= 225$$

20 The points (10, 5); (12, 6); and (4, 2) lie on the straight line $y = kx$. What
is k?

$k = 0.5$

It is easy to see that for all the three points (10, 5); (12, 6); and (4, 2), the
y coordinate is half the x coordinate. Thus they all lie on the line
$y = 0.5x$.
If you substitute $x = 10$ and $y = 5$ into the equation you get a true
result: $5 = 0.5 \times 10$.
Thus the values satisfy the equation and the points lie on the line.

Section 2

21 Find the solution of the equation $5x - 9 = 4x$.

$x = 9$

Using simple rules for equations:

$$5x - 9 = 4x$$
$$\underline{ + 9 \qquad + 9}$$
$$5x \quad = 4x + 9$$
$$\underline{{}^-4x \qquad {}^-4x}$$
$$x \quad = \quad 9 \qquad \textit{Check}: \text{LHS} = 45 - 9 = 36$$
$$\text{RHS} = \ 4 \times 9 = 36$$

22 Write an inequation to represent the number line shown.

$^-1 < x \leqslant 2$

Clearly x lies between $^-1$ and 2. The only problem is to deal with the 'end-points' of the line.

... means that $^-1 < x$, or x is a number greater than $^-1$.
x cannot be equal to $^-1$ itself.

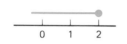

... means that x can be less than or equal to 2.

23 Solve the pair of equations $2m + n = 5$
$$6m - 2n = {}^-15$$

$m = {}^-\frac{1}{2}, n = 6$

(a) $2m + n = 5 \quad \rightarrow 4m + 2n = 10$
(b) $6m - 2n = {}^-15 \rightarrow \underline{6m - 2n = {}^-15}$
$$10m \quad = {}^-5$$
$$m \quad = {}^-\tfrac{1}{2}$$
Using (a): $\ {}^-1 + n = 5$
$$n = 6$$
Check in equation (b): $\text{LHS} = 6m - 2n = 6({}^-\tfrac{1}{2}) - 2(6)$
$$= {}^-3 - 12 = {}^-15$$
$$\text{RHS} = {}^-15$$

24 Solve the equations $x + 3y = 7$
$$x - y = 3$$

$x = 4, y = 1$

$$x + 3y = 7$$
$$\underline{x - \ y = 3}$$
Subtract $\qquad\qquad 4y = 4$
$$y = 1$$
Using second equation: $x - 1 = 3$
$$x = 4 \quad \textit{Check}: \text{LHS} = x + 3y = 4 + 3 = 7$$
$$\text{RHS} = 7$$

This pair of equations is easy to solve by guessing but in an examination your working should be shown.

25 Simplify $x^{10} \div x^4$

x^6

Using rules of indices: $x^{10} \div x^4 = x^{10-4} = x^6$
If you cannot remember the rules, write it out in full:

$$x^{10} \div x^4 = \frac{x \times x \times x \times x \times x \times x \times x \times x \times x \times x \times x^1 \times x^1 \times x^1 \times x^1}{x^1 \times x^1 \times x^1 \times x^1} \quad \text{cancelling}$$

$$= \frac{x \times x \times x \times x \times x \times x \times x \times x \times x \times x}{1}$$

$$= x^6.$$

26 Simplify $\dfrac{25x^2yz}{100xyz^3}$

$\dfrac{x}{4z^2}$

This is a simple exercise in cancelling.

$$\frac{25x^2yz}{100xyz^3} \rightarrow \frac{\overset{1}{25} \times x \times x \times y \times z}{\underset{4}{100} \times x \times y \times z \times z \times z} \rightarrow \frac{x}{4z^2}$$

Check by giving simple values to x, y and z.
Using $x = 1$, $y = 2$, $z = 3$:

$$\frac{25x^2yz}{100xyz^3} = \frac{25 \times 1 \times 2 \times 3}{100 \times 1 \times 2 \times 27} - \frac{150}{5400} = 0.0277 \dots$$

$$\frac{x}{4z^2} = \frac{1}{4 \times 9} = \frac{1}{36} = 0.0277 \dots$$

27 The diagram shows the two graphs $y = 2x$
and $x + y = 9$. R represents the point where
they meet.
  (a) What are the coordinates of any point
       on $y = 2x$?
  (b) Write down the coordinates of P and Q.
  (c) Solve the simultaneous equations
       $y = 2x$
       $x + y = 9$ to find the coordinates of R.

  (a) $(a, 2a)$ (b) P $(0, 9)$; Q $(9; 0)$ (c) R $(3, 6)$

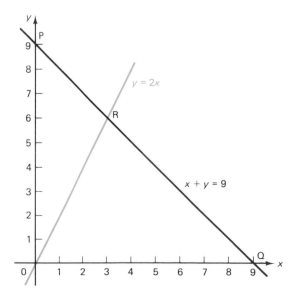

(a) Any point on the line $y = 2x$ will have its y-coordinate twice as large as its x-coordinate. So the point $(a, 2a)$ always lies on the line whatever the value of a.

(c)
$$\left.\begin{array}{r} y = 2x \\ x + y = 9 \end{array}\right\} \Rightarrow x + 2x = 9$$
$$\Rightarrow 3x = 9$$
$$\Rightarrow \quad x = 3.$$
$$\text{and} \quad y = 6.$$

R is the point $(3, 6)$. This can be seen from the graph or by guessing but the question asks you to solve the equations so you must show a solution to obtain full marks!

28 Find the value of $\sqrt[3]{\dfrac{3V}{4\pi}}$ where $V = 58 \cdot 93$ and $\pi = 3 \cdot 14$.

$2 \cdot 4145$

This question checks whether you can substitute correctly in a formula. [In fact it gives the radius of a sphere whose volume is V.]
Use $3 \cdot 14$ for π and not the value on your $\boxed{\pi}$ button.

- If your calculator has $\boxed{x^y}$ or $\boxed{x^{1/y}}$ the sequence is

  $3 \boxed{\times} 58 \cdot 93 \boxed{=} \boxed{\div} 4 \boxed{\div} 3 \cdot 14 \boxed{=} \boxed{x^{1/y}} 3 \boxed{=}$

  $\qquad\qquad\qquad\uparrow\quad\uparrow$

  Note the 2 'divides' because both 4 and π are on the bottom of the fraction.

  or $\quad 3 \boxed{\times} 58 \cdot 93 \boxed{=} \boxed{\div} 4 \boxed{\div} 3 \cdot 14 \boxed{=} \boxed{x^y} 0 \cdot 3333 \ldots \boxed{=}$

- Without $\boxed{x^y}$, first calculate $\dfrac{3V}{4\pi} = 14 \cdot 0756 \ldots$

Now you must find the cube root by trial and error. You know $2^3 = 8$ and $3^3 = 27$ so the number wanted is nearer 2 than 3.

$(2 \cdot 5)^3 \quad = 15 \cdot 625 \qquad$ too big
$(2 \cdot 4)^3 \quad = 13 \cdot 824 \qquad$ too small but close
$(2 \cdot 42)^3 \quad = 14 \cdot 17 \ldots \qquad$ too big but close
$(2 \cdot 41)^3 \quad = 13 \cdot 99 \ldots \qquad$ too small but close
$(2 \cdot 415)^3 = 14 \cdot 08 \ldots, \quad$ which is near enough.

29 Given $F = 1 \cdot 8C + 32$, find C in terms of F.

$$C = \frac{F - 32}{1 \cdot 8}$$

Use the rules for equations to isolate C:

$$F = 1 \cdot 8C + 32$$
$$\Rightarrow F - 32 = 1 \cdot 8C \qquad \text{Subtract 32}$$
$$\Rightarrow \frac{F - 32}{1 \cdot 8} = C \qquad \text{Divide by } 1 \cdot 8$$

Or use inverse functions:

$$C \xrightarrow{\times 1\cdot 8} 1\cdot 8C \xrightarrow{+32} 1\cdot 8C + 32$$

$$\frac{F - 32}{1\cdot 8} \xleftarrow{\div 1\cdot 8} F - 32 \xleftarrow{-32} F$$

30 $V = \dfrac{\pi r^2 h}{2}$

(a) Taking $\pi = 3\cdot 1$, find V if $r = 3$ and $h = 20$.

(b) Find r, given that $V = 8\pi$ and $h = 2r$.

(c) Rearrange the formula to find r in terms of h and V.

(a) $V = 279$　(b) $r = 2$　(c) $r = \sqrt{\dfrac{2V}{\pi h}}$

(a) Using your calculator: $V = \dfrac{\pi \times 3^2 \times 20}{2}$

$$3\cdot 1 \; \boxed{\times} \; 9 \; \boxed{\times} \; 20 \; \boxed{\div} \; 2$$

(b) Replace V by 8π and h by $2r$ in the formula:

$$V = \frac{\pi r^2 h}{2} \rightarrow 8\pi = \frac{\pi \times r^2 \times 2r}{2}$$

$$\Rightarrow 8 = r^3$$

$$\Rightarrow 2 = r$$

(c) Using inverse functions:

$$r \xrightarrow{(\;)^2} r^2 \xrightarrow{\times \pi} \pi r^2 \xrightarrow{\times h} \pi r^2 h \xrightarrow{\div 2} \frac{\pi r^2 h}{2}$$

$$\sqrt{\frac{2V}{\pi h}} \xleftarrow{\sqrt{}} \frac{2V}{\pi h} \xleftarrow{\div \pi} \frac{2V}{h} \xleftarrow{\div h} 2V \xleftarrow{\times 2} V$$

Or use rules of equations: $V = \dfrac{\pi r^2 h}{2} \Rightarrow 2V = \pi r^2 h$

$$\Rightarrow \frac{2V}{\pi h} = r^2$$

$$\Rightarrow \sqrt{\frac{2V}{\pi h}} = r.$$

Use the method you like best.

31 What are the factors of $x^2 + 10x - 24$? Use your answer to solve the equation $x^2 + 10x - 24 = 0$.

$(x + 12)$　$(x - 2)$　$x = 2$ or $^-12$

$x^2 + 10x - 24 = (x + a)(x + b)$

$\qquad\qquad\qquad = x^2 + (a + b)x + ab.$

We need values for a and b whose product is $^-24$ and whose sum is $^+10$.

a	b	ab	$a + b$
24	⁻1	⁻24	23
12	⁻2	⁻24	10

No need to go further.

Factors are $(x + 12)$ and $(x - 2)$

$$x^2 + 10x - 24 = 0 \Rightarrow (x + 12)(x - 2) = 0$$
$$\Rightarrow x + 12 = 0 \Rightarrow x = {}^{-}12$$
$$\text{or}$$
$$x - 2 = 0 \Rightarrow x = 2$$

- Check by substituting $x = 2$ and $x = {}^{-}12$ in $x^2 + 10x - 24$:
  $$2^2 + (10 \times 2) - 24 = 0$$
  $$({}^{-}12)^2 + (10 \times {}^{-}12) - 24 = 144 - 120 - 24 = 0.$$

32 If $(x - 2)(x + 3) = x^2 + ax - 6$, what is the value of a?

$a = 1$

Multiplying out: $(x - 2)(x + 3) = x^2 - 2x + 3x - 6$
$$= x^2 + x - 6$$
If this is to be the same as $x^2 + ax - 6$, then $ax = x$
$$\Rightarrow a = 1.$$

- Another way of approaching this problem is to give x any value.
  $(x - 2)(x + 3) = x^2 + ax - 6$ put $x = 3$
       1   ×   6 $9 + 3a - 6$
  $$\Rightarrow 6 = 3 + 3a.$$
  $$\Rightarrow a = 1.$$

33 Work out the value of $(3 + \sqrt{2})(3 - \sqrt{2})$.

7

$(3 + \sqrt{2})(3 - \sqrt{2})$ has the same value as $3^2 - (\sqrt{2})^2 \dots$ difference of squares.
Thus the value is $9 - 2 = 7$.
Check on your calculator.

- Reading straight into the calculator will not work unless you have brackets ⌊ ( ) ⌋ . Try it on your calculator.

34 Solve the equation $x^2 + 4x = 0$.

$x = 0$ or ⁻4

It is obvious that $x = 0$ is a solution to this equation. Since the equation is quadratic another solution is to be expected.
$x^2 + 4x = 0 \Rightarrow x^2 = {}^{-}4x$ $x = 0$ or
$$\Rightarrow x = {}^{-}4 \quad \text{dividing through by } x \text{ if } x \neq 0$$
A slightly different argument: $x^2 + 4x = 0 \Rightarrow x(x + 4) = 0$
$$\Rightarrow x = 0 \quad \text{or} \quad x + 4 = 0$$
$$\Rightarrow x = 0 \quad \text{or} \quad x = {}^{-}4.$$

35 The mappings f: $x \rightarrow 2x$ and g: $x \rightarrow x + 2$ are combined to form a single mapping fg. Find the result of mapping the number 3 by fg.

fg(3) = 10

The 'trap' in this question is to get the mappings in the wrong order.
fg is written for 'g first, then f'.* So ...
    g maps $3 \rightarrow 3 + 2 = 5$
then f maps $5 \rightarrow 2 \times 5 = 10$

36 If f: $x \rightarrow x^2 - 2x + 1$ [i.e. $f(x) = x^2 - 2x + 1$], what is the value of
(a) f(10)   (b) f(3)?

(a) 81   (b) 4

$f(10) = 10^2 - (2 \times 10) + 1 = 100 - 20 + 1 = 81$
$f(3)\ \ =\ \ 3^2 - (2 \times 3)\ \ + 1 =\ \ 9 -\ \ 6 + 1 =\ \ 4$

Note: The mapping is $x \rightarrow (x - 1)^2$ so that a quick way of finding f(n) is to subtract 1 and square.

37 (a) Which of the numbers 9, 11, 16, 10 or 14 should be written in the small square?
(b) Which of the mappings given below corresponds to the diagram?
    $x \rightarrow x^2$; $x \rightarrow 4x - 3$; $x \rightarrow 3x - 2$; $x \rightarrow 2x - 1$;
    or $x \rightarrow 2x^2 - 1$?

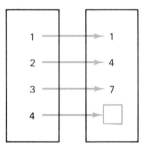

(a) 10   (b) $x \rightarrow 3x - 2$

The best way to answer this question is by trial and error.
First, the pattern 1   4   7   grows by 3 each time giving 10 as the
           +3 +3 +3
number for the small square.
This suggests $x \rightarrow 3x - 2$ is the correct mapping as it too grows by 3 each time (because of the $3x$)
None of the other 4 mappings will give correct images for 1, 2, 3 and 4.

38 f is the mapping $x \rightarrow 4x$.
(a) Which of the ordered pairs (0, 4); (2, 8); ($^-$1, $^-$4); ($\frac{1}{2}$, 2); (5, 20) does not belong to the mapping?
(b) Which of the following mappings is the inverse of f?
    $x \rightarrow \frac{1}{4}$; $x \rightarrow x - 4$; $x \rightarrow \frac{x}{4}$; $x \rightarrow\ ^-4x$; $x \rightarrow \frac{1}{4x}$

(a) (0, 4)   (b) $x \rightarrow \frac{x}{4}$

The function $x \rightarrow 4x$ maps 0 into 0 not 4. Therefore (0, 4) is the wrong ordered pair.

---

* The reason for this is to avoid any confusion. It has been agreed internationally by mathematicians.

If you look on the mapping as $\xrightarrow{\times 4}$, this becomes obvious:

$2 \xrightarrow{\times 4} 8; \quad ^-1 \xrightarrow{\times 4} {}^-4; \quad \frac{1}{2} \xrightarrow{\times 4} 2; \quad 5 \xrightarrow{\times 4} 20.$

So $(2, 8)$; $(^-1, ^-4)$; $(\frac{1}{2}, 2)$ and $(5, 20)$ all fit the mapping.

The inverse of $\xrightarrow{\times 4}$ is $\xrightarrow{\div 4}$ so $x \to \dfrac{x}{4}$ is the correct inverse of $x \to 4x$.

This can be checked by choosing a value for x, say 20, to see if the mapping and inverse bring you back to 20 again.

$x: \to 4x \qquad 20 \to 80 \xrightarrow{\;x\, \to\, \frac{1}{4}\;} \frac{1}{4}$

$\qquad\qquad\qquad\qquad 80 \xrightarrow{\;x\, \to\, x-4\;} 76$

$\qquad\qquad\qquad\qquad 80 \xrightarrow{\;x\, \to\, \frac{x}{4}\;} 20 \qquad$ This must be the inverse function.

$\qquad\qquad\qquad\qquad 80 \xrightarrow{\;x\, \to\, {}^-4x\;} {}^-320$

$\qquad\qquad\qquad\qquad 80 \xrightarrow{\;x\, \to\, \frac{1}{4x}\;} \dfrac{1}{320}$

39 Given that $f(x) = 3x^2 + 2$ and $x > 0$,
(a) find the value of $f(2)$.   (b) find the values of x for which $f(x) = 11$.
(c) find the inverse of the function $f: x \to 3x^2 + 2$. If this is f^{-1}, show that $f^{-1}(14) = 2$

(a) 14   (b) $x = \pm \sqrt{3}$ (c) $x \to \sqrt{\dfrac{x-2}{3}}$

(a) $3(2^2) + 2 = 12 + 2 = 14.$

(b) $3x^2 + 2 = 11 \Rightarrow 3x^2 = 9$

$\qquad\qquad\qquad \Rightarrow \quad x^2 = 3$

$\qquad\qquad\qquad\qquad x \;\; = \pm \sqrt{3}$

(c) $x \to 3x^2 + 2$ can be shown as the mappings

$x \xrightarrow{\;(\;)^2\;} x^2 \xrightarrow{\;\times 3\;} 3x^2 \xrightarrow{\;+2\;} 3x^2 + 2$

$\sqrt{\dfrac{y-2}{3}} \xleftarrow{\;\sqrt{\;}\;} \dfrac{y-2}{3} \xleftarrow{\;\div 3\;} y - 2 \xleftarrow{\;-2\;} y$

The inverse will 'extract' x out again, so the inverse function is

$x \to + \sqrt{\dfrac{x-2}{3}}.^{*}$

$f^{-1}(14) = + \sqrt{\dfrac{14-2}{3}} = + \sqrt{\dfrac{12}{3}} = + \sqrt{4} = 2.$

*Note we take the positive square root only.

40 The graph of the line $y = mx + c$ passes through A (4, 0) and B (0, 6).
(a) Find the values of c and m.
(b) Find the coordinates of a point on the line and on $y = x$.

(a) $m = -\frac{3}{2}, c = 6$ (b) $x = \dfrac{12}{5}, y = \dfrac{12}{5}$

Use the point B (0, 6) to find c: $y = mx + c \ldots 6 = c \ldots$ putting $x = 0$
$$y = 6$$

Now use A (4, 0) to find m: $0 = 4m + 6, \quad m = \dfrac{-6}{4} = \dfrac{-3}{2} \ldots$ putting $x = 4$
$$y = 0$$

To find the point which is also on $y = x$ we have $y = \dfrac{-3}{2}x + 6$,

but $y = x$ as well so $x = \dfrac{-3}{2}x + 6$

$\Rightarrow \dfrac{5}{2}x = 6$

$\Rightarrow 5x = 12$

$\Rightarrow \quad x = \dfrac{12}{5}$ and $y = \dfrac{12}{5}$.

Check with a quick sketch.

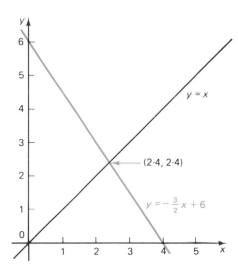

(2·4, 2·4)

$y = x$

$y = -\frac{3}{2}x + 6$

Topic G **Trigonometry**

Contents

Enlargement; sine, cosine, tangent; Pythagoras' theorem; bearings; constructions

Self assessment

The purpose of this task is to find out whether or not you need revision on topic G. There is no time limit.

- Make a table in your book, like the one on page vi. You need space for 20 questions.
- Write down your answers to all the following questions.
- When you have finished calculate your score from the answers on page 434.
- If you score more than 80% go on to Topic H self assessment (pp. 365–366).

1 Which of these changes when a figure is enlarged:
   (i) lengths   (ii) angles
  (iii) ratios   (iv) areas?
  A All   B (i), (ii) and (iii) but not (iv)
  C (i) only   D (i) and (iv) but not (ii) and (iii)

2 (i) Which side is opposite to θ?
  (ii) Which side is the hypotenuse?
  (iii) What is the name of the third side?

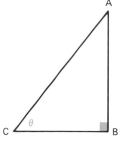

3 Which one of these is not true?
  A $\sin \theta = O/H$
  B $\cos \theta = H/O$
  C $\tan \theta = O/A$
  D $O^2 + A^2 = H^2$

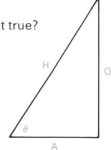

4 Only one of these relationships is true for all angles between 0° and 90°. Which one is it?
  A $\cos \theta > \sin \theta$ B $\sin \theta > \cos \theta$
  C $\tan \theta > \cos \theta$ D $\tan \theta > \sin \theta$

5 The circle with centre B is an enlargement of the circle with centre A.
  (i) Where is the centre of enlargement?
  (ii) How far is the centre of enlargement from A and B?
  [*Hint*: It may help to make a copy of the diagram first.]

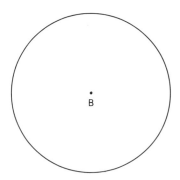

6 The correct value for sin 36° is
  A 0·587 785   B 0·891 006
  C 0·809 017   D 0·726 543

7 The three wrong answers in question 6 were the results of mistakes in using the calculator. Can you discover what mistakes were made?

8 The 16 ft ladder is leaning against a wall. The angle between ladder and ground is 67°. *h* can be found by calculating ...
A 16 × cos 67°   B 16 × sin 67°
C 16 ÷ cos 67°   D 16 ÷ sin 67°

9 The isosceles triangle has 6 cm sides and its base angles are each 70°. Calculate
   (i) the height of the triangle,
   (ii) the base of the triangle,
   (iii) the area of the triangle.

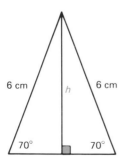

10 An interceptor is fired at a missile flying at 4000 m. The point on earth directly below the missile is 18 km from the interceptor launch pad. Calculate the angle of elevation (θ) of the interceptor launcher. [You can add a comment if you wish!]

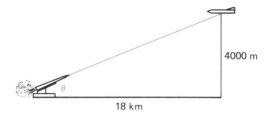

11 If sin θ is 0·5000, cos θ will be
A 0·5000   B 0·8660
C 0·3000   D 1·0000

12 Calculate the lengths of the diagonals of rectangle ABCD.

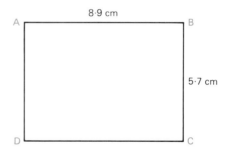

13 P can be any point on the circumference of a semicircle drawn with XY as diameter. XY is 10 cm long.
  (i) Calculate the length of PY if PX = 4 cm.
  (ii) Calculate PX̂Y.

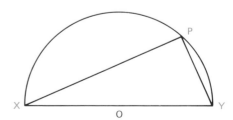

14 Copy the diagram and colour or shade
  (i) two different sizes of equilateral triangle,
  (ii) two different sizes of isosceles triangles which are not equilateral,
  (iii) two different sizes of right-angled triangle.

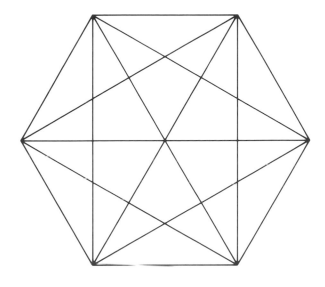

15 A ship leaves port and travels on bearing 090° for 60 miles. It then proceeds on bearing 120° for a further 60 miles. How far is the ship from the port (in a direct line)? [Scale drawing.]

16 Describe what you would need to know to be able to find the bearing of your school from your home.

◆ **17** The vertices of △ABC are (1, 1), (2, 1), and (2, 3). Draw the triangle on a grid. Enlarge the triangle by a factor of ⁻2 taking (0, 0) as the centre of the enlargement. What are the coordinates of A', B' and C', the vertices of the enlarged triangle?

◆ **18** P is the vertex of a pyramid on a square base. The sloping sides of the pyramids are equilateral triangles whose sides are 3 cm long. Calculate the height of the pyramid in two different ways.

19 Use the given graph of cos θ to estimate the value of
  (i) cos 75°   (iii) cos 300°
  (ii) cos 180°   (iv) sin 150°
  check on your calculator.

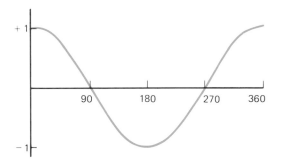

◆ **20** An isosceles triangle has two sides 5 cm long. The angle between them is 40°. Calculate the third side using the cosine rule ... $a^2 = b^2 + c^2 - 2bc \cos A$, and confirm your result by another method.

Key facts G

G.1 Enlargement

An enlargement is a transformation which increases the size of a shape without changing any angles.

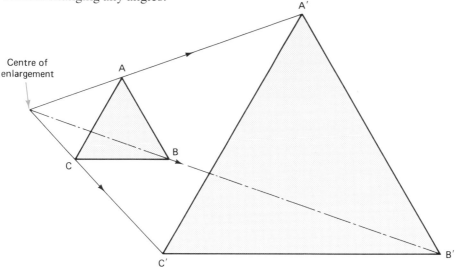

Each enlargement has a centre and a scale factor. The scale factor of the above enlargement is 3.

- Each line is enlarged to 3 times its size.
- All the angles are unchanged.
- The area is enlarged 9 times ($=3^2$).

△ABC is itself an 'enlargement' of △A′B′C′, the scale factor being $\frac{1}{3}$ instead of 3.

♦ *A negative enlargement* is demonstrated in the drawing below.

The image point A′ is found from the relationship OA′ = 2OA but OA′ is measured in the opposite direction from OA.
The negative enlargement thus corresponds to
(i)   positive enlargement followed by half turn
or
(ii) half turn followed by positive enlargement.

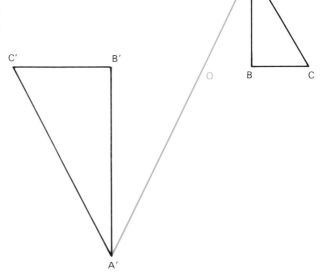

Exercise G.1

1 Every circle is an enlargement of every other one. Find the centre of enlargement for each diagram. Estimate the scale factor of the enlargement by measurement.

(a)

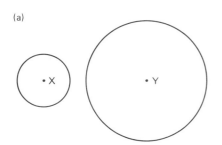

(b)

C

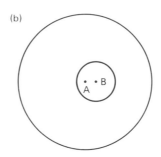

2 The square CDEF is an enlargement of square ABFG. The scale factor is 3 : 2 (or 1·5).
If the area of ABFG is 645 mm², calculate the area of CDEF.

3 An elephant 10 ft high weighs 2 tons. Her baby is exactly half her height, and is also half size in all its other dimensions. How much would you expect the baby elephant to weigh? B

4 Paul caught a salmon weighing 10 kg. It was 60 cm long. How long would you expect a 5 kg salmon to be? B

5 Draw a quadrilateral ABCD given that
(i) ABCD is cyclic (iii) AB = AC = 4 cm
(ii) $A\hat{B}C = 73°$ (iv) $B\hat{A}D = 105°$
From the figure you have just drawn, construct an enlargement, scale factor $-\frac{1}{2}$, with centre A. A

C

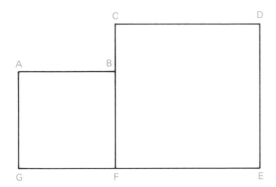

G.2 Sine, cosine, tangent

This is the basic diagram which shows the sides of a right-angled triangle.

Side	Length
Hypotenuse	R
Opposite θ	$R \sin \theta$
Next to θ (adjacent)	$R \cos \theta$

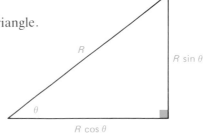

You should practise drawing this basic diagram until you are quite sure of it.

Example

A ladder 4 metres long leans against a wall at an angle of 72°.

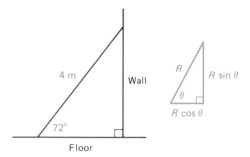

The height up the wall of the top of the ladder is 4 sin 72°.

4 $\boxed{\times}$ 72 $\boxed{\sin}$ $\boxed{=}$ 3·8 m

The distance from the base of the ladder to the bottom of the wall is 4 cos 72°.

4 $\boxed{\times}$ 72 $\boxed{\cos}$ $\boxed{=}$ 1·24 m

The functions $\boxed{\sin}$, $\boxed{\cos}$ and $\boxed{\tan}$ are ratios.

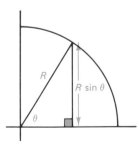
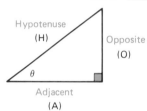
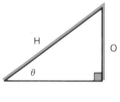
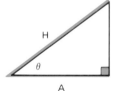

$$\sin \theta = \frac{O}{H}$$

$$\cos \theta = \frac{A}{H}$$

$$\tan \theta = \frac{O}{A}$$

The functions sin, cos, tan can be shown clearly on a circle, radius R.

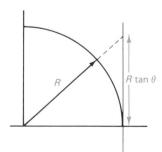
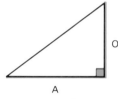

This line is a tangent to the circle

◆ G.2.1 Angles > 90°

The functions sin, cos and tan of angles can still be shown on a circle, radius R. The whole circle will be needed however.
The values of the functions can be checked on your calculator.

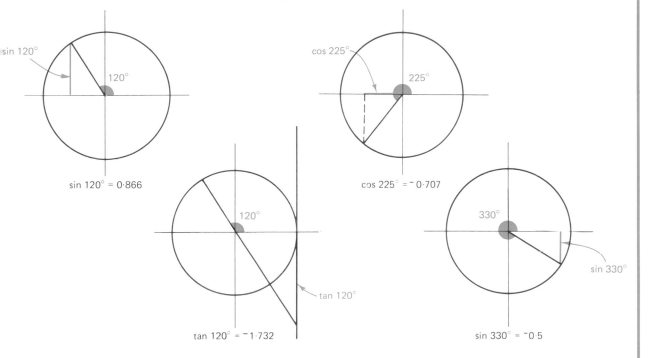

sin 120° = 0·866

cos 225° = ⁻0·707

tan 120° = ⁻1·732

sin 330° = ⁻0·5

◆ G.2.2 Graphs of sin θ, cos θ and tan θ

Using values of θ from 0 to 360°, graphs of each of the functions may be drawn.

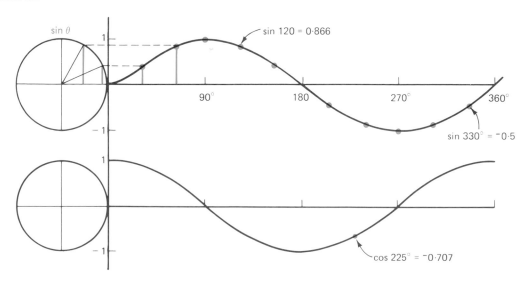

321

G.2.3 Relationships worth knowing for angles <90°

- $(\sin \theta)^2 + (\cos \theta)^2 = 1$ for every value of θ ...   Pythagoras' theorem.
- $\dfrac{\sin \theta}{\cos \theta} = \tan \theta$ for every value of θ O/H ÷ A/H = O/A.
- $\sin (90° - \theta) = \cos \theta$ $\cos (90° - \theta) = \sin \theta$ ... from rotating the triangle.
- $\tan \theta > \sin \theta$ ... from the diagram of $R \tan \theta$.

These relationships can easily be checked on the calculator. They should be checked for angles >90°.

G.2.4 Useful values for sin θ, cos θ and tan θ

θ	$\sin \theta$	$\cos \theta$	$\tan \theta$
0°	0	1	0
30°	0·5	0·866	
45°	0·7071	0·7071	1
60°	0·866	0·5	
90°	1	0	∞

Your calculator will give error for tan 90°. Why is this?

G.2.5 Drawing

In this drawing, an angle of 42° is used to find sin 42°, cos 42° and tan 42°. R has been chosen as 10 cm to make the calculations more obvious.

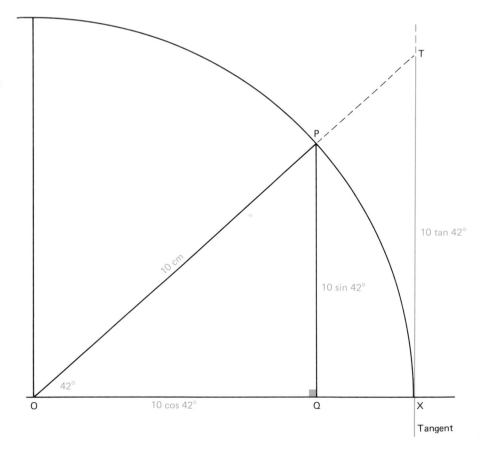

10 tan 42°

10 sin 42°

10 cm

42°

O   10 cos 42°   Q   X

P

T

Tangent

OP = 10 cm = R

			By drawing	*By calculator*
OP	= 10 cm	= R		
PQ	= 6·7 cm	= R sin 42°	so sin 42° = 0·67	0·6691
OQ	= 7·5 cm	= R cos 42°	so cos 42° = 0·75	0·7431
TX	= 9 cm	= R tan 42°	so tan 42° = 0·90	0·9004

G.2.6 Inverse functions

In some problems the value of $\sin \theta$ can be found. This can be used to find the value of θ, as shown in the example.

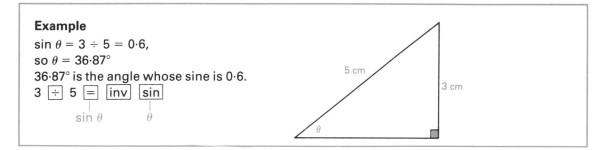

Example

$\sin \theta = 3 \div 5 = 0\cdot6$,

so $\theta = 36\cdot87°$

36·87° is the angle whose sine is 0·6.

3 ÷ 5 = inv sin

     | |

   sin θ θ

5 cm

3 cm

θ

The inverses of $\sin x$, $\cos x$, $\tan x$ are often written $\sin^{-1} x$, $\cos^{-1} x$, $\tan^{-1} x$.

$\sin^{-1} 0\cdot4$ is an angle whose sin is 0·4 . . . (actually 23·58°)

$\tan^{-1} 5$ is an angle whose tan is 5 . . . (actually 78·69°)

- If you are working with angles between 0 and 360°, there are two possible values for $\sin^{-1} 0\cdot4$. These are 23·58° and $180 - 23\cdot58° = 156\cdot42°$.

The calculator will only give the principle value between 0° and 90°, so the other value must be deduced from the graph of $\sin x$ or from the full circular diagram.

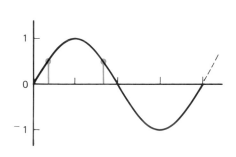

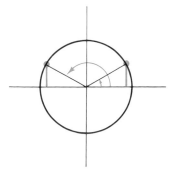

- $\sin^{-1} x$, $\cos^{-1} x$ and $\tan^{-1} x$ each have two possible values between 0 and 360°.
- $\sin^{-1} x$ and $\cos^{-1} x$ do not have any values at all for values of x which are greater than $^+1$ or less than $^-1$.
  Can you see why?
  e.g. 2 inv sin = . . . ERROR (or E)

G.2.7 Problems

You will only be asked to solve two types of simple problem.

Type 1 . . . Right-angled triangle, one other known angle and one known side.
    Find the lengths of the other sides.
Type 2 . . . Right-angled triangle, two sides of known length.
    Find the angles of the triangle.

Examples

1 The angle of elevation to a tower from a
point 150 m from the base is 37°. What is
the height of the tower?

$$\frac{h}{150} = \tan 37° \Rightarrow h = 150 \tan 37°$$
$$= 150 \times 0.753 \ldots$$
$$= 113 \text{ m}$$
150 ☒ 37 tan =

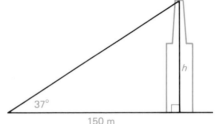

2 A flagpole is held up by three ropes each
14 metres long. The ropes are pegged to the
ground at points 12 m from the foot of the
flagpole. Find the angles of elevation of
the ropes.
Each rope forms a triangle with the flagpole
and the ground. The angle asked for is θ.

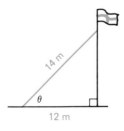

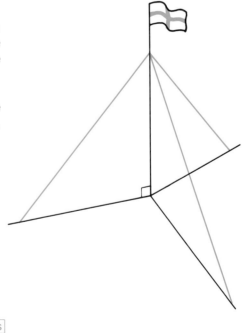

$$\cos \theta = 12 \div 14 = 0.8571 \ldots$$
$$\theta = 31° \qquad \ldots \cos^{-1} 0.8571 \ldots$$
12 ÷ 14 = inv cos

Note: The third angle of the triangle is 90° − 31° = 59°.

◆ **3** A lantern hangs vertically from a wall (shown in the diagram). It is supported by two metal spars at angles of 65° and 31° to the wall. If the shortest distance from C to the wall is 50 cm, calculate the distance from A to B.

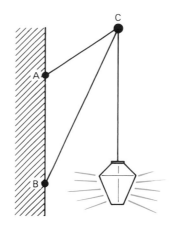

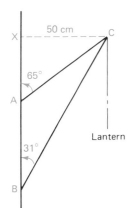

Lantern

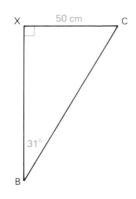

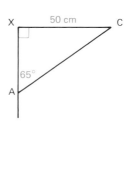

Both triangles CXB and CXA can be solved using $\boxed{\sin}$, $\boxed{\cos}$.

(i) $CB = \dfrac{50}{\sin 31°}$; $BX = CB \cos 31°$

   50 $\boxed{÷}$ 31 $\boxed{\sin}$ $\boxed{=}$ $\boxed{×}$ 31 $\boxed{\cos}$ $\boxed{=}$ 83·214

(ii) $CA = \dfrac{50}{\sin 65°}$; $AX = CA \cos 65°$

   50 $\boxed{÷}$ 65 $\boxed{\sin}$ $\boxed{=}$ $\boxed{×}$ 65 $\boxed{\cos}$ $\boxed{=}$ 23·315

$AB = BX - AX = 59·9$ cm

● The solution is even simpler using $\boxed{\tan}$ and the co-angles 59° and 25°.

   (i) $BX = 50 \tan 59° = 83·214$

   (ii) $AX = 50 \tan 25° = 23·315$

Exercise G.2

1 Use your calculator to find the length of AC.

C

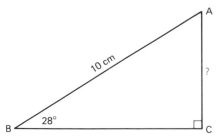

2 Use your calculator to find FD̂E.

C

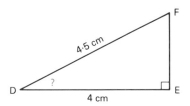

3 Make a diagram on graph paper which will enable you to measure sin 45°, cos 45° and tan 45°.
[Indicate the scale you use.]

C

4 The diagram shows how two students found the width of a river without crossing it. They used two sighting poles and a surveyor's tape. Calculate the width of the river.

B

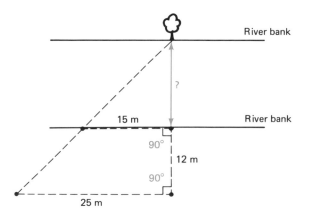

5 Find two values of θ, both between 0° and 360°, given that
(a) sin θ = 0·6
(b) cos θ = ⁻0·45
(c) tan θ = ⁻6·4

B

6 The rectangle is shown with three corners on the sides of the square. Can it be moved so that all four corners lie on the sides of the square. If so, what angles are made between the sides of the rectangle and the sides of the square.

A

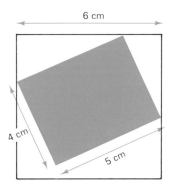

7 The diagram shows a cylindrical pole in a cylindrical hole which is too large for the post.

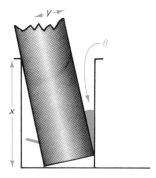

The hole has been dug to a depth of x cm and the radius of the post is y cm. Find the diameter of the hole in terms of x, y and $θ$.

A

8 A motorway 30 m wide passes through a cutting and into two tunnels. The tops of the cutting are level and 80 m apart. The motorway is 30 m vertically below the top of the cutting on each side. The angle of slope of one side is 64°, calculate the angle of slope of the other side.

A

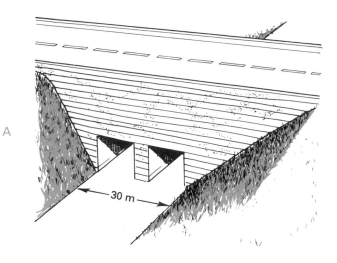

30 m

G.3 Pythagoras' theorem

Pythagoras' theorem is the most famous theorem in mathematics. It is usually stated: In any right-angled triangle the square on the hypotenuse is the sum of the squares on the other two sides.

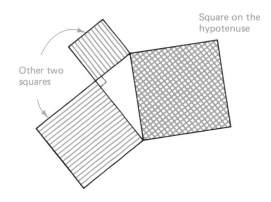

Square on the hypotenuse

Other two squares

Another way of writing the theorem is to use a, b and c for the lengths of the three sides: then $a^2 + b^2 = c^2$.

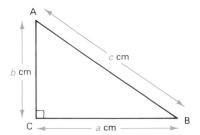

A

c cm

b cm

C ← a cm → B

G.3.1 The inverse of Pythagoras' theorem

The inverse of Pythagoras' theorem is also very useful: any triangle with sides a, b and c, such that $a^2 + b^2 = c^2$, has a right angle opposite side c. The most common example is the 3, 4, 5 triangle (and any triangle made by enlarging the 3, 4, 5 triangle):

$3^2 + 4^2 = 9 + 16 = 25$
$\quad\quad 5^2 = 25.$

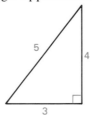

G.3.2 Triangles worth remembering

The half square

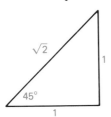

Half of an equilateral triangle

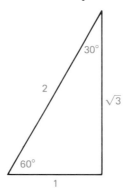

The figure shows the four 3, 4, 5 triangles found in a quarter circle, radius 5 cm.

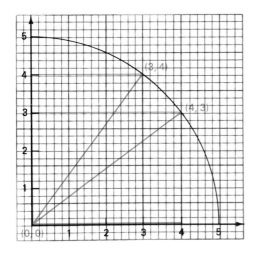

The 5, 12, 13 triangle gives another family of right-angled triangles:
$5^2 + 12^2 = 25 + 144 = 169$
$\quad\quad 13^2 = 169.$

G.3.3   Using Pythagoras' theorem

If two sides are known in a right-angled triangle, the length of the third can
be found.

Example

1   $c^2 = (2{\cdot}9)^2 + (3{\cdot}8)^2$
   $\quad = 8{\cdot}41 + 14{\cdot}44 = 22{\cdot}85$
   $c = \sqrt{22{\cdot}85} = 4{\cdot}78$ cm

   2·9 $\boxed{x^2}$ $\boxed{+}$ 3·8 $\boxed{x^2}$ $\boxed{=}$ $\boxed{\sqrt{}}$

2   $a^2 + (3{\cdot}8)^2 = (4{\cdot}3)^2$
   $a^2 = (4{\cdot}3)^2 - (3{\cdot}8)^2$
   $\quad = 18{\cdot}49 - 14{\cdot}44 = 4{\cdot}05$
   $a = \sqrt{4{\cdot}05} = 2{\cdot}01$ cm

   4·3 $\boxed{x^2}$ $\boxed{-}$ 3·8 $\boxed{x^2}$ $\boxed{=}$ $\boxed{\sqrt{}}$

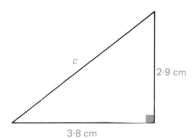

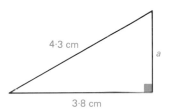

[If you complete the whole calculation on the calculator make sure you
check with a careful drawing!]

◆ 3   The distance between two points (x_1, y_1) and (x_2, y_2) whose
   coordinates are known is $d = \sqrt{(x_1 - x_2)^2 + (y_1 - y_2)^2}$

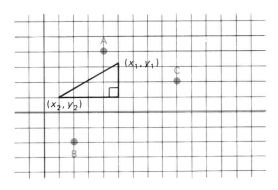

A is (4, 4)
B is (2, ⁻2)
C is (9, 2)
Length of AB is $\sqrt{(4 - 2)^2 + (4 - {}^-2)^2} = \sqrt{40}$
Length of BC is $\sqrt{(2 - 9)^2 + ({}^-2 - 2)^2} = \sqrt{65}$
Length of AC is $\sqrt{(4 - 9)^2 + (4 - 2)^2} = \sqrt{29}$
Check these lengths by measurement.

◆ **4** Pythagoras' theorem is often used to find lengths on 3-D objects.

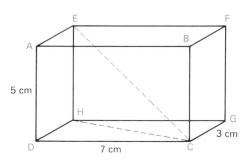

$HC^2 = (7^2 + 3^2)$
$EC^2 = EH^2 + HC^2$
$\quad\ = 5^2 + (7^2 + 3^2)$
$EC = \sqrt{5^2 + 7^2 + 3^2} = \sqrt{83}$

The diagonals of this cuboid are $\sqrt{83}$ cm in length.
[The longest diagonals of a cube, side 1 unit, are $\sqrt{3}$ units in length.]

Exercise G.3

1 A right-angled isosceles triangle has two sides 6 cm long. Calculate the length of the third side.   C

2 Prove (without drawing) that a triangle with sides 4 cm, 5 cm and 6 cm is not a right-angled triangle.   C

3 The diagram shown can be used to measure an estimate of both $\sqrt{2}$ and $\sqrt{3}$. Extend the drawing to estimate $\sqrt{5}$.   B

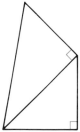

4 Show that all the short diagonals of this hexagon are $\sqrt{3}$ units in length.   B

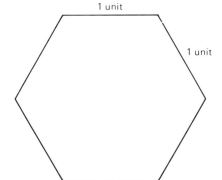

5 Given that $\sin \theta = 0.3$, calculate without the use of [sin] or [sin⁻¹] the values of $\cos \theta$ and $\tan \theta$.   B

6 Prove, without measurement, that △XYZ is not isosceles. Given X is (4, 8), Y is (2, 2), Z is (8, 2). B

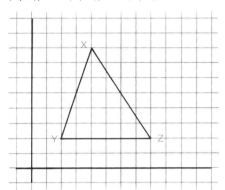

7 (i) Calculate the lengths of EB and BH.
(ii) Construct △EBH and estimate the size of EB̂H. A

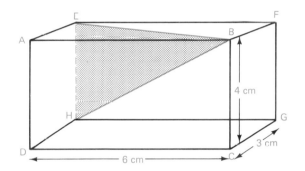

8 The height of this tower to the top of the spire is 55 m. The tower itself is built on a square base 5 m × 5 m and is exactly 30 m high.

Calculate
(i) the length of edges of the spire,
(ii) the surface area of the sloping sides of the spire. A

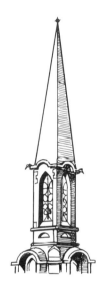

G.4 Bearings

Navigators use bearings to describe direction. Directions are measured from north, through 360° clockwise back to north again. Bearings are always given in three figures, e.g. 090°, not 90°.

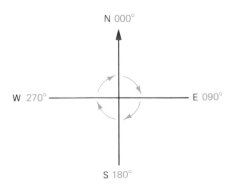

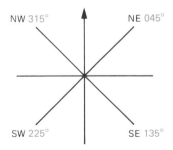

Example

Bearings

Ship to lighthouse	035°
Lighthouse to island	160°
Island to ship	290°

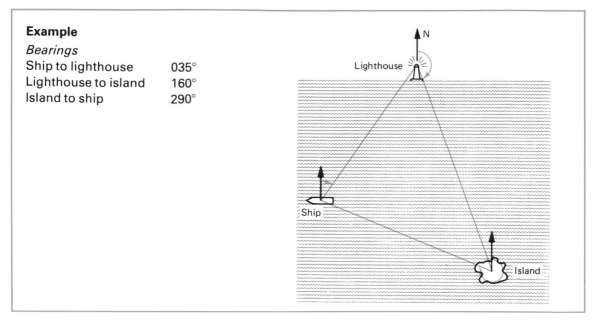

It is very helpful to use a 360° protractor in all
work on bearings. [This is what navigators use.]

G.4.1   Fixing position

A ship or aircraft can find its position at sea if it is told its bearings from two
radar stations. The position is found by drawing.

Example

Bearing from A ... 027°
Bearing from B ... 295°

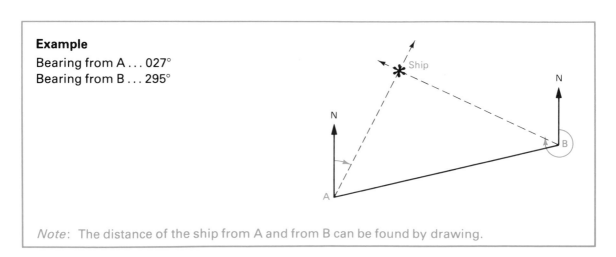

Note: The distance of the ship from A and from B can be found by drawing.

G.4.2 Back bearing

The bearing of A from B and the bearing of B from A are simply related. The second is called the back bearing

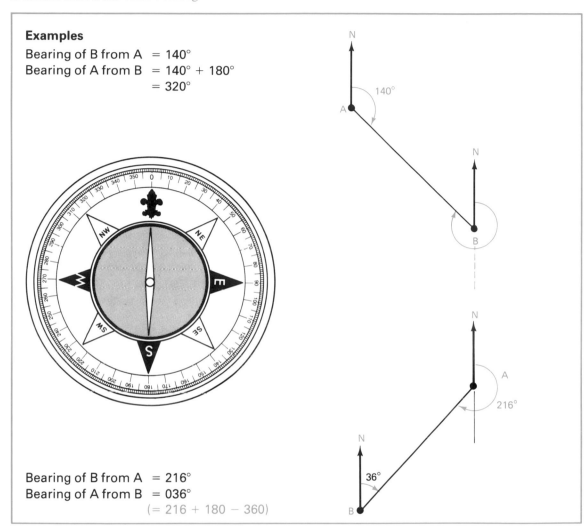

Examples
Bearing of B from A = 140°
Bearing of A from B = 140° + 180°
= 320°

Bearing of B from A = 216°
Bearing of A from B = 036°
(= 216 + 180 − 360)

Investigate this rule. The back bearing is the bearing + 180°, but 360° is subtracted if the total is over 360.

Exercise G.4

1 Draw a diagram which shows a ship sailing 400 km on bearing 070° and then 200 km on bearing 140°. How far will the ship be from its starting point?   C

2 Two forest observation posts are 5 km apart. The bearing of the second post from the first is 133°. What is the bearing of the first post from the second?   C

333

3 In the same forest, a fire is spotted on bearing 080° from the first post and on bearing 340° from the second post. Make a diagram which could pin-point the position of the fire. C

4 Explain how the bearings of two beacons on the coast could be used to fix the position of a ship at sea. B

5 Make careful measurements to find
(i) the bearings of the white from each of the far corners of the snooker table,
(ii) the bearing of each green ball from the white,
(iii) the bearing of the white from each green. A

6 An aircraft pilot sees a fighter approaching on bearing 047°. What is the back bearing? Make a drawing of the position after 10 seconds given that

(i) the aircraft is travelling at a steady speed of 850 km/hr on a bearing of 350°,

(ii) the fighter is travelling at 1400 km/hr,

(iii) the distance between the two aircraft was 5 km when the fighter was first spotted. A

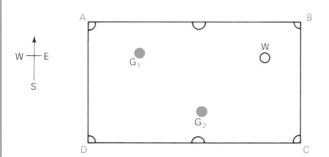

G.5   Constructions

G.5.1   Triangles

A triangle can be drawn if your information fits one of these sets of data:

(i) All three sides are known lengths.
Note: But any two sides together must be longer than the third side or a triangle cannot be formed.

(ii) Two sides are known and the angle between them is known.

(iii) Two angles are known so the third one can be found, and one side is known.

(iv) The triangle has a right angle and any two sides are known.

Examples

1 Construction of a triangle
   with sides 3 cm, 4 cm
   and 5 cm.

2 Construction of a triangle
   with two angles of 40°
   and the side between them
   5 cm long.

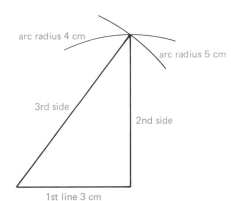

arc radius 4 cm

arc radius 5 cm

3rd side

2nd side

1st line 3 cm

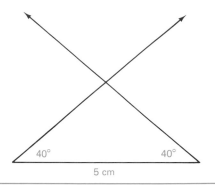

40°   40°

5 cm

G.5.2. Quadrilaterals

Knowing the lengths of the four sides of a quadrilateral is not enough to
enable you to draw it. A fifth fact is needed. This can be the length of a
diagonal, an angle, or that there are a pair of parallel sides.

Examples

1 Draw the quadrilateral ABCD given AB = 4 cm, BC = 3·5 cm, CD = 5·7 cm,
   DA = 6 cm and AC = 5·7 cm.
   1∅ Draw AB
   2∅ Find C
   3∅ Draw AC, BC
   4∅ Find D
   5∅ Draw CD, AD

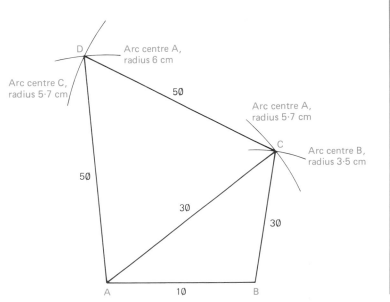

D

Arc centre A,
radius 6 cm

Arc centre C,
radius 5·7 cm

5∅

Arc centre A,
radius 5·7 cm

C

Arc centre B,
radius 3·5 cm

5∅

3∅

3∅

A   1∅   B

335

2 Draw the trapezium PQRS, given PQ//RS, PQ = 4 cm, QR = 3 cm, RS = 6 cm and SP = 3·5 cm.

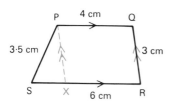

Since PQRX is a parallelogram,
PX = 3 cm and XR = 4 cm.

1Ø Draw SR
2Ø Find X
3Ø Find P
4Ø Draw SP
5Ø Find Q
6Ø Draw PQ, RQ

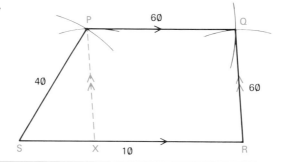

- If both pairs of opposite sides are parallel, an angle is still needed to select just one figure.

Examples

Two of the infinite number of parallelograms with sides 4 cm and 2·5 cm.

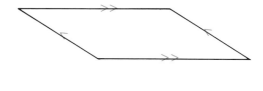

Exercise G.5

1 Draw a triangle whose sides are 7 cm, 5 cm and 4 cm in length. Measure its angles.   C

2 What can you say about a group of three numbers *a*, *b* and *c*, if it is not possible to draw a triangle whose sides are *a* cm, *b* cm and *c* cm in length?   C

3 Draw a rhombus whose sides are 4 cm long and which has one diagonal of 7 cm. Measure the length of the other diagonal.   C

4 Draw an isosceles trapezium with parallel sides 8 cm and 6 cm long and with the other two sides each 7 cm long. Explain your method.   B

Examination questions G

1 A printer makes a 'template' as shown, to be the base of a pattern. Draw another grid and use it to enlarge the template to double size.

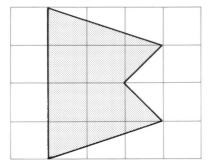

2 Which one of the triangles drawn below is not exactly right-angled?

(a)

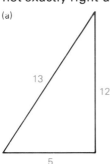

13
12
5

(b)

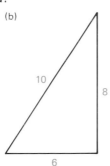

10
8
6

(c)

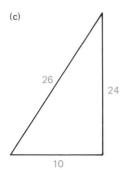

26
24
10

(d)

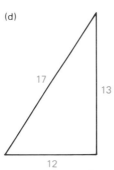

17
13
12

3 Calculate the size of angles PQ̂R and PR̂Q.

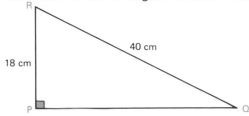

R
40 cm
18 cm
P
Q

4 Calculate the value of *c* if *a* = 9 cm and *b* = 40 cm. Use your result to help complete the last three lines in the table.

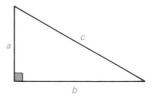

a	b	c
3	4	5
5	12	13
7	24	25
9	40	
11		
13		

a
c
b

5 The angle of depression from a coastguard station to a ship at sea is 3·2°. The coastguard station is on the top of a cliff 140 m high. How far is the ship from the base of the cliff?

6 Two look-out posts A and B lie on a straight coastline running east to west. The distance between them is 5 km. A ship is sighted on a bearing 067° from A and 337° from B.
  (a) Explain why the angle AŜB must be 90°.
  (b) Calculate the distance of the ship from A and B.
  (c) The ship sails on a course such that AŜB is always 90°.
    (i) Describe the path taken by the ship.
    (ii) What is the bearing of the ship from A when it is 3 km from A? (SEG)

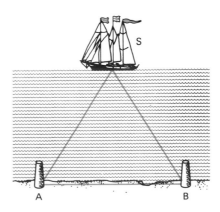

S
A
B

7 The diagram shows the cross-section of a studio roof. For strength, angle AB̂C must always be 90° but BÂC can vary. The length AC is 10 metres.

(a) Calculate the length of AB when BÂC is 25°.

(b) Complete the table given below to show the lengths of AB and BC for various angles BÂC.

(c) Draw a graph (using axes as shown below) to show the lengths AB and BC.

(d) What is the length of AB when it is twice the length of BC?   (SEG)

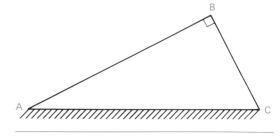

Angle BÂC	Length of AB	Length of BC
10°	9·85 m	1·74 m
20°	9·40 m	3·42 m
30°	8·66 m	5·00 m
40°	7·66 m	6·43 m
50°		
60°		
70°		
80°		

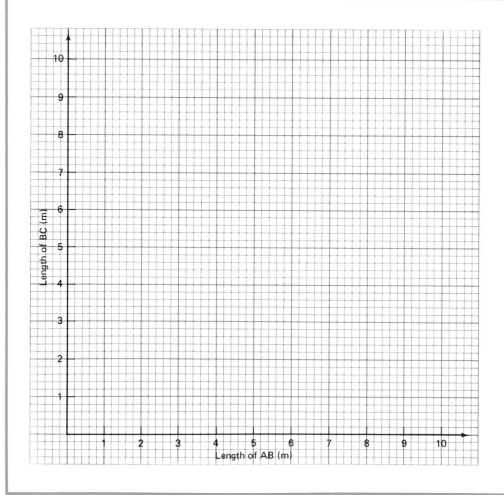

8 The diagram shows three posts A, B and C on a building site.
(a) Use a scale of 1 cm ↔ 50 m to make an accurate drawing of the positions of A, B and C.
(b) (i) Join AC and measure the length to the nearest mm.
(ii) What is the distance on the building site between the two posts A and C?
(c) (i) Measure and write down the size of BÂC.
(ii) What is the bearing of C from A?
(iii) What is the bearing of A from C?
(d) By drawing further lines on your scale drawing, find how far the post C is east of the post A. (SEG)

9 A ship sails from X on a bearing 050° for a distance of 65 km. It continues due south for 100 km.
(a) How far is the ship from X?
(b) What is the bearing of the ship from X?

10 A park is a quadrilateral, PQRS: PQ = 400 m, RS = 550 m, QR = 350 m, $\hat{Q}$ = 80° and $\hat{R}$ = 120°.
Use a scale 1:5000 (or 1 cm ↔ 50 metres) and make an accurate scale drawing of the park. Use your drawing to find the length of the fourth side of the park.

11 Six sticks have lengths 1 m, 2 m, 3 m, 4 m, 5 m and 6 m. List three different selections of three sticks which cannot be made into a triangle.

12 The drawing below shows part of a coastline. A and B are observation posts. C is a lifeboat centre.
(a) Measure the length of AB in cm.
(b) How far apart are the observation posts?
(c) In a storm a ship sends out an SOS. The signal is picked up by A and B. The bearing of the ship is 030° from A and 270° from B. Locate the position of the ship.
(d) How far must the lifeboat travel from C to the ship? On what bearing should the lifeboat steer?

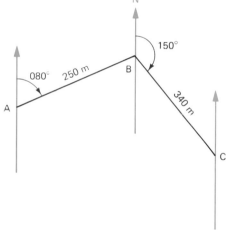

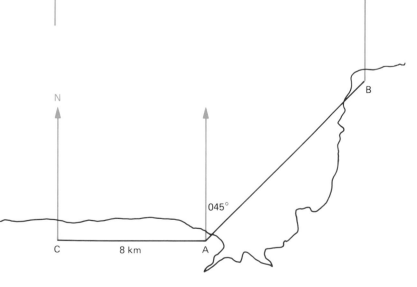

13 (a) Show that $(n + 4)^2 - n^2 = 4(2n + 4)$.
    (b) Use the above relationship to find a pythagorean triple.
    (c) Extend your work on (b) to find two more pythagorean triples and enter your results in a table. Use the patterns in the table to find more right angled triangles in which the hypotenuse is 4 units longer than one of the other sides.

14 Find two solutions to each of the equations below.
    (a) $\sin x = 0.4$
    (b) $\tan x = {}^-1.3$
    (c) $\cos x = 0.85\ldots$ correct to two decimal places.

15 A twin pair of tower blocks are 80 metres apart. From the window marked W, the angle of elevation to the top of the other block is 35° while the angle of depression to the foot of the other block is 40°. Calculate
   (i) the height of both blocks,
   (ii) the floor on which W is found, given that each block has 30 floors above ground.

16 The angles of elevation to the top of a mining slag heap are shown in the diagram. P and Q are points at the same level and 1·4 km apart. The line PQ goes directly below R, the vertex of the heap. Calculate the height of the heap above the level of PQ.

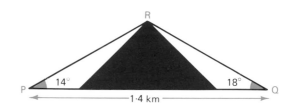

17 When the mid points of faces of a cube are joined a figure called an octahedron is formed.
Give all the facts you can about the octahedron, if the cube's edges are each 6 cm in length.

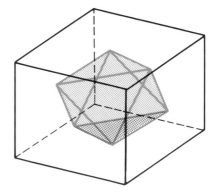

18 A pyramid stands on a square base, side x cm. Its sloping edges are also x cm long and its volume is exactly 1000 cm³. Calculate the value of x.

Activities and investigations G

Trig or bust ... a game for two

You need a scientific calculator or trig table, and you will have to make a
simple set of cards: ten 'θ' cards and nine 'function' cards, as shown here.
These function cards are labelled 'f' on the back.
The θ cards are, of course, labelled θ.

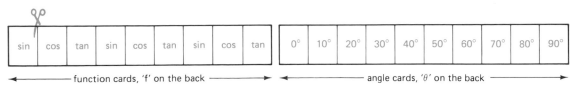

sin	cos	tan	sin	cos	tan	sin	cos	tan

0°	10°	20°	30°	40°	50°	60°	70°	80°	90°

◀———————— function cards, 'f' on the back ————————▶   ◀———————— angle cards, 'θ' on the back ————————▶

How to play

(i) The cards are spread face down in two separate groups.
(ii) The first player (A) turns over one from each group.
(iii) The second player (B) also turns over a pair of cards.

If A turns 10° and cos, and B turns over 40° and tan, player A wins the
round because cos 10° > tan 40°   2 points to A.
        0·9848 > 0·839

(iv) Equal values score 1 point for each player.
(v) After each round the cards are placed back face down in their groups.

The game goes on for as long as you like—it is a good idea to set a time limit,
or a score target, before you start.

Variation 1   Extend the θ cards to 180° and play as above.
Variation 2   Extend the functions to include sec, cosec and cot.
            [see Investigation 1 on next page.]

A solo project

Making your own protractor

A protractor can be made easily on a rectangle using values of tan x from
your calculator. Find out how to do it, and then ...

1. Make an accurate protractor on
   stiff card. (You will need a
   well-graduated perspex ruler.)
2. Use your protractor to construct
   (i) a regular pentagon,
   (ii) a regular nonagon (9 sides).
3. Design and make a rectangular
   protractor which has the 30°
   and 150° divisions exactly at the
   top corners of the rectangle.

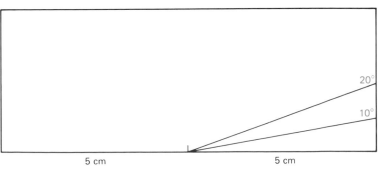

Investigations

1 Measuring for sin, cos and tan

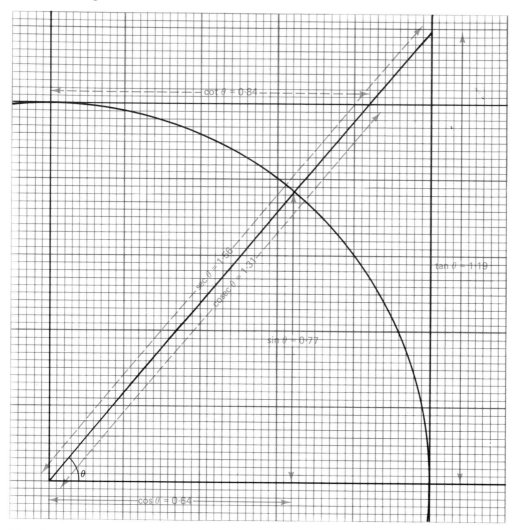

The diagram shows how values can be found from measuring distances. The radius of the arc is 10 cm for convenience.

Use this type of diagram and a protractor to find the values of sin, cos and tan required to complete the table opposite.

- $\cot \theta = \dfrac{1}{\tan \theta}$ $\sec \theta = \dfrac{1}{\cos \theta}$ $\csc \theta = \dfrac{1}{\sin \theta}$

θ	$\sin \theta$	$\cos \theta$	$\tan \theta$
10°			
20°			
30°			
40°			
50°			
60°			
70°			
80°			
90°			

2 Special triangles

Make models of the special triangles. Use them to create designs. Use colour! Use imagination! Use skill!

 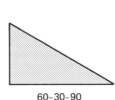 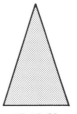 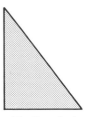

60–60–60	45–45–90	60–30–90	72–72–36	'The Egyptian'
'The equilateral'	'The half square'	'The semi-equi'	'The golden' what's so special??	or the 3, 4, 5

3 Finding heights ... working in pairs

The diagram shows how the height of buildings, trees, etc., can be found using a table of tangents.

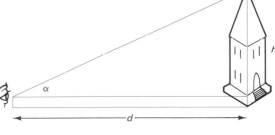

$$h = d \tan \alpha$$

You will need to consider the following points.

- How to measure a straight distance. (Standardise your pace by counting the number of steady steps it takes you to walk a measured 50 metres.)
- How to measure an angle of elevation using a protractor, drinking straw and plumbline.

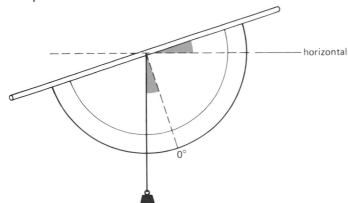

horizontal

0°

- Do not forget to allow for the height of your eye above the ground.

IMPORTANT—Never look directly at the sun.

Find the height of some tall objects in your area. Write up your results.

4 Estimating the diameter of the moon

You can investigate the diameter of the moon by catching it exactly
between two marks on a window. [You will have to adjust your distance
from the window.]

All you need to know is that the distance of the moon from the earth is
238 840 miles ... and a few other simple measurements!

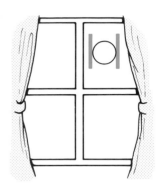

5 Bearings from home (or school)

Make a direction chart for your home or school.
Make it look interesting!

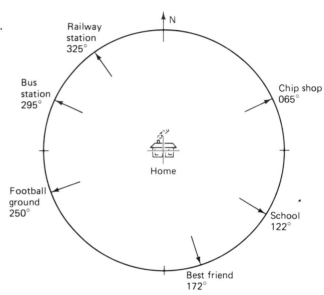

Railway
station
325°

Chip shop
065°

Bus
station
295°

Home

Football
ground
250°

School
122°

Best friend
172°

6 Drawing a graph of sin x

The graph below shows part of the graph of $y = \sin x$. Find out how it has
been constructed and make your own version.

(a) Add a similar graph for cos x.
(b) Make a graph of tan x.

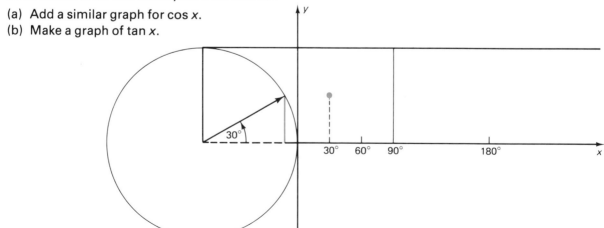

7 Getting to know the Trig family

The functions sin x, cos x and tan x have many relationships, some of which are listed below. You should verify and prove the relationships, and see if you can add to the list.

For $0 \leqslant x \leqslant 90°$

- $(\sin x)^2 + (\cos x)^2 = 1$
- $\dfrac{\sin x}{\cos x} = \tan x$
- $\sin x = \cos(90 - x)$
- $(\tan x)^2 = \left(\dfrac{1}{\cos x}\right)^2 - 1$
- $\tan(90 - x) = \dfrac{1}{\tan x}$

- $\sin x + \cos x \geqslant 1$
- $\dfrac{1}{\sin x} + \dfrac{1}{\cos x} \geqslant 2$
- $\cos x = \sin(90 - x)$
- $\left(\dfrac{1}{\tan x}\right)^2 + 1 = \left(\dfrac{1}{\sin x}\right)^2$

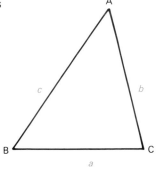

Check which of the relationships are still true if $x > 90°$.

8 Solving the general triangle

The general triangle is usually marked with vertices A, B, C and side lengths a, b, c units.
Note that side a is opposite vertex A and so on.
Two important rules can be proved for the general triangle.

sine rule . . . . . $\dfrac{a}{\sin A} = \dfrac{b}{\sin B} = \dfrac{c}{\sin C}$

cosine rule . . . . . $a^2 = b^2 + c^2 - 2bc \cos A$

(three forms of this rule are possible)

Check that the rules can be used for any length and for any size of angle.

Prove the rules, starting from the figures drawn below.

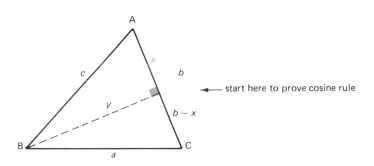

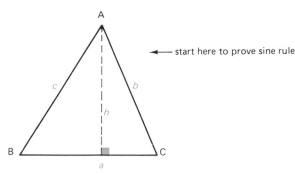

start here to prove sine rule

start here to prove cosine rule

Show how the rules change in the special case of a right angled triangle.

9   Area formulae for the triangles

Two important area formulae for triangles are
(i) Area $= \frac{1}{2}ab \sin C = \frac{1}{2}bc \sin A = \frac{1}{2}ac \sin B$
(ii) Area $= \sqrt{s(s-a)(s-b)(s-c)}$ where $s = \frac{1}{2}(a + b + c)$
Show that both formulae give the same result for different triangles chosen at random.

How do the formulae change
(i) if one angle is a right angle,
(ii) if the triangle is equilateral,
(iii) if the triangle is isosceles.

● Use of $\frac{1}{2}ab \sin C$ gives the area of a circle, radius 1 unit, as $\dfrac{n}{2} \sin \dfrac{360}{n}$.

Check that this is true and use it to find an accurate value of π (correct to 6 decimal places).

10   Double angles

A simple check shows that $\sin 60°$ is not $2 \times \sin 30°$.
Can you find simple relationships between $\sin 2x$ and $\sin x$; $\cos x$ and $\cos 2x$; ...
The diagram below might help (or invent one of your own)

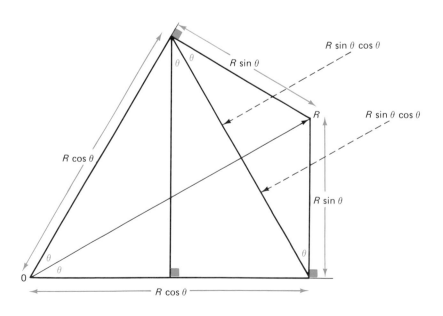

Worked answers to examination questions G

1 A printer makes a 'template' as shown, to be the base of a pattern.
Draw another grid and use it to enlarge the template to double size.

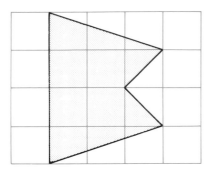

There are three ways to answer this question.

Method 1
Double the size of the grid spaces, then choose the vertices to match
the original.

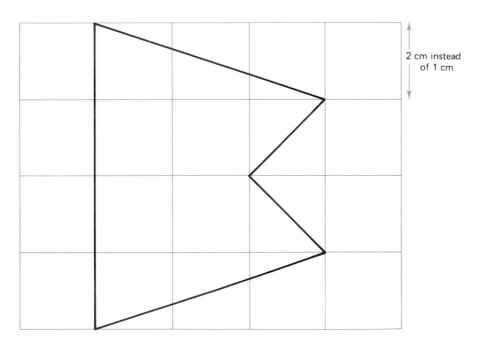

2 cm instead
of 1 cm

Method 2
Double the number of squares on the background grid. Increase the vertical line from 4 cm to 8 cm. For all the diagonal lines double the dimensions of rectangles they cross, e.g. PQ crosses a 3 × 1 rectangle in the original and a 6 × 2 rectangle in the enlargement.

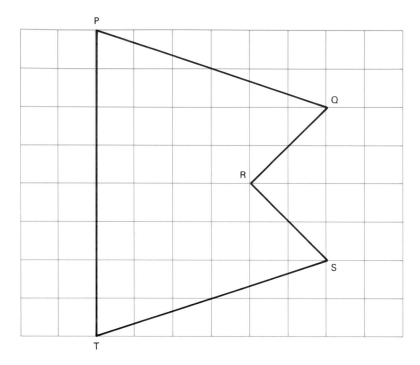

QR now crosses an area 2 × 2 instead of 1 × 1.
RS now crosses an area 2 × 2 instead of 1 × 1.
ST now crosses an area 6 × 2 instead of 3 × 1.
As you can see, this method is really the same as the first.

Method 3
Each of the vertices is given coordinates based on an *x*-axis through T and a *y*-axis along TP. The vertices of the enlargement have double the coordinates of the original points.

Point	Original	Enlargement
T	(0, 0)	(0, 0)
P	(0, 4)	(0, 8)
Q	(3, 3)	(6, 6)
R	(2, 2)	(4, 4)
S	(3, 1)	(6, 2)

Note: It doesn't really matter where you choose the *x* and *y* axes. The method still produces the same enlargement.

2 Which one of the triangles below is not exactly right-angled?

(a)

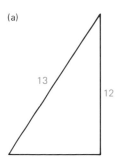

13 · 12 · 5

(b)

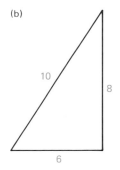

10 · 8 · 6

(c)

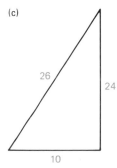

26 · 24 · 10

(d)

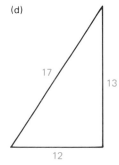

17 · 13 · 12

12, 13, 17 is not right-angled

Each triangle can be checked by Pythagoras' theorem. If $a^2 + b^2 = c^2$
then the triangle is right-angled:
$12^2 + 13^2 = 144 + 169 = 313$
$17^2 = 289.$

3 Calculate the size of angles PQ̂R and PR̂Q.

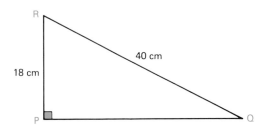

PQ̂R = 26·7°   PR̂Q = 63·3°

From the diagram 18 = 40 sin PQ̂R
$\Rightarrow$ sin PQ̂R = 0·45
$\Rightarrow$ PQ̂R = 26·7°
PR̂Q = 90° − PQ̂R
= 90° − 26·7° = 63·3°

18 ÷ 40 = inv sin − 90 = +/−
↑   ↑   ↑
sin PQ̂R   PQ̂R   PR̂Q

349

4 Calculate the value of c if $a = 9$ cm and $b = 40$ cm. Use your result to help complete the last three lines in the table.

a	b	c
3	4	5
5	12	13
7	24	25
9	40	
11		
13		

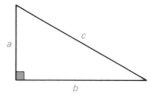

$c = 41$ Completed table [last 3 lines]:

a	b	c
9	40	41
11	60	61
13	84	85

Using Pythagoras $a^2 + b^2 = c^2$
Since $a = 9$ and $b = 40$ $9^2 + 40^2 = c^2$
$$1681 = c^2$$
$$41 = c$$ 9 $\boxed{(\ )^2}$ $\boxed{+}$ 40 $\boxed{(\ )^2}$ $\boxed{=}$ $\boxed{\sqrt{\ }}$

The last two lines can be found by looking at the patterns of differences and also noticing that $c = b + 1$ in each case.

a		b		c	
3		4		5	
	2		8		8
5		12		13	
	2		12		12
7		24		25	
	2		16		16
9		40		41	
	2		20		20
11		60		61	
	2		24		24
13		84		85	

5 The angle of depression from a coastguard station to a ship at sea is 3·2°. The coastguard station is on the top of a cliff 140 m high. How far is the ship from the base of the cliff?

The ship is 2504 m from the base of the cliff.

Draw a diagram using the information in the question.

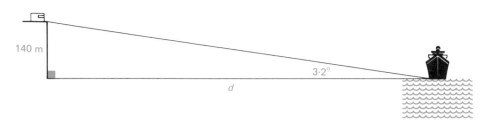

Method 1

$$\frac{140}{d} = \tan 3.2°$$

$$\Rightarrow \frac{d}{140} = \frac{1}{\tan 3.2°} \qquad \text{inversing both sides}$$

$$\Rightarrow \quad d = 140 \div \tan 3.2° \qquad 140 \;\boxed{\div}\; 3.2 \;\boxed{\tan}\; \boxed{=}$$

$$= 2504 \text{ m}$$

Method 2

Using the other angle: $\qquad \dfrac{d}{140} = \tan(90° - 3.2°)$

$$\Rightarrow d = 140 \tan 86.8° \qquad 90 \;\boxed{-}\; 3.2 \;\boxed{=}\; \boxed{\tan}\; \boxed{\times}\; 140 \;\boxed{=}$$

$$- 2504 \text{ m}$$

It is worth using both methods. You will then have an independent check of your answer.

6 Two look-out posts A and B lie on a straight coastline running east to west. The distance between them is 5 km. A ship is sighted on a bearing 067° from A and 337° from B.
 (a) Explain why the angle AŜB must be 90°.
 (b) Calculate the distance of the ship from A and B.
 (c) The ship sails on a course such that AŜB is always 90°.
   (i) Describe the path taken by the ship.
   (ii) What is the bearing of the ship from A when it is 3 km from A?

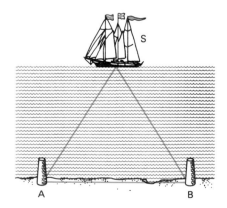

(a) AŜB = 90°   (b) AS = 4·6 km   BS = 1·95 km
(c) (i) The ship is sailing along a semicircle.   (ii) 037° to nearest degree.

(a) $\widehat{SBA} = 337° - 270° = 67°$
$\widehat{SAB} = 90° - 67° = 23°$
All three angles of $\triangle SAB$ must add up to 180°, so $\widehat{ASB}$ must be 90°.

(b) Since $\widehat{ASB} = 90°$
$AS = AB \sin 67° = 4.6$ km
$BS = AB \sin 23° = 1.95$ km

(c) Since $\widehat{ASB}$ is a right angle the point S is always on a semicircle, diameter AB.
When $AS = 3$ km
$\cos \widehat{SAB} = 0.6 \ldots (3 \div 5)$
$\Rightarrow \widehat{SAB} = 53.1°$
$\Rightarrow$ Bearing of S from A $= 90° - 53.1°$
$= 036.9°$.

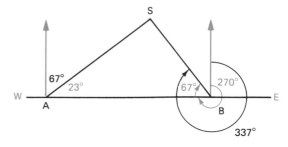

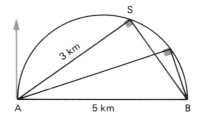

7 The diagram shows the cross-section of a studio roof. For strength angle $\widehat{ABC}$ must always be 90°, but $\widehat{BAC}$ can vary. The length AC is 10 metres.
(a) Calculate the length of AB when $\widehat{BAC}$ is 25°.
(b) Complete the table given below to show the lengths of AB and BC for various angles $\widehat{BAC}$.
(c) Draw a graph to show the lengths AB and BC.
(d) What is the length of AB when it is twice the length of BC? (SEG)

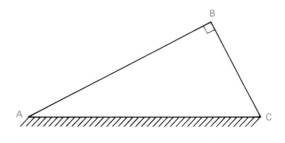

Angle $\widehat{BAC}$	Length of AB	Length of BC
10°	9.85 m	1.74 m
20°	9.40 m	3.42 m
30°	8.66 m	5.00 m
40°	7.66 m	6.43 m
50°		
60°		
70°		
80°		

(a) $AB = 9.06$ m

(b)

Angle $\widehat{BAC}$	Length AB	Length BC
50°	6.43 m	7.66 m
60°	5.00 m	8.66 m
70°	3.42 m	9.40 m
80°	1.74 m	9.85 m

(c)

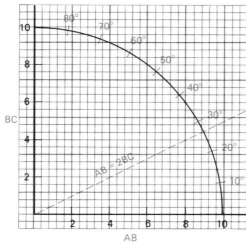

(d) AB = 8·95 m.

(a) AB = 10 sin 65° = 10 × 0·906 = 9·06 m.
(b) The lengths will be the same as for 10° to 40°, with AB ↔ BC.
You could work out each one separately but it is not necessary.
(c) The graph is a quarter circle.
(d) Since $\dfrac{BC}{AB}$ = tan Â, when AB = 2BC: tan Â = $\dfrac{BC}{2BC}$ = 0·5

$$A = 26·5° *$$

AB = 10 cos 26·5°
  = 8·95 m.

* This is confirmed by the graph. Where the line AB = 2BC cuts the curve
  corresponds to about 27°.

8 The diagram shows three posts A, B and C
on a building site.
  (a) Use a scale of 1 cm ↔ 50 m to make an
    accurate drawing of the positions of A,
    B and C.
  (b) (i) Join AC and measure the length to
      the nearest mm.
    (ii) What is the distance on the building
      site between the two posts A and C?
  (c) (i) Measure and write down the size of
      BÂC.
    (ii) What is the bearing of C from A?
    (iii) What is the bearing of A from C?
  (d) By drawing further lines on your scale
    drawing find how far the post C is east
    of the post A.   (SEG)

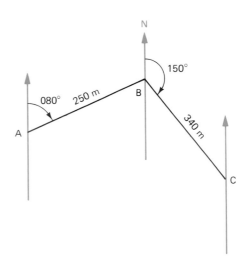

353

(a)

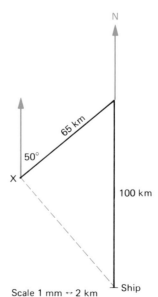

(b) (i) AC = 97 mm   (ii) 485 metres
(c) (i) BÂC = 41°   (ii) 121°   (iii) 301°
(d) 416 metres (8·32 cm)

(a) AB will be 5 cm long. BC will be 6·8 cm long.
(b) AC = 97 mm = 9·7 cm. Each cm represents 50 m so the actual
      length of AC on site is 9·7 × 50 = 485 m.
(c) (ii) Bearing of C from A is 80° + 41° = 121°.
      (iii) Bearing of A from C is 180° + 121°   [360° − (180° − 121°)]
            180° + 121° = 301°.

9 A ship sails from X on a bearing 050° for a distance of 65 km. It
    continues due south for 100 km.
    (a) How far is the ship from X?
    (b) What is the bearing of the ship from X?

(a) 77 km   (b) 140°

The drawing gives the distance from X to
the ship as 38·5 mm → 77 km.
Bearing 050° + 090° ... by measurement.

Scale 1 mm ↔ 2 km

354

10 A park is a quadrilateral, PQRS: PQ = 400 m, RS = 550 m, QR = 350 m,
$\hat{Q}$ = 80° and $\hat{R}$ = 120°.
Use a scale 1 : 5000 (or 1 cm ↔ 50 metres) and make an accurate scale
drawing of the park. Use your drawing to find the length of the fourth
side of the park.

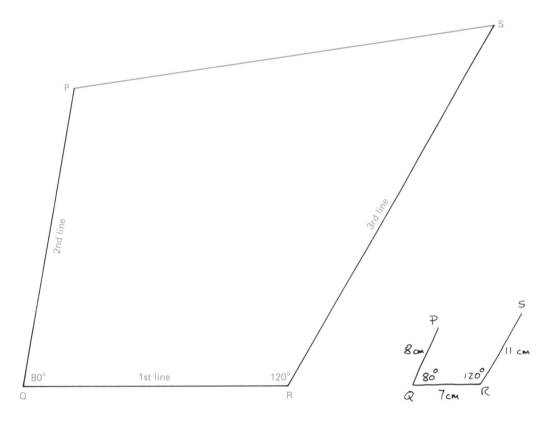

PS = 11·3 cm.   Fourth side of the park is 565 metres long.

First make a sketch from the data. Use QR as the starting line because
you know an angle at each end. Then add QP, 8 cm long, at 80° to QR.
Next add RS, 11 cm long, at 120° to QR. It only remains to draw and
measure PS. PS = 11·3 cm, so the fourth side is 11·3 × 50 = 565 m.

11 Six sticks have lengths 1 m, 2 m, 3 m, 4 m, 5 m, and 6 m. List three
different selections of three sticks which cannot be made into a
triangle.

1, 2, 3; 1, 2, 4; 1, 2, 5 [Or any other three from the list below.]

If a triangle is to be formed, the sum of any two sides must be greater
than the third side. Any three of the following would get full marks:
1, 2, 3   1, 3, 4   1, 4, 5   1, 5, 6   2, 3, 5   2, 4, 6
1, 2, 4   1, 3, 5   1, 4, 6   2, 3, 6
1, 2, 5   1, 3, 6
1, 2, 6

12 The drawing below shows part of a coastline. A and B are observation posts. C is a lifeboat centre.
(a) Measure the length of AB in cm.
(b) How far apart are the observation posts?
(c) In a storm a ship sends out an SOS. The signal is picked up by A and B. The bearing of the ship is 030° from A and 270° from B. Locate the position of the ship.
(d) How far must the lifeboat travel from C to the ship? On what bearing should the lifeboat steer?

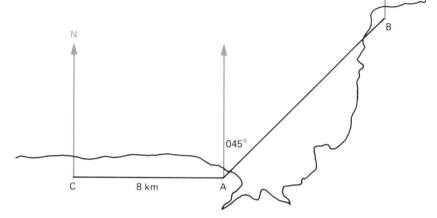

(a) AB = 6 cm
(b) 12 km
(c) The ship is located at X, on the drawing.
(d) 15·4 km; bearing 057°

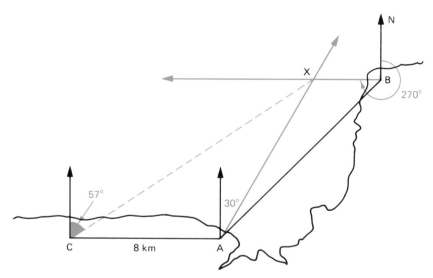

(b) The scale can be found because CA is marked as 8 km. The actual length of CA is 4 cm, thus the scale is 1 cm ↔ 2 km. So AB represents a distance of 12 km.
(d) CX = 7·7 cm, which corresponds to 15·4 km.

13 (a) Show that $(n + 4)^2 - n^2 = 4(2n + 4)$.

(b) Use the above relationship to find a pythagorean triple.

(c) Extend your work on (b) to find two more pythagorean triples and enter your results in a table. Use the patterns in the table to find more right angled triangles in which the hypotenuse is 4 units longer than one of the other sides.

(a) $(n + 4)^2 - n^2 = n^2 + 8n + 16 - n^2$
$= 8n + 16$
$= 4(2n + 4)$

(b) $n, n + 4$ and $\sqrt{4(2n + 4)}$ will form a pythagorean triple when $\sqrt{4(2n + 4)}$ is an exact number, i.e. when $4(2n + 4)$ is an exact square. This is only the case when $2n + 4$ is an exact square. The triple is found by putting $2n + 4$ equal to 1, 4, 9, 16, etc and seeing what happens.

$2n + 4 = 1 \Rightarrow 2n = {}^-3 \ldots$ impossible
$2n + 4 = 4 \Rightarrow n = 0 \ldots$ impossible
$2n + 4 = 9 \Rightarrow n = 2\frac{1}{2} \ldots$ not a whole number
$2n + 4 = 16 \Rightarrow n = 6$
This gives the sides of the triangle as 6, 10 and 8.

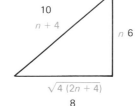

(c) The table below can be built up by the differences (shown in colour).

$2n + 4$ (must be an even square)	n		$n + 4$		$\sqrt{4(2n + 4)}$	
16	6		10		8	
		10		10		4
36	16		20		12	
		14		14		4
64	30		34		16	
		18		18		4
100	48		52		20	
		22		22		4
.	.		.		.	
.	.		.		.	
.	.		.		.	
.	.		.		.	

This table shows that as many triples as you like can be formed by continuing the table. Note that $3 : 4 : 5$ appears as $6 : 10 : 8$, and $5 : 12 : 13$ appears as $20 : 48 : 52$

14 Find two solutions to each of the equations below.
(a) $\sin x = 0 \cdot 4$
(b) $\tan x = {}^-1 \cdot 3$
(c) $\cos x = 0 \cdot 85 \ldots$ correct to two decimal places.

(a) 23·6°, 156·4°   (b) 127·6°, 232·4°   (c) 31·8°, 328·2°

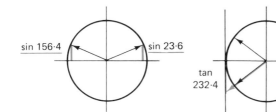

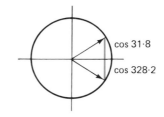

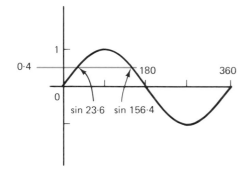

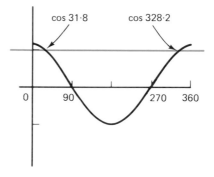

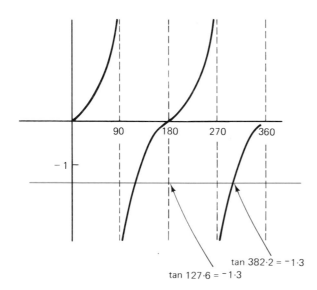

tan 382·2 = ⁻1·3

tan 127·6 = ⁻1·3

The question can be answered by reference to the circles or to the graphs.
The size of the angle is found using [inv] [sin] etc, and then the second value deduced from the diagram.

15 A twin pair of tower blocks are 80 metres apart.

From the window marked W, the angle of elevation to the top of the other block is 35° while the angle of depression to the foot of the other block is 40°. Calculate

(i) the height of both blocks,

(ii) the floor on which W is found, given that each block has 30 floors above ground.

(i) 123 metres   (ii) Probably 17th floor

The total height is $80 \tan 35 + 80 \tan 40 = 123 \cdot 1$ m.

The window divides the height into two parts ... 67 m and 56 m.

Thus there are $\dfrac{56}{123} \times 30$ floors above the window

and $\dfrac{67}{123} \times 30$ floors below the window.

$\dfrac{56}{123} \times 30 \simeq 13\frac{1}{2}$

$\dfrac{67}{123} \times 30 \simeq 16\frac{1}{2}$

Thus there are 16 whole floors below the window and the window will be on the 17th floor.

- In many buildings the ground and 1st floors are loftier than upper floors. That is why the answer is modified by adding probably.

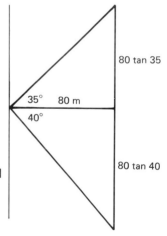

16 The angles of elevation to the top of a mining slag heap are shown in the diagram. P and Q are points at the same level and 1·4 km apart. The line PQ goes directly below R, the vertex of the heap. Calculate the height of the heap above the level of PQ.

197·5 metres

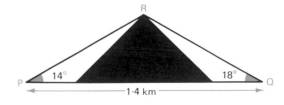

10    $\dfrac{h}{x} = \tan 14°$ $\dfrac{h}{1\cdot4 - x} = \tan 18°$

20    $\Rightarrow x \tan 14 = (1\cdot4 - x) \tan 18$

30    $\Rightarrow x \tan 14 + x \tan 18 = 1\cdot4 \tan 18$

40    $\Rightarrow x (\tan 14 + \tan 18) = 1\cdot4 \tan 18$

50    $\Rightarrow x = \dfrac{1\cdot4 \tan 18}{\tan 14 + \tan 18} = 792$ m

60    $\Rightarrow h = x \tan 14 \ldots$ from 10

70    $\Rightarrow h = 792 \tan 14 = 197\cdot5$ m $\ldots$ from 50

Notes: (i)   This problem could have been solved by drawing and therefore can be solved by trigonometry.

(ii)   You cannot calculate values in lines 20, 30 and 40 because you do not know what x is.

(iii)   This is an example of a general type of problem where a height is found without access to the base point. [See diagram.]

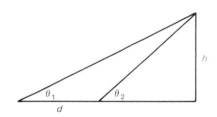

17   When the mid points of faces of a cube are joined a figure called an octahedron is formed.

Give all the facts you can about the octahedron, if the cube's edges are each 6 cm in length.

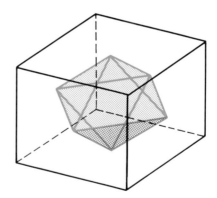

All the edges of the octahedron are $\sqrt{18} = 3\sqrt{2}$ cm in length. Each of the 8 faces consist of an equilateral triangle, so all the angles are 60°.

The diagonals joining opposite vertices are 6 cm long.

The volume of the octahedron is 36 cm³ which is exactly $\frac{1}{6}$ of the volume of the cube.

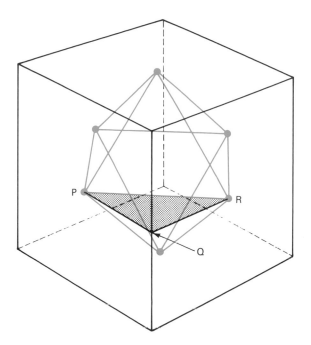

The triangle PQR gives the length of edge of the octahedron.

PQ = 3 cm

QR = 3 cm

PR = $\sqrt{9 + 9}$ = $\sqrt{18}$ cm.

The opposite vertices are centres of faces of the cube so the diagonals are all 6 cm.

The octahedron is composed of two pyramids, height 3 cm, on bases which are squares of side $\sqrt{18}$ cm.

Volume of each pyramid = $\frac{1}{3} \times (\sqrt{18})^2 \times 3$ = 18 cm³

Volume of octahedron = 36 cm³

Volume of the cube = 6 × 6 × 6 = 216 cm³.

Note: Since the area of an equilateral triangle, side x cm, is $\frac{\sqrt{3}}{4}x^2$,

the surface area of the whole octahedron is

$8 \times \frac{\sqrt{3}}{4} \times 18 = 36\sqrt{3}$ cm²,

while the surface area of the cube is 216 cm², but perhaps this is going too far for the question.

18 A pyramid stands on a square base, side x cm. Its sloping edges are also x cm long and its volume is exactly 1000 cm³. Calculate the value of x.

16·19 cm

The height of the pyramid can be found from two different triangles.

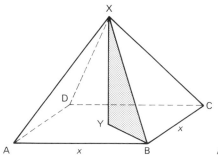
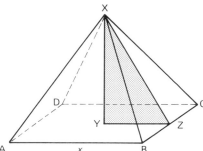

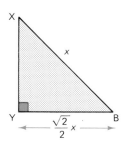
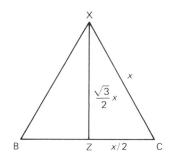

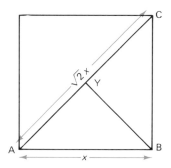

$$(XY)^2 = x^2 - \left(\frac{\sqrt{2}}{2}x\right)^2$$

$$= x^2 - \frac{2}{4}x^2$$

$$= \frac{1}{2}x^2$$

$$XY = \frac{x}{\sqrt{2}}$$

$$(XY)^2 = \left(\frac{\sqrt{3}}{2}x\right)^2 - \left(\frac{x}{2}\right)^2$$

$$= \frac{3}{4}x^2 - \frac{1}{4}x^2$$

$$= \frac{1}{2}x^2$$

$$XY = \frac{x}{\sqrt{2}}$$

The volume of the pyramid is $\frac{1}{3} \times$ height $\times$ area of base

$$\text{Vol} = \tfrac{1}{3} \times \frac{x}{\sqrt{2}} \times x^2 = 1000 \text{ cm}^3$$

$$x^3 = 1000 \times 3 \times \sqrt{2}$$

$$x = 16\cdot19 \qquad\qquad [3000 \;\boxed{\times}\; 2 \;\boxed{\checkmark}\; \boxed{=}\; \boxed{x^{1/y}}\; 3 \;\boxed{=}\;]$$

Notes: (i) This gives the sides of a square pyramid cup which would hold 1 litre of liquid.

(ii) The fact that △XYB is isosceles may come as a surprise. If you think of the pyramid as being half of a regular octahedron then clearly XY is half of a long diagonal and so is BY.

Topic H **Vectors and matrices**

Contents

Vectors; vectors and multiplication; applications in geometry; matrices; matrices of transformations; some applications of matrices.

Self assessment

The purpose of this task is to find out whether or not you need revision on this last topic. There is no time limit. If you reach the target score of 80% (or more) go back over other topics in which you did not score so well. Alternatively you could concentrate on practice on past examination papers.

Make a table with space for scoring your answers to the 16 questions in this section (see page vi). Answers are on pages 435–436.

1 Mark the position vectors $\begin{pmatrix} 0 \\ 2 \end{pmatrix}$, $\begin{pmatrix} -3 \\ 1 \end{pmatrix}$ and $\begin{pmatrix} 3 \\ -3 \end{pmatrix}$ on a grid. Show on the same diagram that the three vectors form a triangle.

2 The vectors $\begin{pmatrix} 1 \\ 0 \end{pmatrix}$ and $\begin{pmatrix} 0 \\ 1 \end{pmatrix}$ are given the symbols **i** and **j**.
Draw vectors corresponding to
(a) 2**i** + 3**j**
(b) 2**i** − 3**j**
How could the symmetry of these two vectors be seen from the **i**, **j** forms?

3 Which of the following are not equivalent vectors to $\begin{pmatrix} 1 \\ 2 \end{pmatrix}$:
(a) **i** + 2**j**   (b) $\frac{1}{2}$(2**i** + 4**j**)
(c) $\begin{pmatrix} 1 \\ 0 \end{pmatrix} + \begin{pmatrix} 0 \\ 2 \end{pmatrix}$
(d) A vector whose length is $\sqrt{5}$.

♦ **4** Draw arrow diagrams which show that
(a) $\begin{pmatrix} a \\ b \end{pmatrix} + \begin{pmatrix} c \\ d \end{pmatrix} = \begin{pmatrix} a + c \\ b + d \end{pmatrix}$
(b) $\begin{pmatrix} p \\ q \end{pmatrix} - \begin{pmatrix} r \\ s \end{pmatrix} = \begin{pmatrix} p - r \\ q - s \end{pmatrix}$
(c) $3\begin{pmatrix} x \\ y \end{pmatrix} = \begin{pmatrix} 3x \\ 3y \end{pmatrix}$

♦ **5** Find the length of the following vectors
(a) $\begin{pmatrix} 2 \\ 3 \end{pmatrix}$ (b) $\begin{pmatrix} 3 \\ -1 \end{pmatrix}$ (c) 3**i** + 4**j**

♦ **6** $\overrightarrow{AB}$ is **p**; $\overrightarrow{BC}$ is **q**; $\overrightarrow{CA}$ is **r**. X is the midpoint of AC. Write $\overrightarrow{CX}$ and $\overrightarrow{BX}$ in terms of **p**, **q** and **r**.

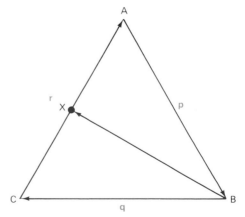

◆ **7** $\overrightarrow{AB} = \mathbf{p}$; $\overrightarrow{AD} = \mathbf{q}$; and ABCD is a parallelogram. Show that X, the midpoint of AC, is also the midpoint of BD.

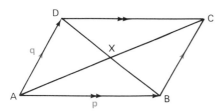

[*Hint*: Find $\overrightarrow{AC}$, $\overrightarrow{AX}$ and $\overrightarrow{BX}$ in terms of **p** and **q**.]

◆ **8** Use vectors to prove that the quadrilateral formed by joining the midpoints of the sides of any quadrilateral is a parallelogram.

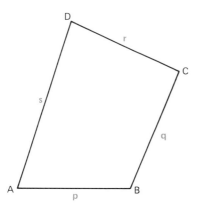

◆ **9** Arrange the information below as a matrix. Bert's Beefburger Cabin sells beefburgers, double beefburgers and super beefburgers. On Monday he sells seven beefburgers, no doubles and ten supers. On Tuesday he sells fourteen beefburgers, twelve doubles and fifteen supers.

◆ **10** $\mathbf{A} = \begin{pmatrix} 2 & 3 \\ 1 & 4 \end{pmatrix}$ and $\mathbf{B} = \begin{pmatrix} 4 & 3 \\ 2 & 1 \end{pmatrix}$. Calculate the product matrices **AB** and **BA**.

◆ **11** Show that the matrix $\mathbf{A} = \begin{pmatrix} 2 & \frac{1}{2} \\ -4 & -1 \end{pmatrix}$ satisfies the matrix equation $\mathbf{A}^2 = \mathbf{A}$. Can you find any other matrices that will also satisfy the equation.

◆ **12** Show that $\begin{pmatrix} 2 & -1 \\ -5 & 3 \end{pmatrix}$ is the inverse of the matrix $\begin{pmatrix} 3 & 1 \\ 5 & 2 \end{pmatrix}$ and use it to solve the simultaneous equations
$3x + y = 7$
$5x + 2y = 30$
(Check your solution by another method).

◆ **13** The matrices $\begin{pmatrix} 0 & 1 \\ 1 & 0 \end{pmatrix}$, $\begin{pmatrix} 0 & -1 \\ 1 & 0 \end{pmatrix}$ and $\begin{pmatrix} 0 & 1 \\ 1 & 1 \end{pmatrix}$ are each used to move the vector $\begin{pmatrix} x \\ y \end{pmatrix}$ in the plane. Describe each transformation and make a diagram in each case.

◆ **14** The diagram shows the main routes connecting four castles.
Complete the incidence matrix below:

	P	Q	R	S
P	0			
Q		0		
R			0	
S				0

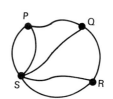

◆ **15** Calculate the determinant of each of the following matrices.

(a) $\begin{pmatrix} 3 & 4 \\ 4 & 3 \end{pmatrix}$ (b) $\begin{pmatrix} 4 & -1 \\ 2 & 3 \end{pmatrix}$

(c) $\begin{pmatrix} -3 & 4 \\ 5 & -1 \end{pmatrix}$ (d) $\begin{pmatrix} x & 1 \\ 1 & y \end{pmatrix}$

(e) $\begin{pmatrix} \cos 72° & \sin 72° \\ -\sin 72° & \cos 72° \end{pmatrix}$ (f) $\begin{pmatrix} \cos\theta & \sin\theta \\ -\sin\theta & \cos\theta \end{pmatrix}$

◆ **16** The matrix $\begin{pmatrix} 3 & 2 \\ 6 & 4 \end{pmatrix}$ is special in that its determinant is zero. Explain why this is so and show that the pair of equations
$3x + 2y = 5$
$6x + 4y = 9$
cannot be solved simultaneously
Illustrate this fact on a simple graph.

Key facts H

H.1   Vectors

Many quantities take more than one number to measure. Such quantities are
called vectors

Examples

1 *An arrow*
The arrow has a length and a direction.

2 A velocity also has a size and direction.
It can be represented by an arrow.

3 *Forces*
Forces can be represented by arrows.

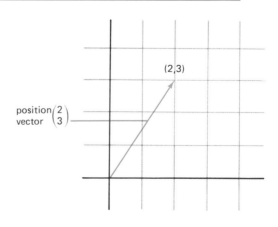

4 Movement by translation

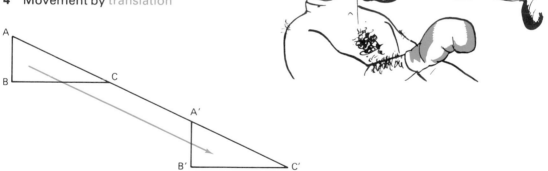

A vector is usually written as a number pair inside

brackets $\begin{pmatrix} 2 \\ 3 \end{pmatrix}$ to distinguish it from a pair of

coordinates. The connection is shown clearly in
the grid diagram.

position $\begin{pmatrix} 2 \\ 3 \end{pmatrix}$ vector

(2,3)

367

H.1.1 Components and equivalence

The vector $\begin{pmatrix} x \\ y \end{pmatrix}$ can be seen to be made up of two components $\begin{pmatrix} x \\ 0 \end{pmatrix}$ and $\begin{pmatrix} 0 \\ y \end{pmatrix}$.

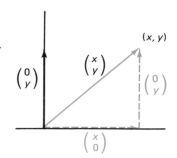

$\begin{pmatrix} x \\ 0 \end{pmatrix}$ is a vector along the x-axis.

$\begin{pmatrix} 0 \\ y \end{pmatrix}$ is a vector along the y-axis.

The vector $\begin{pmatrix} x \\ y \end{pmatrix}$ can be described in words as x along and y up.

Two vectors are equivalent if they can both be represented by arrows with the same size and direction.

Example

The vectors $\overrightarrow{AB}$ and $\overrightarrow{CD}$ are equivalent to the position vector $\begin{pmatrix} -4 \\ -2 \end{pmatrix}$.

Note that the components are also equivalent.

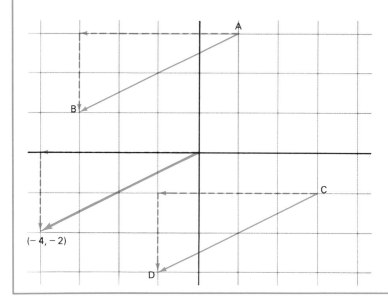

H.1.2 Addition and multiplication

The sum of two vectors $\begin{pmatrix} a \\ b \end{pmatrix}$ and $\begin{pmatrix} c \\ d \end{pmatrix}$ is another vector, $\begin{pmatrix} a + c \\ b + d \end{pmatrix}$.

This is what you would expect. Adding corresponds to drawing the second vector arrow on to the end of the first.

Example

$$\begin{pmatrix} 2 \\ 3 \end{pmatrix} + \begin{pmatrix} 4 \\ 1 \end{pmatrix} = \begin{pmatrix} 6 \\ 4 \end{pmatrix}$$

Components

$$\begin{pmatrix} 2 \\ 0 \end{pmatrix} + \begin{pmatrix} 0 \\ 3 \end{pmatrix} + \begin{pmatrix} 4 \\ 0 \end{pmatrix} + \begin{pmatrix} 0 \\ 1 \end{pmatrix}$$

$$= \begin{pmatrix} 6 \\ 0 \end{pmatrix} + \begin{pmatrix} 0 \\ 4 \end{pmatrix}$$

$$= \begin{pmatrix} 6 \\ 4 \end{pmatrix}$$

The diagram shows both the addition of arrows 'end on' and the addition of components.

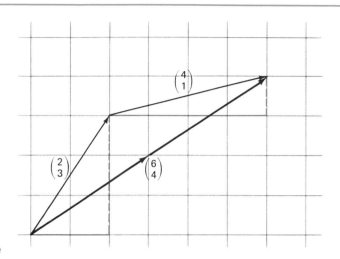

The basic rule for the addition of two vectors is

$$\begin{pmatrix} a \\ b \end{pmatrix} + \begin{pmatrix} c \\ d \end{pmatrix} = \begin{pmatrix} a + c \\ b + d \end{pmatrix}.$$

If the two vectors are the same this leads to

$$\begin{pmatrix} a \\ b \end{pmatrix} + \begin{pmatrix} a \\ b \end{pmatrix} = \begin{pmatrix} 2a \\ 2b \end{pmatrix}, \quad \text{ie.} \quad 2\begin{pmatrix} a \\ b \end{pmatrix} = \begin{pmatrix} 2a \\ 2b \end{pmatrix}$$

which can be extended a step at a time to the result

$$k\begin{pmatrix} a \\ b \end{pmatrix} = \begin{pmatrix} ka \\ kb \end{pmatrix}$$

Example

$$3\begin{pmatrix} 4 \\ -2 \end{pmatrix} = \begin{pmatrix} 12 \\ -6 \end{pmatrix}$$

Note that the vector $k\mathbf{p}$ will be parallel to $\mathbf{p}$ and k times as long as $\mathbf{p}$. This is very useful in geometry.

This diagram shows how $\begin{pmatrix} 12 \\ -6 \end{pmatrix}$ is built

up from $3\begin{pmatrix} 4 \\ -2 \end{pmatrix}$, and that $\begin{pmatrix} 12 \\ -6 \end{pmatrix}$ is

parallel to $\begin{pmatrix} 4 \\ -2 \end{pmatrix}$.

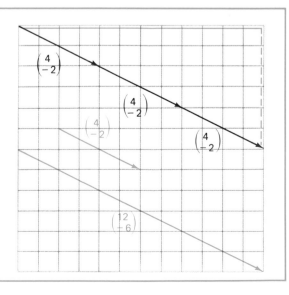

369

◆ H.1.3 Negative vectors; subtraction

Common sense suggests that the negative of the
vector $\begin{pmatrix} a \\ b \end{pmatrix}$ should be the vector $\begin{pmatrix} {}^-a \\ {}^-b \end{pmatrix}$.

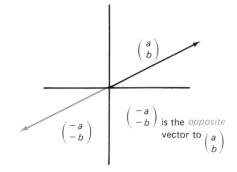

$\begin{pmatrix} {}^-a \\ {}^-b \end{pmatrix}$ is the *opposite*
vector to $\begin{pmatrix} a \\ b \end{pmatrix}$

This gives rise to the subtraction of vectors
p − **q** = **p** + **⁻q**
and

$$\begin{pmatrix} a \\ b \end{pmatrix} - \begin{pmatrix} c \\ d \end{pmatrix} = \begin{pmatrix} a \\ b \end{pmatrix} + \begin{pmatrix} {}^-c \\ {}^-d \end{pmatrix} = \begin{pmatrix} a - c \\ b - d \end{pmatrix}.$$

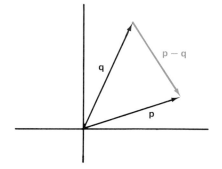

p − **q** is the vector you have to add to **q** to get **p**
(just as 6–4 is the number you have to add to 4 to
get 6).

This diagram shows **p** − **q** as **p** + **⁻q**.

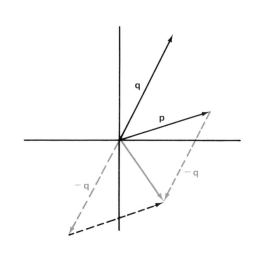

Example

$$\begin{pmatrix} 2 \\ 1 \end{pmatrix} - \begin{pmatrix} ^-1 \\ 4 \end{pmatrix} = \begin{pmatrix} 3 \\ ^-3 \end{pmatrix}$$

The diagram shows $\begin{pmatrix} 2 \\ 1 \end{pmatrix} - \begin{pmatrix} ^-1 \\ 4 \end{pmatrix}$ and

$\begin{pmatrix} 2 \\ 1 \end{pmatrix} + \begin{pmatrix} 1 \\ ^-4 \end{pmatrix}$, both giving the same

vector $\begin{pmatrix} 3 \\ ^-3 \end{pmatrix}$.

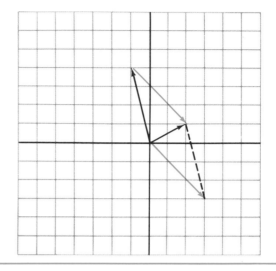

♦ **H.1.4 Modulus of a vector**

The size of a vector, independent of its direction, is called a modulus, written $|\mathbf{p}|$.
It is easily calculated by Pythagoras's theorem, from the components.

$$\mathbf{p} = \begin{pmatrix} a \\ b \end{pmatrix}$$

$$|\mathbf{p}| = \sqrt{a^2 + b^2}$$

The modulus is always positive.

Example

The modulus of $\begin{pmatrix} 2 \\ 5 \end{pmatrix}$ is $\sqrt{29}$.

Measuring the length $\overrightarrow{OP}$ in mm with a
ruler gives $|\overrightarrow{OP}|$ = 5·4 cm

$\sqrt{2^2 + 5^2} = \sqrt{4 + 25}$
$\qquad\quad = \sqrt{29}$ = 5·38 cm

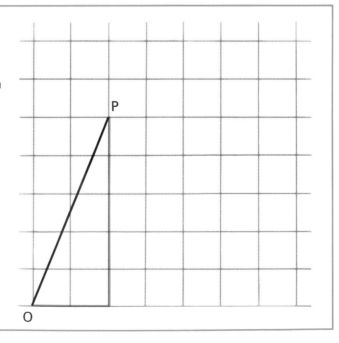

Exercise H.1

1 Draw the following vectors on a grid

$$\begin{pmatrix} 0 \\ 4 \end{pmatrix}, \begin{pmatrix} 2 \\ 3 \end{pmatrix}, \begin{pmatrix} 3 \\ -2 \end{pmatrix}, \begin{pmatrix} -4 \\ -1 \end{pmatrix}$$

C

2 $\overrightarrow{PQ}$ is the vector $\begin{pmatrix} 2 \\ -3 \end{pmatrix}$, which arrows correspond to

$$\begin{pmatrix} 5 \\ -1 \end{pmatrix}; \begin{pmatrix} -4 \\ 0 \end{pmatrix}; \begin{pmatrix} -2 \\ 4 \end{pmatrix}; \begin{pmatrix} -2 \\ -4 \end{pmatrix}; \begin{pmatrix} 1 \\ 4 \end{pmatrix}$$

What do you notice about all six vectors combined?

C

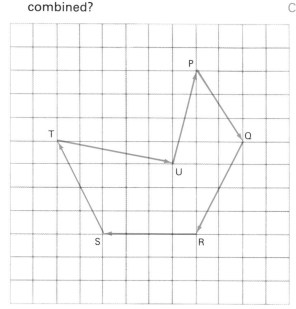

3 The vectors **p** and **q** are shown as sides of the parallelogram ABCD.

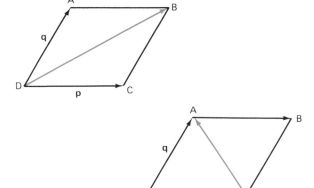

(a) Write the vectors which represent the two diagonals in terms of **p** and **q**.
(b) What do you obtain when the two diagonal vectors are added together?
(c) Demonstrate your result (b) on the diagram below.

B

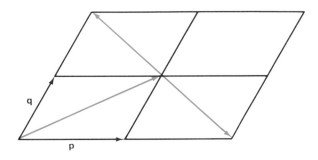

4 Which of the following is not equivalent to $\begin{pmatrix} 2 \\ -3 \end{pmatrix}$?

(a) $\begin{pmatrix} 2 \\ 0 \end{pmatrix} + \begin{pmatrix} 0 \\ -3 \end{pmatrix}$ (b) $\begin{pmatrix} 3 \\ 5 \end{pmatrix} + \begin{pmatrix} -1 \\ -8 \end{pmatrix}$

(c) $\begin{pmatrix} 4 \\ 5 \end{pmatrix} + \begin{pmatrix} -2 \\ -2 \end{pmatrix}$ (d) $2\begin{pmatrix} 1 \\ -1 \end{pmatrix} + \begin{pmatrix} 0 \\ -1 \end{pmatrix}$

Demonstrate all four vector sums on a grid.

B

5 Calculate the modulus for each of the following vectors.

(a) $\begin{pmatrix} 5 \\ 3 \end{pmatrix}$ (b) $\begin{pmatrix} 5 \\ -3 \end{pmatrix}$ (c) $\begin{pmatrix} 3 \\ 4 \end{pmatrix}$

(d) $\begin{pmatrix} 5 \\ 3 \end{pmatrix} + \begin{pmatrix} 3 \\ 4 \end{pmatrix}$ (e) $\begin{pmatrix} 5 \\ 3 \end{pmatrix} - \begin{pmatrix} 3 \\ 4 \end{pmatrix}$

A

6 Explain why it is always true that $|\mathbf{p} + \mathbf{q}| \leq |\mathbf{p}| + |\mathbf{q}|$.

A

H.2 Vectors and multiplication

Note: It is possible that this topic is not included in your examination syllabus. Check with your teacher and then decide whether to continue or skip to H.4.

◆ H.2.1 Scalar product

Two vectors may be multiplied to form a scalar product in two ways (shown below).

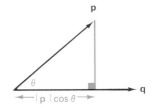

$$\mathbf{p} = \begin{pmatrix} p_1 \\ p_2 \end{pmatrix} \qquad \mathbf{q} = \begin{pmatrix} q_1 \\ q_2 \end{pmatrix}$$

The scalar product $\mathbf{p} \cdot \mathbf{q} = (p_1 q_1 + p_2 q_2)$

$\qquad\qquad\qquad = |\mathbf{p}|\,|\mathbf{q}|\cos\theta \ldots$ where θ is the angle between $\mathbf{p}$ and $\mathbf{q}$

Example

$$\mathbf{p} = \begin{pmatrix} 2 \\ 2 \end{pmatrix}; \quad \mathbf{q} = \begin{pmatrix} 3 \\ 1 \end{pmatrix}; \quad \mathbf{p} \cdot \mathbf{q} = (2 \times 3 + 2 \times 1)$$

$$= 8$$

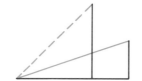

$$\left. \begin{array}{l} |\mathbf{p}| = \sqrt{8} \\ |\mathbf{q}| = \sqrt{10} \end{array} \right\} \quad \mathbf{p} \cdot \mathbf{q} = |\mathbf{p}|\,|\mathbf{q}|\cos\theta = \sqrt{8}\sqrt{10}\cos\theta$$

Thus, $\quad \cos\theta = \dfrac{8}{\sqrt{8}\sqrt{10}} = \dfrac{\sqrt{8}}{\sqrt{10}} = \sqrt{\dfrac{8}{10}} = 0{\cdot}89\ldots$

$\qquad\qquad \Rightarrow \theta = 26{\cdot}565°$

● Thus the two forms of scalar product have been used to find the angle between the vectors.

● The scalar product can be illustrated by the sale of ice cream etc.

	cones	tubs	blocks	Costs	
Sales	(50	70	30)	50p	cones
				80p	tubs
				140p	blocks

The scalar product is the total money taken . . .
$50 \times 50 + 70 \times 80 + 30 \times 140$
$= 12300\text{p} = £123$

Make up examples of your own.

H.2.2 Perpendicular vectors

If the angle between two vectors is 90°, the scalar product is 0 [since cos 90° = 0]. This means that scalar product can be used as a test for perpendicularity.

$\mathbf{p} \cdot \mathbf{q} = 0 \Rightarrow \mathbf{p} \perp \mathbf{q}$.

Example

The vectors shown are $\begin{pmatrix} 4 \\ 2 \end{pmatrix}$ and $\begin{pmatrix} 1 \\ -2 \end{pmatrix}$.

The scalar product is $(1 \times 4 + {}^-2 \times 2)$
$\mathbf{p} \cdot \mathbf{q} = 4 - 4 = 0$

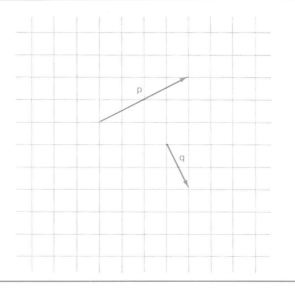

Note: $\mathbf{p} \cdot \mathbf{p} = |\mathbf{p}|^2$ since $\cos 0° = 1$.

Exercise H.2

1 Calculate the scalar product $\mathbf{p} \cdot \mathbf{q}$ if

$\mathbf{p} = \begin{pmatrix} 2 \\ 3 \end{pmatrix}$ and $\mathbf{q} = \begin{pmatrix} -1 \\ 4 \end{pmatrix}$. B

2 Use scalar products to find the angle between vectors $\mathbf{a}$ and $\mathbf{b}$

where $\mathbf{a} = \begin{pmatrix} 3 \\ 3 \end{pmatrix}$ and $\mathbf{b} = \begin{pmatrix} 4 \\ 5 \end{pmatrix}$. A

3 Choose vectors for $\mathbf{p}$, $\mathbf{q}$ and $\mathbf{r}$ to see whether
(a) $\mathbf{p} \cdot \mathbf{q} = \mathbf{q} \cdot \mathbf{p}$
(b) $\mathbf{p} \cdot (\mathbf{q} + \mathbf{r}) = \mathbf{p} \cdot \mathbf{q} + \mathbf{p} \cdot \mathbf{r}$ A

4 Given $\mathbf{x} = \begin{pmatrix} 1 \\ 2 \end{pmatrix}$ and $\mathbf{y} = \begin{pmatrix} -1 \\ 3 \end{pmatrix}$ find
the values of $\mathbf{x} \cdot \mathbf{x}$, $\mathbf{y} \cdot \mathbf{x}$ and $\mathbf{y} \cdot \mathbf{y}$.
Is it true that
$(\mathbf{x} + \mathbf{y}) \cdot (\mathbf{x} + \mathbf{y}) = \mathbf{x} \cdot \mathbf{x} + \mathbf{y} \cdot \mathbf{y} + 2\mathbf{x} \cdot \mathbf{y}$? A

H.3 Applications in geometry

Many geometrical properties can be proved very simply using vectors. The basic ideas are

(a) addition of vectors to show position,

(b) multiplication by scalar produces parallel vectors ... $\mathbf{p} = k\mathbf{q} \Rightarrow \mathbf{p} \mathbin{/\mkern-4mu/} \mathbf{q}$,

(c) scalar product $= 0$ implies perpendicularity.

Example 1

X, Y are the midpoints of AB and AC.
It is proved that XY is parallel to BC and half its length.

Proof   1Ø $\overrightarrow{BX} = \tfrac{1}{2}\mathbf{c} = \overrightarrow{XA}$

          2Ø $\overrightarrow{AC} = \mathbf{a} - \mathbf{c}$

          3Ø $\overrightarrow{AY} = \tfrac{1}{2}(\mathbf{a} - \mathbf{c})$

          4Ø $\overrightarrow{XY} = \overrightarrow{XA} + \overrightarrow{AY}$

               $= \tfrac{1}{2}\mathbf{c} + \tfrac{1}{2}(\mathbf{a} - \mathbf{c})$

               $= \tfrac{1}{2}\mathbf{a}$

          5Ø XY is parallel to BC and half its length

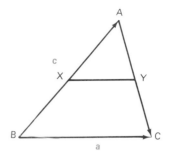

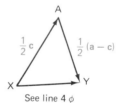

See line 4 ϕ

Example 2

ABCD is a parallelogram whose diagonals are perpendicular. It is proved that the parallelogram is a rhombus.

Proof   1Ø $\overrightarrow{DB} = \mathbf{p} + \mathbf{q}$

          2Ø $\overrightarrow{CA} = \mathbf{q} - \mathbf{p}$

          3Ø $(\mathbf{p} + \mathbf{q}) \cdot (\mathbf{q} - \mathbf{p}) = 0$

          4Ø $\mathbf{q} \cdot \mathbf{q} - \mathbf{p} \cdot \mathbf{p} = 0$

          5Ø $\mathbf{q} \cdot \mathbf{q} = \mathbf{p} \cdot \mathbf{p}$

          6Ø $|\mathbf{q}|^2 = |\mathbf{p}|^2$

          7Ø $|\mathbf{q}| = |\mathbf{p}|$

             So the figure is a rhombus.

Line 5Ø: remember $\mathbf{q} \cdot \mathbf{q} = |\mathbf{q}|^2$

                          $\mathbf{p} \cdot \mathbf{p} = |\mathbf{p}|^2$

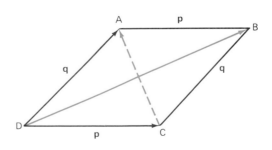

Exercise H.3

1 (a) **a**, **b** and **c** are the position vectors of the vertices A, B and C of a parallelogram. Write down an equation connecting the three vectors.

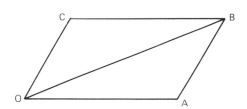

(b) Express the following vectors in terms of **w**, **x**, **y** and **z**:
(i) $\overrightarrow{AC}$ (ii) $\overrightarrow{DB}$ (iii) $\overrightarrow{AD}$
(iv) $\overrightarrow{EB}$ (v) $\overrightarrow{AE}$

If M is the midpoint of AE find
(vi) $\overrightarrow{MB}$ (vii) $\overrightarrow{CM}$ (viii) $\overrightarrow{MD}$
in terms of **w**, **x**, **y** and **z**.   B

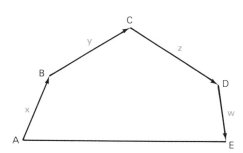

2 In the trapezium ABCD, AB // DC and AB = $\frac{2}{3}$DC.
Write vectors for
(i) $\overrightarrow{AB}$ (ii) $\overrightarrow{DB}$ (iii) $\overrightarrow{BC}$
in terms of **x** and **y**.   B

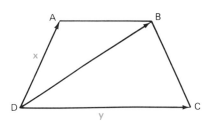

3 In triangle ABC, D is the midpoint of BC.

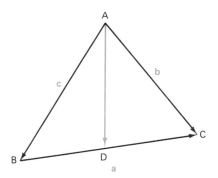

(a) Write the vectors $\overrightarrow{AD}$, $\overrightarrow{BD}$, $\overrightarrow{DC}$ in terms of **a**, **b** and **c**.
(b) Use your results to prove that
$$\overrightarrow{AD} = \frac{\mathbf{b} + \mathbf{c}}{2}.$$
Explain geometrically why this result must be true.   A

4 Calculate the angle between $\begin{pmatrix} 3 \\ 1 \end{pmatrix}$ and $\begin{pmatrix} 2 \\ -2 \end{pmatrix}$. Check by a careful drawing.   A

5 Find the column vector forms of $\overrightarrow{CX}$ and $\overrightarrow{OX}$.

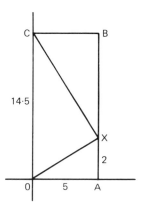

Use your results to prove that $C\hat{X}O$ is a right angle.   A

6 The symbols **i** and **j** stand for $\begin{pmatrix}1\\0\end{pmatrix}$ and $\begin{pmatrix}0\\1\end{pmatrix}$.

Three vectors **p**, **q**, **r** are given by the equations

$$\mathbf{p} = 4\mathbf{i} - 3\mathbf{j} \quad \mathbf{q} = a\mathbf{i} + b\mathbf{j} \quad \mathbf{r} = c\mathbf{i} + d\mathbf{j}$$

(a) Calculate $|\mathbf{p}|$, $|\mathbf{q}|$, $|\mathbf{r}|$ and $|\mathbf{q} + \mathbf{r}|$.

(b) Given that **q** is parallel to **p**, find a relationship between a and b.

(c) Given that **p** and **r** are perpendicular show that $4c = 3d$.

(d) Deduce from (b) and (c) that $|\mathbf{q} + \mathbf{r}|^2 = |\mathbf{q}|^2 + |\mathbf{r}|^2$ and illustrate this by a diagram.   A

7 Use vectors to prove that the diagonals of a rectangle must be equal.   A

8 Show that every isosceles triangle can be described in terms of two vectors, $a\mathbf{i} + b\mathbf{j}$ and $a\mathbf{i} - b\mathbf{j}$. Find the scalar product of these two vectors. How does the result relate to the original triangle?   A

◆ H.4   Matrices

A set of vectors can be arranged as a block of numbers called a matrix.

$$\begin{pmatrix} a & b \\ c & d \end{pmatrix} \rightarrow \quad \begin{matrix}(a & b)\\(c & d)\end{matrix} \quad \text{or} \quad \begin{pmatrix}a\\c\end{pmatrix}\begin{pmatrix}b\\d\end{pmatrix}$$

matrix   pair of   pair of

            row vectors   column vectors

This means that two sorts of information can be stored in a single matrix.

Example

Petrol pump sales

1st quarter sales from each pump (thousand gallons)

	✱✱	✱✱	lead free
Jan	8	14	6
Feb	3	12	4
Mch	11	21	10

(8   14   6) ↖
(3   12   14) ← row
(11   21   10) ↙ vectors

The row vectors show the total sales each month. The column vectors show the different month's sales for each type of petrol.

H.4.1   Matrix multiplication

The multiplication of matrices makes use of the scalar product of vectors (see section 8.2). The three situations

(a) vector times vector

(b) matrix times vector

(c) matrix times matrix

are shown below.

(a) $\quad (a_1 \quad b_1)\begin{pmatrix}a_2\\b_2\end{pmatrix} = a_1a_2 + b_1b_2$

      row   col   scalar product

Example

$$(2 \quad 5)\begin{pmatrix} 3 \\ 4 \end{pmatrix} = 6 + 20 = 26$$

(b) $\begin{pmatrix} (a_1 & b_1) \\ (c_1 & d_1) \end{pmatrix}\begin{pmatrix} a_2 \\ b_2 \end{pmatrix} = \begin{pmatrix} a_1a_2 + b_1b_2 \\ c_1a_2 + d_1b_2 \end{pmatrix}$

$$\begin{pmatrix} \mathbf{r}_1 \\ \mathbf{r}_2 \end{pmatrix} \quad \times \mathbf{c} \quad = \quad \begin{pmatrix} \mathbf{r}_1 \cdot \mathbf{c} \\ \mathbf{r}_2 \cdot \mathbf{c} \end{pmatrix}$$

matrix   col. v.   col. vector

Example

$$\begin{pmatrix} 2 & 5 \\ 1 & 7 \end{pmatrix}\begin{pmatrix} 3 \\ 4 \end{pmatrix} = \begin{pmatrix} 6 + 20 \\ 3 + 28 \end{pmatrix} = \begin{pmatrix} 26 \\ 31 \end{pmatrix}$$

matrix × col. v. ⟶ col. v.

(c) $\begin{pmatrix} (a_1 & b_1) \\ (c_1 & d_1) \end{pmatrix}\left(\begin{pmatrix} a_2 \\ b_2 \end{pmatrix}\begin{pmatrix} c_2 \\ d_2 \end{pmatrix}\right) = \begin{pmatrix} a_1a_2 + b_1b_2 & a_1c_2 + b_1d_2 \\ c_1a_2 + d_1b_2 & c_1c_2 + d_1d_2 \end{pmatrix}$

$$\begin{pmatrix} \mathbf{r}_1 \\ \mathbf{r}_2 \end{pmatrix} \quad \times (\mathbf{c}_1 \quad \mathbf{c}_2) = \begin{pmatrix} \mathbf{r}_1 \cdot \mathbf{c}_1 & \mathbf{r}_1 \cdot \mathbf{c}_2 \\ \mathbf{r}_2 \cdot \mathbf{c}_1 & \mathbf{r}_2 \cdot \mathbf{c}_2 \end{pmatrix}$$

matrix × matrix   =   matrix

Example

$$\begin{pmatrix} 2 & 5 \\ 1 & 7 \end{pmatrix}\begin{pmatrix} 3 & 6 \\ 4 & ^-1 \end{pmatrix} = \begin{pmatrix} 26 & 7 \\ 31 & ^-1 \end{pmatrix}$$

matrix × matrix → matrix

- The arrangements above hold for all matrices whatever their size. It should be noted that matrices have to match if they can be multiplied.
- It is a convention that matrix products are always formed by multiplying row vectors by column vectors in order, and not multiplying columns by rows. [See Exercise H.4.]

H.4.2 Unit matrix I

The matrix $\begin{pmatrix} 1 & 0 \\ 0 & 1 \end{pmatrix}$ is the unit matrix for two-by-two matrices.

It has the same property as 1 in ordinary numbers.

$a \times 1 = a$ for all numbers

$\mathbf{A} \cdot \mathbf{I} = \mathbf{A}$ where $\mathbf{A}$ is any 2×2 matrix

Proof: part I

$$\begin{pmatrix} a & b \\ c & d \end{pmatrix}\begin{pmatrix} p & q \\ r & s \end{pmatrix} = \begin{pmatrix} a & b \\ c & d \end{pmatrix} \Rightarrow \begin{array}{ll} ap + br = a & \text{(i)} \\ aq + bs = b & \text{(ii)} \\ cp + dr = c & \text{(iii)} \\ cq + ds = d & \text{(iv)} \end{array}$$

$\left.\begin{array}{l} ap + br = a \\ cp + dr = c \end{array}\right\}$ ... obviously $p = 1, r = 0$ satisfies the equations.

$\left.\begin{array}{l} aq + bs = b \\ cq + ds = d \end{array}\right\}$ ... obviously $q = 0, s = 1$ satisfies the equations.

So $\begin{pmatrix} 1 & 0 \\ 0 & 1 \end{pmatrix}$ behaves like the unit matrix.

Part II

$\begin{pmatrix} 1 & 0 \\ 0 & 1 \end{pmatrix}$ is a unit matrix. We need to prove that there is no

other ... $\mathbf{I} = \begin{pmatrix} 1 & 0 \\ 0 & 1 \end{pmatrix}$.

Suppose $\mathbf{J}$ is another matrix so that $\mathbf{AJ} = \mathbf{A}$ for every matrix $\mathbf{A}$, then
$\mathbf{IJ} = \mathbf{I}$.
But $\mathbf{IJ} = \mathbf{J}$ because $\mathbf{I}$ is a unit matrix.
So $\mathbf{I} = \mathbf{J}$.

(Margin: OPTIONAL BUT INTERESTING)

Example
$$\begin{pmatrix} 2 & 3 \\ 4 & 5 \end{pmatrix}\begin{pmatrix} 1 & 0 \\ 0 & 1 \end{pmatrix} = \begin{pmatrix} 2 & 3 \\ 4 & 5 \end{pmatrix} \quad \text{and} \quad \begin{pmatrix} 1 & 0 \\ 0 & 1 \end{pmatrix}\begin{pmatrix} 2 & 3 \\ 4 & 5 \end{pmatrix} = \begin{pmatrix} 2 & 3 \\ 4 & 5 \end{pmatrix}$$
Check these by matrix multiplication.

H.4.3 Determinant of a matrix ... |A|

The number $(ad - bc)$ is called the determinant of the matrix $\begin{pmatrix} a & b \\ c & d \end{pmatrix}$. It is the difference of the diagonal products.

The ad diagonal is called the leading diagonal of the matrix.

Examples

A	$\begin{pmatrix} 2 & 5 \\ 3 & 1 \end{pmatrix}$	$\begin{pmatrix} 1 & 0 \\ 1 & 0 \end{pmatrix}$	$\begin{pmatrix} ^-1 & 2 \\ 1 & 1 \end{pmatrix}$	$\begin{pmatrix} 4 & 0 \\ 0 & 4 \end{pmatrix}$
|A|	$^-13$	0	$^-3$	16

Please check the values of the determinant in each case.

H.4.4 Inverse of a matrix ... A^{-1}

The inverse of the matrix $A = \begin{pmatrix} a & b \\ c & d \end{pmatrix}$ is $\dfrac{1}{|A|}\begin{pmatrix} d & ^-b \\ ^-c & a \end{pmatrix}$.

Note that the elements of the leading diagonal have been switched, while the elements on the other diagonal have been made negative.

● When a matrix A is multiplied by its inverse A^{-1}, the unit matrix is formed.

● If $|A| = 0$, the matrix A does not have an inverse.

● If $|A| = 1$, ie. $ad - bc = 1$, then $\begin{pmatrix} d & ^-b \\ ^-c & a \end{pmatrix}$ is the inverse of $\begin{pmatrix} a & b \\ c & d \end{pmatrix}$.

Example

The inverse of $\begin{pmatrix} 3 & 2 \\ 7 & ^-5 \end{pmatrix}$ ... $A = \begin{pmatrix} 3 & 2 \\ 7 & ^-5 \end{pmatrix}$; $|A| = ^-15 - 14 = ^-29$

$$A^{-1} = \frac{1}{^-29}\begin{pmatrix} ^-5 & ^-2 \\ ^-7 & 3 \end{pmatrix} = \frac{1}{29}\begin{pmatrix} 5 & 2 \\ 7 & ^-3 \end{pmatrix}$$

Checks

$$AA^{-1} = \frac{1}{29}\begin{pmatrix} 3 & 2 \\ 7 & ^-5 \end{pmatrix}\begin{pmatrix} 5 & 2 \\ 7 & ^-3 \end{pmatrix} = \frac{1}{29}\begin{pmatrix} 29 & 0 \\ 0 & 29 \end{pmatrix} = \begin{pmatrix} 1 & 0 \\ 0 & 1 \end{pmatrix}$$

$$A^{-1}A = \frac{1}{29}\begin{pmatrix} 5 & 2 \\ 7 & ^-3 \end{pmatrix}\begin{pmatrix} 3 & 2 \\ 7 & ^-5 \end{pmatrix} = \frac{1}{29}\begin{pmatrix} 29 & 0 \\ 0 & 29 \end{pmatrix} = \begin{pmatrix} 1 & 0 \\ 0 & 1 \end{pmatrix}$$

Note the demonstration that $AA^{-1} = A^{-1}A$

Exercise H.4

1 Mrs Green bought 7 lb of potatoes at 20p per lb, 4 lb of apples at 35p per lb and 1 lb of strawberries at 45p per lb. Set out the data as a pair of vectors and show their scalar product. What does the scalar product represent?   B

2 Mrs Green (of question 1) called in on her neighbour, Mrs Brown, and offered to do her shopping. Mrs Brown also wanted potatoes, apples and strawberries but not in the same quantity (see below). Calculate how much money Mrs Brown's shopping costs.

Mrs Green $(7 \quad 4 \quad 1)$ $\begin{pmatrix} 20 \\ 35 \\ 45 \end{pmatrix}$
Mrs Brown $(4 \quad 3 \quad 2)$ B

3 Carry out the multiplications below, where possible.

(a) $\begin{pmatrix} 1 & 1 & 2 \\ 1 & 3 & 1 \end{pmatrix} \begin{pmatrix} 0 \\ 0 \\ 1 \end{pmatrix}$ (b) $\begin{pmatrix} 3 & 4 \\ 5 & 6 \end{pmatrix} \begin{pmatrix} 1 \\ ^-1 \end{pmatrix}$

(c) $(2 \quad 6) \begin{pmatrix} 0 \\ ^-1 \\ 0 \end{pmatrix}$ (d) $\begin{pmatrix} a & b \\ c & d \end{pmatrix} \begin{pmatrix} 5 \\ 6 \end{pmatrix}$ B

4 (a) Prove that $\begin{pmatrix} a & b \\ c & d \end{pmatrix} \begin{pmatrix} 1 & 0 \\ 0 & 1 \end{pmatrix} = \begin{pmatrix} a & b \\ c & d \end{pmatrix}$.

(b) Find a matrix which enlarges $\begin{pmatrix} a & b \\ c & d \end{pmatrix}$ by a factor of 4.

(i.e. increases each element by 4 times ... $a \rightarrow 4a$ $b \rightarrow 4b$ etc.)   A

5 Use the method of section H.4.4 to write down the inverses of the following matrices.

(a) $\begin{pmatrix} 1 & 2 \\ 2 & 1 \end{pmatrix}$ (b) $\begin{pmatrix} 2 & ^-3 \\ 1 & 5 \end{pmatrix}$

(c) $\begin{pmatrix} 1 & 0 \\ 0 & 3 \end{pmatrix}$ (d) $\begin{pmatrix} 3 & ^-1 \\ 4 & 2 \end{pmatrix}$

Check both products $\mathbf{AA}^{-1}$ and $\mathbf{A}^{-1}\mathbf{A}$ in each case.   B

6 (a) Choose pairs of matrices to show that $\mathbf{AB}$ is not generally equal to $\mathbf{BA}$, where $\mathbf{A}$ and $\mathbf{B}$ are 2×2 matrices.

(b) Matrices of the form $\begin{pmatrix} k & 0 \\ 0 & k \end{pmatrix}$ do obey the commutative law of multiplication $\mathbf{AB} = \mathbf{BA}$.

Investigate $\begin{pmatrix} k & 0 \\ 0 & ^-k \end{pmatrix}$ matrices for commutativity and other properties of real numbers.   A

7 Construct examples of pairs of matrices $\begin{pmatrix} a_1 & b_1 \\ c_1 & d_1 \end{pmatrix}$ and $\begin{pmatrix} a_2 & b_2 \\ c_2 & d_2 \end{pmatrix}$ such that $a_1 d_2 = a_2 d_1$ and $b_1 c_2 = b_2 c_1$. Investigate the $\mathbf{AB}$, $\mathbf{BA}$ products for each example. Comment.   A

8 Find matrices so that
(a) $\mathbf{A}^2 = \mathbf{A}$ (b) $\mathbf{A}^2 = {}^-\mathbf{A}$ A

H.5   Matrices of transformations

The transformations of geometry, enlargement, reflection and rotation can be represented by matrices acting on vectors.

H.5.1 Enlargement

Matrices of the form $\begin{pmatrix} k & 0 \\ 0 & k \end{pmatrix}$ produce an

enlargement, scale factor k.
The square whose vertices are $(0,0)$, $(0,1)$, $(1,0)$
and $(1,1)$ is enlarged to the square whose vertices
are $(0,0)$, $(0,4)$, $(4,0)$ and $(4,4)$ by the

matrix $\begin{pmatrix} 4 & 0 \\ 0 & 4 \end{pmatrix}$.

This corresponds to 'stretching the whole plane'.

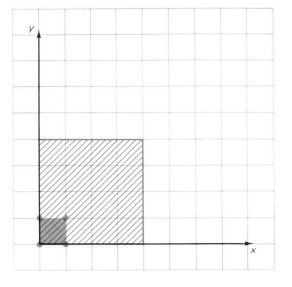

$$\begin{pmatrix} 4 & 0 \\ 0 & 4 \end{pmatrix}\begin{pmatrix} 0 \\ 0 \end{pmatrix} = \begin{pmatrix} 0 \\ 0 \end{pmatrix}$$

$$\begin{pmatrix} 4 & 0 \\ 0 & 4 \end{pmatrix}\begin{pmatrix} 0 \\ 1 \end{pmatrix} = \begin{pmatrix} 0 \\ 4 \end{pmatrix}$$

$$\begin{pmatrix} 4 & 0 \\ 0 & 4 \end{pmatrix}\begin{pmatrix} 1 \\ 0 \end{pmatrix} = \begin{pmatrix} 4 \\ 0 \end{pmatrix}$$

$$\begin{pmatrix} 4 & 0 \\ 0 & 4 \end{pmatrix}\begin{pmatrix} 1 \\ 1 \end{pmatrix} = \begin{pmatrix} 4 \\ 4 \end{pmatrix}$$

Check these matrix multiplications.

H.5.2 Reflection

The matrix $\begin{pmatrix} 1 & 0 \\ 0 & -1 \end{pmatrix}$ produces reflection in the x axis.

Example

Point A $\quad \begin{pmatrix} 1 & 0 \\ 0 & -1 \end{pmatrix}\begin{pmatrix} 2 \\ 1 \end{pmatrix} = \begin{pmatrix} 2 \\ -1 \end{pmatrix}$

Point B $\quad \begin{pmatrix} 1 & 0 \\ 0 & -1 \end{pmatrix}\begin{pmatrix} 4 \\ 1 \end{pmatrix} = \begin{pmatrix} 4 \\ -1 \end{pmatrix}$

Point C $\quad \begin{pmatrix} 1 & 0 \\ 0 & -1 \end{pmatrix}\begin{pmatrix} 4 \\ 4 \end{pmatrix} = \begin{pmatrix} 4 \\ -4 \end{pmatrix}$

Point (2,3) $\begin{pmatrix} 1 & 0 \\ 0 & -1 \end{pmatrix}\begin{pmatrix} 2 \\ 3 \end{pmatrix} = \begin{pmatrix} 2 \\ -3 \end{pmatrix}$

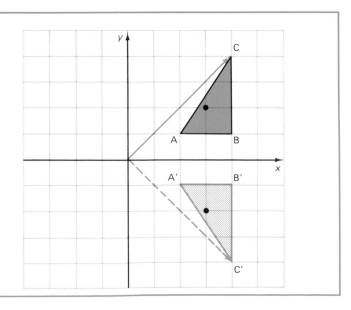

- This matrix can be found by considering it as a function which maps (x, y) into $(x, ^-y)$ . . .

$$\begin{pmatrix} a & b \\ c & d \end{pmatrix}\begin{pmatrix} x \\ y \end{pmatrix} = \begin{pmatrix} x \\ ^-y \end{pmatrix} \Rightarrow \left.\begin{matrix} ax + by = x \\ cx + dy = ^-y \end{matrix}\right\} \Rightarrow \begin{matrix} a = 1, b = 0 \\ c = 0, d = ^-1 \end{matrix}$$

• • The matrix $\begin{pmatrix} ^-1 & 0 \\ 0 & 1 \end{pmatrix}$ produces reflection in the y-axis.

   Prove this for yourself

• • The matrix $\begin{pmatrix} 0 & 1 \\ 1 & 0 \end{pmatrix}$ produces reflection in the line $y = x$ (diagonal line).

   Prove this for yourself

• • The matrix $\begin{pmatrix} 0 & ^-1 \\ ^-1 & 0 \end{pmatrix}$ produces reflection in the line $y = ^-x$ (negative

diagonal line).

   Prove this for yourself

•• Reflection in the y axis followed by reflection in the x axis produces a rotation of 180° . . . i.e. a half turn

$$\begin{pmatrix} 1 & 0 \\ 0 & ^-1 \end{pmatrix}\begin{pmatrix} ^-1 & 0 \\ 0 & 1 \end{pmatrix}\begin{pmatrix} x \\ y \end{pmatrix} = \begin{pmatrix} ^-x \\ ^-y \end{pmatrix}$$

So the half turn corresponds to

$$\begin{pmatrix} 1 & 0 \\ 0 & ^-1 \end{pmatrix}\begin{pmatrix} ^-1 & 0 \\ 0 & 1 \end{pmatrix} = \begin{pmatrix} ^-1 & 0 \\ 0 & ^-1 \end{pmatrix}.$$

   Confirm this by another method.

H.5.3 Rotation

The matrix $\begin{pmatrix} 0 & ^-1 \\ 1 & 0 \end{pmatrix}$ produces an anticlockwise rotation of 90°.

Example

Point A $\begin{pmatrix} 0 & ^-1 \\ 1 & 0 \end{pmatrix}\begin{pmatrix} 3 \\ ^-1 \end{pmatrix} = \begin{pmatrix} 1 \\ 3 \end{pmatrix}$

Point B $\begin{pmatrix} 0 & ^-1 \\ 1 & 0 \end{pmatrix}\begin{pmatrix} 5 \\ ^-1 \end{pmatrix} = \begin{pmatrix} 1 \\ 5 \end{pmatrix}$

Point C $\begin{pmatrix} 0 & ^-1 \\ 1 & 0 \end{pmatrix}\begin{pmatrix} 5 \\ 3 \end{pmatrix} = \begin{pmatrix} ^-3 \\ 5 \end{pmatrix}$

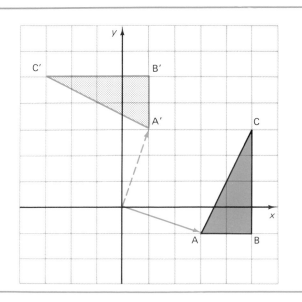

- This matrix can be found by considering it as a function which maps (x, y) into $(^-y, x)$ . . .

$$\begin{pmatrix} a & b \\ c & d \end{pmatrix}\begin{pmatrix} x \\ y \end{pmatrix} = \begin{pmatrix} ^-y \\ x \end{pmatrix} \Rightarrow \left.\begin{array}{c} ax + by = ^-y \\ cx + dy = x \end{array}\right\} \Rightarrow \begin{array}{c} a = 0, b = ^-1 \\ c = 1, d = 0 \end{array}$$

- • The matrix $\begin{pmatrix} 0 & 1 \\ ^-1 & 0 \end{pmatrix}$ produces a clockwise rotation of 90°.

  Prove this for yourself

- • Two rotations of 90° clockwise or anticlockwise produce a half turn.

  Show this by matrix multiplication

- • The matrix $\begin{bmatrix} \cos\theta & ^-\sin\theta \\ \sin\theta & \cos\theta \end{bmatrix}$ produces an anticlockwise rotation of $\theta°$

  while $\begin{bmatrix} \cos\theta & \sin\theta \\ ^-\sin\theta & \cos\theta \end{bmatrix}$ produces a clockwise rotation of $\theta°$.

The anticlockwise rotation followed by the clockwise rotation will take the vector back to where it started. Thus the two matrices must be inverses.

Their product is $\begin{bmatrix} \cos^2\theta + \sin^2\theta & 0 \\ 0 & \cos^2\theta + \sin^2\theta \end{bmatrix} = \begin{pmatrix} 1 & 0 \\ 0 & 1 \end{pmatrix}$

Exercise H.5

1 Write down matrices which would produce the transformation in the diagrams.

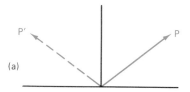
(a)

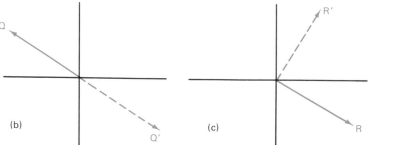

(b)

(c)

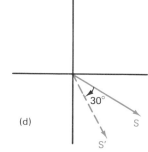
(d)

2 E_1 and E_2 are two enlargement matrices such that $E_1 E_2 = I$.
What can you say about the enlargements they produce. Draw a diagram.

3 $\triangle ABC$ has its vertices at $(1, 1)$, $(3, 1)$ and $(3, 4)$. Draw the images of this triangle under the transformations

$$T_1 = \begin{pmatrix} ^-1 & 0 \\ 0 & 1 \end{pmatrix} \text{ and } T_2 = \begin{pmatrix} 0 & ^-1 \\ 1 & 0 \end{pmatrix}.$$

What transformations would be produced by $T_1 T_2$ and $T_2 T_1$?

4 The rotation matrix $\mathbf{R} = \begin{pmatrix} \frac{1}{2}\sqrt{3} & -\frac{1}{2} \\ \frac{1}{2} & \frac{1}{2}\sqrt{3} \end{pmatrix}$

turns the vector $\begin{pmatrix} x \\ y \end{pmatrix}$ through an angle θ.

Find θ and show that $\mathbf{R}^3 = \begin{pmatrix} 0 & -1 \\ 1 & 0 \end{pmatrix}$.

Explain why this must be so from a geometrical point of view. A

5 The transformation **T** consists of a reflection in the x axis followed by an enlargement, centre (0, 0) and scale factor 3. Find the matrix of the transformation and the images of

$\begin{pmatrix} 1 \\ 1 \end{pmatrix}$, $\begin{pmatrix} 1 \\ -1 \end{pmatrix}$ and $\begin{pmatrix} 2 \\ 3 \end{pmatrix}$. A

6 The six transformations
  (i)   rotation through 90° anticlockwise ↻
  (ii) rotation through 90° clockwise ↺
  (iii) half turn (or rotation through 180°) H
  (iv) reflection in the x axis ↕
  (v)   reflection in the y axis ↔
  (vi) no change I
  (vii) reflection in $y = x$ ↘
  (viii) reflection in $y = {}^-x$ ↗
  are given the symbols shown.

(a) Write a matrix for each transformation.
(b) Complete the composition table
(c) Find which transformations satisfy
$$\mathbf{A}^2 = \mathbf{I}$$
$$\mathbf{A}^4 = \mathbf{I}$$
$$(\mathbf{A}^{-1})^2 = \mathbf{A}$$
A

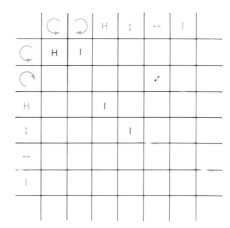

The side operation is followed by the top operation.

◆ H.6 Some applications of matrices

Matrices have many applications in the mathematical solution of problems. Two examples are given here in addition to the matrix transformations described above.

H.6.1 Incidence matrices (route matrices)

Routes round a network can be easily described by a matrix.

Example

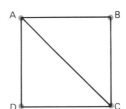

The matrix shows how many direct routes can be found from one node to another. E.g. There is one direct route from B to C, but no direct route from B to D.

If **M** is the route matrix, $\mathbf{M}^2$ will be the route matrix for 2nd order journeys, i.e. journeys which are completed in two steps

---

Example

$$\mathbf{M} = \begin{pmatrix} 0 & 1 & 1 & 1 \\ 1 & 0 & 1 & 0 \\ 1 & 1 & 0 & 1 \\ 1 & 0 & 1 & 0 \end{pmatrix} \qquad \mathbf{M}^2 = \begin{pmatrix} 3 & 1 & 2 & 1 \\ 1 & 2 & 1 & 2 \\ 2 & 1 & 3 & 1 \\ 1 & 2 & 1 & 2 \end{pmatrix}$$

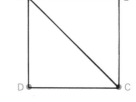

This suggests   3 routes A → A
                   1 route   A → B
                   2 routes A → C
                   1 route   A → D

Checking 2nd order routes on the network
For A → A   A → B → A
               A → C → A
               A → D → A . . . 3 routes as expected.

- Check that $\mathbf{M}^2$ is correct by multiplying **M** by itself.
- Check that $\mathbf{M}^2$ gives the correct number of 2nd order routes.

H.6.2   Solution of sets of simultaneous equations

Although the method is used on a pair of simultaneous equations with two unknowns, it can easily be extended. At this stage however you will not be asked to solve more than two linear equations at a time.

The method is shown in an example.

Example

Solve the simultaneous equations $2x + 3y = 13$
                                     $3x - y \;= 3$

10   Write as a matrix equation $\begin{pmatrix} 2 & 3 \\ 3 & {}^-1 \end{pmatrix}\begin{pmatrix} x \\ y \end{pmatrix} = \begin{pmatrix} 13 \\ 3 \end{pmatrix}$ **Ax = x′**

15   Calculate $|\mathbf{A}|$ . . . ${}^-2 - 9 = {}^-11$

20   Write down $\mathbf{A}^{-1}$ (see section H.4.4). . . $\dfrac{1}{{}^-11}\begin{pmatrix} {}^-1 & {}^-3 \\ {}^-3 & 2 \end{pmatrix} = \begin{pmatrix} \frac{1}{11} & \frac{3}{11} \\ \frac{3}{11} & \frac{{}^-2}{11} \end{pmatrix}$

30   $\begin{pmatrix} x \\ y \end{pmatrix} = \begin{pmatrix} \frac{1}{11} & \frac{3}{11} \\ \frac{3}{11} & \frac{{}^-2}{11} \end{pmatrix}\begin{pmatrix} 13 \\ 3 \end{pmatrix} = \begin{pmatrix} \frac{22}{11} \\ \frac{33}{11} \end{pmatrix} = \begin{pmatrix} 2 \\ 3 \end{pmatrix}$
$\begin{aligned} \mathbf{Ax} &= \mathbf{x'} \\ \Rightarrow \mathbf{A}^{-1}\mathbf{Ax} &= \mathbf{A}^{-1}\mathbf{x'} \\ \Rightarrow \quad\quad \mathbf{x} &= \mathbf{A}^{-1}\mathbf{x'} \end{aligned}$

40   $x = 2, \quad y = 3$

The method boils down to finding the inverse of matrix **A**.

Exercise H.6

1 (a) Write down the route matrix for the diagram.
(b) Find the square of this matrix and use it to find the number of routes from P to R which take exactly two steps.

B

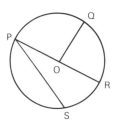

2 Construct a network of arcs and nodes, given the following incidence matrix.

$$\begin{array}{c c} & \begin{array}{c c c c} A & B & C & D \end{array} \\ \begin{array}{c} A \\ B \\ C \\ D \end{array} & \left(\begin{array}{c c c c} 0 & 2 & 0 & 1 \\ 2 & 0 & 2 & 1 \\ 0 & 2 & 0 & 1 \\ 1 & 1 & 1 & 0 \end{array}\right) \end{array}$$

Show that there are 9 second order routes from B back to B on this network.

A

3 Use a matrix method to solve the simultaneous equations
(a) $2x + y = 3$
$x - 2y = 9$
(b) $3x - 4y + 3 = 0$
$x = 2y - 2$

B

4 Show that the simultaneous equations
$2x + 4y = 9$
$3x + 6y = 10$
cannot be solved by matrix methods. Do you think the equations can be solved by any other methods. Give reasons for your answer.

A

Examination questions H

The following questions are typical of the questions you can expect. Worked out answers are given on pages 396–408.

1 A police patrol car is controlled using a grid, with the police station at (0, 0).
Write down vectors which represent each 'action point' and vectors which represent journeys between action points.
What is the sum of all the journey vectors when the patrol car has returned to the station via -A-B-C-D-E-.

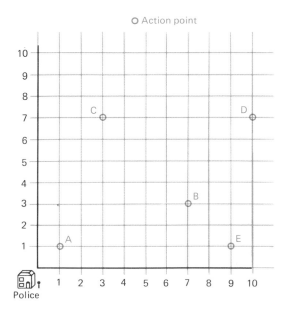

2 Vector **a** is $\begin{pmatrix} 3 \\ -2 \end{pmatrix}$ and vector **b** is $\begin{pmatrix} 5 \\ 4 \end{pmatrix}$.

    (a) What is the vector $\frac{1}{2}(\mathbf{a} + \mathbf{b})$? Illustrate this vector on a diagram.

    (b) Write down a vector which is perpendicular to $\begin{pmatrix} 3 \\ -2 \end{pmatrix}$ and another which is perpendicular to $\begin{pmatrix} 5 \\ 4 \end{pmatrix}$.

3 (a) Find the magnitude of the vectors $\begin{pmatrix} 4 \\ 5 \end{pmatrix}$ and $\begin{pmatrix} -4 \\ -5 \end{pmatrix}$. Draw a diagram to illustrate your answer.

    (b) If $\mathbf{u} + \mathbf{v}$ and $\mathbf{u} - \mathbf{v}$ have the same magnitude, what can you say about the vectors **u** and **v**.

4 X and Y are $\frac{3}{4}$ points along OA and OB.

    (a) Find $\overrightarrow{AB}$ in terms of **a** and **b**.

    (b) Find $\overrightarrow{XY}$ in terms of **a** and **b**.

    (c) What can be deduced about XY and AB.

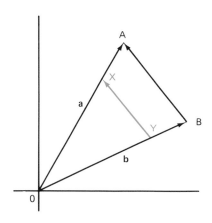

5 ABCD is a parallelogram. P and Q are the midpoints of AB and CD. Prove that X and Y are trisection points of BD, AQ and PC.

6 (a) Prove that $(\mathbf{u} + \mathbf{v}) \cdot \mathbf{w} = \mathbf{u} \cdot \mathbf{w} + \mathbf{v} \cdot \mathbf{w}$, where $\mathbf{u} = \begin{pmatrix} u_1 \\ u_2 \end{pmatrix}$; $\mathbf{v} = \begin{pmatrix} v_1 \\ v_2 \end{pmatrix}$; and $\mathbf{w} = \begin{pmatrix} w_1 \\ w_2 \end{pmatrix}$

    (b) Find the angle between the vectors $\begin{pmatrix} 1 \\ 1 \end{pmatrix}$ and $\begin{pmatrix} 1 \\ 3 \end{pmatrix}$. Confirm by drawing and measurement.

7 Unit vectors **i** and **j** are at right angles to each other.

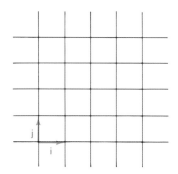

Given $\mathbf{p} = 3\mathbf{i} + 4\mathbf{j}$
           $\mathbf{q} = 5\mathbf{i}$
        $4\mathbf{r} = \mathbf{p} + \mathbf{q}$
        $2\mathbf{s} = \mathbf{p} - \mathbf{q}$

show that
    (a) $|\mathbf{p}| = |\mathbf{q}|$
    (b) $|\mathbf{r}| = |\mathbf{s}|$
    (c) $\mathbf{r} \perp \mathbf{s}$
    (d) $|\mathbf{r} + \mathbf{s}| = |\mathbf{r} - \mathbf{s}|$
    (e) $(\mathbf{r} + \mathbf{s}) \perp (\mathbf{r} - \mathbf{s})$
    (f) $|\mathbf{r} + k\mathbf{s}| = |\mathbf{r} - k\mathbf{s}|$ where k is any number.

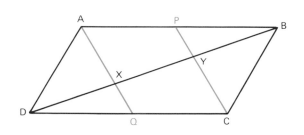

◆ **8** (a) ABCD is a parallelogram. A is (1, 2), B is (6, ⁻2), and D is (3, 5). Calculate the coordinates of C.

(b) OXYZ is a parallelogram with T as the midpoint of YZ.
OT meets ZX at U, and YU meets OZ at V.
If $\overrightarrow{OX} = \mathbf{x}$ and $\overrightarrow{OZ} = \mathbf{z}$ show that
(i) $\overrightarrow{XZ} = \mathbf{z} - \mathbf{x}$
(ii) $\overrightarrow{OU} = \frac{2}{3}(\mathbf{z} + \frac{1}{2}\mathbf{x})$
(iii) $\overrightarrow{YU} = \frac{-2}{3}\mathbf{x} - \frac{1}{3}\mathbf{z}$

9 $\mathbf{A} = \begin{pmatrix} 1 & 1 \\ 1 & 2 \end{pmatrix}$; $\mathbf{B} = \begin{pmatrix} 2 & 1 \\ 1 & 0 \end{pmatrix}$; $\mathbf{C} = \begin{pmatrix} 2 & ^-1 \\ ^-1 & 1 \end{pmatrix}$.

(a) Calculate $\mathbf{A} + \mathbf{B} + \mathbf{C}$.
(b) Calculate $\mathbf{AC}$ and $\mathbf{BC}$.
(c) Find the inverse of $\mathbf{A}$ and the inverse of $\mathbf{B}$.
(d) Is it true that $(\mathbf{AB})^{-1} = \mathbf{B}^{-1} \cdot \mathbf{A}^{-1}$?

10 T is the transformation with matrix $\begin{pmatrix} 0 & 1 \\ ^-1 & 0 \end{pmatrix}$.

What transformations on $\begin{pmatrix} x \\ y \end{pmatrix}$ are caused by

$\mathbf{T}^2$, $\mathbf{T}^3$ and $\mathbf{T}^4$.

◆ **11** Under a transformation whose matrix is $\begin{pmatrix} p & q \\ r & s \end{pmatrix}$, the images of (1, 1) and (1, 0) are (⁻1, 0) and (2, 3). Find the values of p, q, r and s.

◆ **12** For the network shown in the diagram
matrix **A** gives the number of routes between nodes,
matrix **B** is a 3 × 6 incidence matrix showing which arcs end at which nodes,

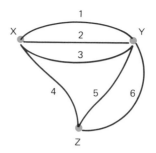

matrix **C** is the incidence matrix showing which nodes are at the ends of which arcs.

(a) Calculate **BC**
(b) Calculate **BC** − **A**. What information does this give?

13 $\mathbf{A} = \begin{pmatrix} 1 & 2 \\ 0 & 3 \end{pmatrix}$; $\mathbf{B} = \begin{pmatrix} 1 & -\frac{2}{3} \\ 0 & \frac{1}{3} \end{pmatrix}$;

$\mathbf{C} = \begin{pmatrix} 2 & 0 \\ 4 & 1 \end{pmatrix}$; $\mathbf{D} = \begin{pmatrix} \frac{1}{2} & 0 \\ p & 1 \end{pmatrix}$

(a) Evaluate **AB**.
(b) Find the value of p which makes **CD** the unit matrix.
(c) Simplify **CABD** with the value of p found in (b). What does this show about the inverse of **CA**?

◆ **14** The matrix represents a network of main roads joining four towns. All roads are dual carriageway.

	P	Q	R	S
P	0	2	1	2
Q	2	0	1	1
R	1	1	0	2
S	2	1	2	0

(a) Calculate the total number of roads involved.
(b) Make a diagram of the network.
(c) How many different ways can a motorist travel P → Q → R → S?

◆ **15** (a) The simultaneous equations

$$2x + 3y = 3$$
$$3x - 4y = 13$$

are solved by writing the pair of equations in matrix form

$$\begin{pmatrix} 2 & 3 \\ 3 & -4 \end{pmatrix} \begin{pmatrix} x \\ y \end{pmatrix} = \begin{pmatrix} 3 \\ 13 \end{pmatrix}$$

Complete the solution.

(b) Explain why the inverse of a matrix

$$\begin{pmatrix} a & b \\ ka & kb \end{pmatrix}$$ cannot be found. Hence or

otherwise show that the equations

$$2x + 3y = 14$$
$$4x + 6y = 21$$

cannot be solved.

[Illustrate your answer with a diagram.]

◆ **16** The matrix

$$\begin{pmatrix} \dfrac{1}{\sqrt{2}} & \dfrac{-1}{\sqrt{2}} \\ \dfrac{1}{\sqrt{2}} & \dfrac{1}{\sqrt{2}} \end{pmatrix}$$

produces a rotation of $\begin{pmatrix} x \\ y \end{pmatrix}$.

(a) Calculate the determinant of the matrix.

(b) Find the angle of rotation.

(c) Construct a matrix that would rotate $\begin{pmatrix} x \\ y \end{pmatrix}$

clockwise through 50°. Comment on any difficulties that might arise in using this rotation.

Activities and investigations H

Games for two to four players

1 Vector race game (up to four people)

You may not have played this game in Topic D. If so, the game fits with the revision of vectors.

2 Vector snap (two players)

This game is played with an ordinary set of dominoes.

Rules

The dominoes are stirred and divided between the players. The players do not look at the dominoes.
The first player selects two dominoes and puts them face upwards: for example,

The second player selects two dominoes and also places them face upwards.

- If the same scalar product can be formed for each pair there is a snap and the first player to say so wins all the dominoes.
  Note that each pair of dominoes can give *two* choices of scalar product.

Scalar product 14

Scalar product 10

Scalar product 14

Scalar product 10

- If a player says snap when it is not true, the other player takes all the dominoes.
- If 'no-snap' or 'false-snap' occurs, the players draw two more dominoes and add them to the face up ones. A 'snap' occurs if any pair can give a scalar product which is the same in both hands.

Investigate and develop this game for yourself.

Puzzles and investigations

1 Vector algebra

What are the rules?
Vectors have simple rules for addition and for multiplication by a scalar.
There is also the scalar product of two vectors.
Compare the behaviour of vectors with the rules of algebra in Section F.1.
[For example, if $\mathbf{p}$, $\mathbf{q}$ and $\mathbf{r}$ are vectors, is it true that $\mathbf{p} \cdot \mathbf{q} = \mathbf{p} \cdot \mathbf{r} \Rightarrow \mathbf{q} = \mathbf{r}$?]

2 Solution of linear equations by vectors

A pair of simultaneous linear equations can be solved very easily by vectors. The steps and an example are given below. Check that the method works and construct some equations of your own to solve by vectors.

1∅ $a_1 x + b_1 y = c_1$
$a_2 x + b_2 y = c_2$

2∅ Write as $\begin{pmatrix} a_1 \\ a_2 \end{pmatrix} x + \begin{pmatrix} b_1 \\ b_2 \end{pmatrix} y = \begin{pmatrix} c_1 \\ c_2 \end{pmatrix}$

3∅ The problem is changed to one of asking how many $\begin{pmatrix} a_1 \\ a_2 \end{pmatrix}'$s plus how many $\begin{pmatrix} b_1 \\ b_2 \end{pmatrix}'$s equals $\begin{pmatrix} c_1 \\ c_2 \end{pmatrix}$.

4∅ This problem of 3∅ is now solved by drawing.
For example,

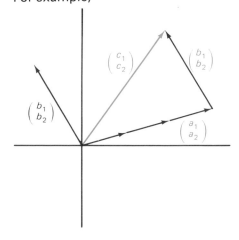

$\begin{pmatrix} c_1 \\ c_2 \end{pmatrix}$ is drawn first and then 'back tracked' in the $\begin{pmatrix} b_1 \\ b_2 \end{pmatrix}$ direction until the $\begin{pmatrix} a_1 \\ a_2 \end{pmatrix}'$s are met. In this case

$$3\begin{pmatrix} a_1 \\ a_2 \end{pmatrix} + 1\begin{pmatrix} b_1 \\ b_2 \end{pmatrix} = \begin{pmatrix} c_1 \\ c_2 \end{pmatrix}$$

so $x = 3$, $y = 1$.

Compare this method with the other methods of solving simultaneous equations.
Algebra ... see section F.7
Matrices ... see section H.6.2
Become an EXPERT.

Example

$x + y = 5$

$2x - y = 1$

$$\begin{pmatrix} 1 \\ 2 \end{pmatrix} x + \begin{pmatrix} 1 \\ -1 \end{pmatrix} y = \begin{pmatrix} 5 \\ 1 \end{pmatrix}$$

How many $\begin{pmatrix} 1 \\ 2 \end{pmatrix}$'s plus how many $\begin{pmatrix} 1 \\ -1 \end{pmatrix}$'s make $\begin{pmatrix} 5 \\ 1 \end{pmatrix}$?

Draw the vectors.

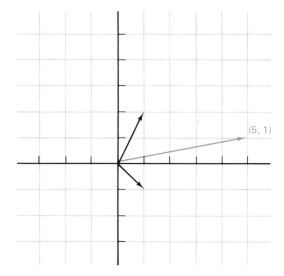

(5, 1)

Step back from $\begin{pmatrix} 5 \\ 1 \end{pmatrix}$, parallel to $\begin{pmatrix} 1 \\ 2 \end{pmatrix}$, until

vector steps continued from $\begin{pmatrix} 1 \\ -1 \end{pmatrix}$

are met.

The diagram shows clearly that

$$2\begin{pmatrix} 1 \\ 2 \end{pmatrix} + 3\begin{pmatrix} 1 \\ -1 \end{pmatrix} = \begin{pmatrix} 5 \\ 1 \end{pmatrix}$$

So $x = 2$, $y = 3$.

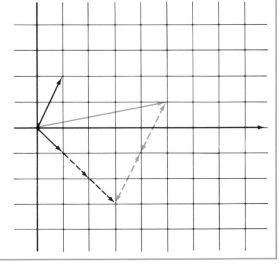

3 Relative motion and other applications

Just as numbers are basic to all forms of measurement, vectors are basic to all forms of movement

Make a collection of the application of vectors in 'real world' movement and force situations.

Here are two examples to start off your collection.

Climbing a rock face
The climber leans out from the rock face so as to increase the vector component towards the rock. This increases the friction.

Swimming a river
To cross the river direct the swimmer must swim against the current.

4 Matrix algebra

2×2 matrices have their own algebra. The rules can be established and checked by examples and by using ordinary algebra on the elements

Here are some ways of writing 2×2 matrices in general.

$$\mathbf{A} = \begin{pmatrix} a & b \\ c & d \end{pmatrix} \ldots \mathbf{A} = \begin{pmatrix} a_1 & a_2 \\ a_3 & a_4 \end{pmatrix}, \quad \mathbf{B} = \begin{pmatrix} b_1 & b_2 \\ b_3 & b_4 \end{pmatrix}.$$

$$\mathbf{A} = \begin{pmatrix} a_{11} & a_{12} \\ a_{21} & a_{22} \end{pmatrix} \ldots \text{this is the most scientific notation}$$

$$\mathbf{B} = \begin{pmatrix} b_{11} & b_{12} \\ b_{21} & b_{22} \end{pmatrix} \ldots \text{the suffices are useful checks}$$

1st row   2nd column

In this notation the basic rules of addition and multiplication become.

$$\mathbf{A} + \mathbf{B} = \begin{pmatrix} a_{11} + b_{11} & a_{12} + b_{12} \\ a_{21} + b_{21} & a_{22} + b_{22} \end{pmatrix}$$

and

$$\mathbf{AB} = \begin{pmatrix} a_{11}b_{11} + a_{12}b_{21} & a_{11}b_{12} + a_{12}b_{22} \\ a_{21}b_{11} + a_{22}b_{21} & a_{21}b_{12} + a_{22}b_{22} \end{pmatrix}$$

Some of the algebra you might check [BEWARE. Not **all** true]

- $\mathbf{A} + \mathbf{B} = \mathbf{B} + \mathbf{A}$
- $\mathbf{A} + (\mathbf{B} + \mathbf{C}) = (\mathbf{A} + \mathbf{B}) + \mathbf{C}$
- $\mathbf{AB} = \mathbf{BA}$
- $\mathbf{A}(\mathbf{B} + \mathbf{C}) = \mathbf{AB} + \mathbf{AC}$
- $\mathbf{AX} = \mathbf{A} \Rightarrow \mathbf{X} = \mathbf{I}$ or $\mathbf{A} = \mathbf{0}$
- $\mathbf{AB} = \mathbf{AC} \Rightarrow \mathbf{B} = \mathbf{C}$
- Every matrix $\mathbf{A}$ has an inverse $\mathbf{A}^{-1}$ such that $\mathbf{AA}^{-1} = \mathbf{A}^{-1}\mathbf{A} = \mathbf{I}$

There are plenty of other relationships to explore as well.

5 Coding and decoding with matrices

Matrices can be used for putting messages into code.
For example . . .

The word blue is changed to the matrix $\begin{pmatrix} 2 & 12 \\ 21 & 5 \end{pmatrix}$.

The numbers correspond to the letters' place in the alphabet.

This matrix is multiplied by the coding matrix

$$\begin{pmatrix} 1 & 1 \\ 2 & 1 \end{pmatrix}\begin{pmatrix} 2 & 12 \\ 21 & 5 \end{pmatrix} = \begin{pmatrix} 23 & 17 \\ 25 & 29 \end{pmatrix}$$

This matrix is 'sent' as an eight figure number 23172529.

The message is decoded by multiplying by the inverse of the coding matrix.

$$\begin{pmatrix} ^-1 & 1 \\ 2 & ^-1 \end{pmatrix} \begin{pmatrix} 23 & 17 \\ 25 & 29 \end{pmatrix} = \begin{pmatrix} 2 & 12 \\ 21 & 5 \end{pmatrix}$$

Explore this method of coding. How could it be broken? How could it be made more subtle? If your interest is aroused do some research on the general process of coding and decoding messages.

6 A special family of transformation matrices

Investigate the set of matrices $\begin{pmatrix} 0 & 1 \\ 1 & 1 \end{pmatrix}, \begin{pmatrix} 1 & 0 \\ 1 & 1 \end{pmatrix}, \begin{pmatrix} 1 & 1 \\ 0 & 1 \end{pmatrix}$ and $\begin{pmatrix} 1 & 1 \\ 1 & 0 \end{pmatrix}$

7 Route matrices and the Königsberg Bridge network

The seven bridges of Königsberg (see page 180). The people of Könisberg tried to find a route which would cross all seven bridges just once. The mathematician Euler changed the Königsberg Bridge problem into that of drawing the network below in a single continuous line.

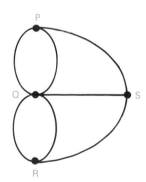

You can use incidence matrices (section H.6.1) to explore the problem further. You can even find out how many 7 stage walks there are altogether (including walks like PQPQPQPQ).

[I made it 31 850 possible walks, but I could be wrong!]

8 Determinants

The value of $ad - bc$ is very important for a matrix. It is called the determinant of the matrix and given a symbol which is the same as that used for the length of a vector.

$$\mathbf{p} = \begin{pmatrix} x \\ y \end{pmatrix} \qquad |\mathbf{p}| = \sqrt{x^2 + y^2}$$

$$\mathbf{A} = \begin{pmatrix} a & b \\ c & d \end{pmatrix} \qquad |\mathbf{A}| = ad - bc = \begin{vmatrix} a & b \\ c & d \end{vmatrix}$$

The determinant is found by subtracting the product of the second diagonal from that of the first.

Investigation 1

$$\begin{pmatrix} 4 & 3 \\ 3 & 1 \end{pmatrix}\begin{pmatrix} 0 \\ 0 \end{pmatrix} \rightarrow \begin{pmatrix} 0 \\ 0 \end{pmatrix}$$

$$\begin{pmatrix} 4 & 3 \\ 3 & 1 \end{pmatrix}\begin{pmatrix} 1 \\ 0 \end{pmatrix} \rightarrow \begin{pmatrix} 4 \\ 3 \end{pmatrix}$$

$$\begin{pmatrix} 4 & 3 \\ 3 & 1 \end{pmatrix}\begin{pmatrix} 0 \\ 1 \end{pmatrix} \rightarrow \begin{pmatrix} 3 \\ 1 \end{pmatrix}$$

$$\begin{pmatrix} 4 & 3 \\ 3 & 1 \end{pmatrix}\begin{pmatrix} 1 \\ 1 \end{pmatrix} \rightarrow \begin{pmatrix} 7 \\ 4 \end{pmatrix}$$

The four vertices of the unit square are

transformed by the matrix $\begin{pmatrix} 4 & 3 \\ 3 & 1 \end{pmatrix}$

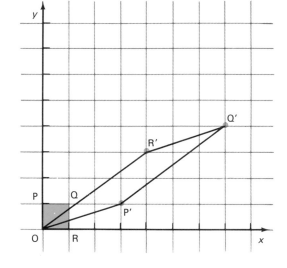

Find the area of OP'Q'R'

What do you notice?
Continue this investigation.

Investigation 2

Adding the first column to the second does not seem to alter the determinant.

$$\mathbf{A} = \begin{pmatrix} 2 & 4 \\ 3 & 5 \end{pmatrix}, \qquad \begin{pmatrix} 2 & 4+2 \\ 3 & 5+3 \end{pmatrix} \rightarrow \begin{pmatrix} 2 & 6 \\ 3 & 8 \end{pmatrix} = \mathbf{B}$$

add c_1 to c_2

$|\mathbf{A}| = {}^-2, \qquad |\mathbf{B}| = {}^-2$ Investigate this further.

Worked answers to examination questions H

1 A police patrol car is controlled using a grid, with the police station at (0, 0).
Write down vectors which represent each 'action point' and vectors which represent journeys between action points.
What is the sum of all the journey vectors when the patrol car has returned to the station via -A-B-C-D-E-.

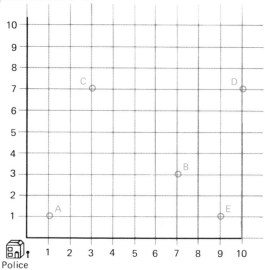

O Action point   Police

The 'action point' vectors are

$$A \begin{pmatrix} 1 \\ 1 \end{pmatrix}; \quad B \begin{pmatrix} 7 \\ 3 \end{pmatrix}; \quad C \begin{pmatrix} 3 \\ 7 \end{pmatrix}; \quad D \begin{pmatrix} 10 \\ 7 \end{pmatrix}; \quad E \begin{pmatrix} 9 \\ 1 \end{pmatrix}$$

Journey vectors are

$$A \to B \begin{pmatrix} 6 \\ 2 \end{pmatrix}; \quad B \to C \begin{pmatrix} ^-4 \\ 4 \end{pmatrix}; \quad C \to D \begin{pmatrix} 7 \\ 0 \end{pmatrix}; \quad D \to E \begin{pmatrix} ^-1 \\ ^-6 \end{pmatrix}$$

The sum of journey vectors is $\begin{pmatrix} 0 \\ 0 \end{pmatrix}$ if $0 \to A$ and $E \to 0$ are included.

Notes: No need to draw arrows.
No working required.

2 Vector **a** is $\begin{pmatrix} 3 \\ ^-2 \end{pmatrix}$ and vector **b** is $\begin{pmatrix} 5 \\ 4 \end{pmatrix}$.

(a) What is the vector $\frac{1}{2}(\mathbf{a} + \mathbf{b})$? Illustrate this vector on a diagram

(b) Write down a vector which is perpendicular to $\begin{pmatrix} 3 \\ ^-2 \end{pmatrix}$ and another

which is perpendicular to $\begin{pmatrix} 5 \\ 4 \end{pmatrix}$.

(a) $\begin{pmatrix} 4 \\ 1 \end{pmatrix}$

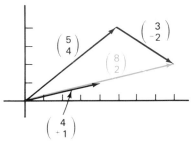

(b) $\begin{pmatrix} 2 \\ 3 \end{pmatrix}$ and $\begin{pmatrix} ^-4 \\ 5 \end{pmatrix}$. Any vector $\begin{pmatrix} a \\ b \end{pmatrix}$ will be

perpendicular to $\begin{pmatrix} ^-4 \\ 5 \end{pmatrix}$ if $5a + 4b = 0$.

(a) The vector can be calculated without reference to arrows.

$$\begin{pmatrix} 3 \\ ^-2 \end{pmatrix} + \begin{pmatrix} 5 \\ 4 \end{pmatrix} = \begin{pmatrix} 8 \\ 2 \end{pmatrix}$$

$$\frac{1}{2}\begin{pmatrix} 8 \\ 2 \end{pmatrix} = \begin{pmatrix} 4 \\ 1 \end{pmatrix}$$

Note that, in the drawing, $\begin{pmatrix} 3 \\ ^-2 \end{pmatrix}$ is added to the end of $\begin{pmatrix} 5 \\ 4 \end{pmatrix}$ for
convenience.

(b) Since $\begin{pmatrix} ^-b \\ a \end{pmatrix}$ is always perpendicular to $\begin{pmatrix} a \\ b \end{pmatrix}$ [as the scalar product is

$^-ab + ab$], it is very easy to write down the vectors required.

3 (a) Find the magnitude of the vectors $\begin{pmatrix} 4 \\ 5 \end{pmatrix}$ and $\begin{pmatrix} ^-4 \\ ^-5 \end{pmatrix}$. Draw a diagram

to illustrate your answer.

(b) If $\mathbf{u} + \mathbf{v}$ and $\mathbf{u} - \mathbf{v}$ have the same magnitude, what can you say
about the vectors **u** and **v**.

(a) Magnitude of both vectors is $\sqrt{41}$.

By pythagoras' theorem
$$OP = OQ = \sqrt{16 + 25} = \sqrt{41}$$

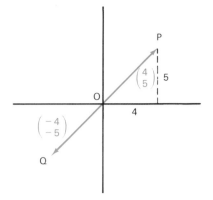

(b) They are perpendicular.

There are two ways of approaching this problem.

(i) Using geometry

If $\mathbf{u} + \mathbf{v}$ and $\mathbf{u} - \mathbf{v}$ have the same length then parallelogram ABCD has equal diagonals. The only type of parallelogram having equal diagonals is a rectangle. Thus $\mathbf{u}$ and $\mathbf{v}$ must be perpendicular.

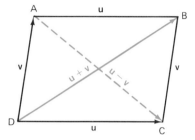

(ii) Using scalar product

Square of length of $\mathbf{u} + \mathbf{v} = (\mathbf{u} + \mathbf{v}) \cdot (\mathbf{u} + \mathbf{v})$ ... since $\mathbf{x} \cdot \mathbf{x} = |\mathbf{x}|^2$
Check this on any vector
Square of length of $\mathbf{u} - \mathbf{v} = (\mathbf{u} - \mathbf{v}) \cdot (\mathbf{u} - \mathbf{v})$
These are equal if $\mathbf{u} \cdot \mathbf{u} + \mathbf{v} \cdot \mathbf{v} + 2\mathbf{u} \cdot \mathbf{v} = \mathbf{u} \cdot \mathbf{u} + \mathbf{v} \cdot \mathbf{v} - 2\mathbf{u} \cdot \mathbf{v}$
$$\Rightarrow \mathbf{u} \cdot \mathbf{v} = 0$$
$$\Rightarrow \mathbf{u} \perp \mathbf{v}$$

4 X and Y are $\frac{3}{4}$ points along OA and OB.

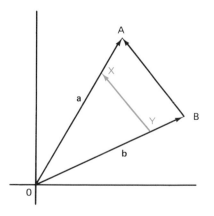

(a) Find $\overrightarrow{AB}$ in terms of $\mathbf{a}$ and $\mathbf{b}$.
(b) Find $\overrightarrow{XY}$ in terms of $\mathbf{a}$ and $\mathbf{b}$.
(c) What can be deduced about XY and AB.

(a) $\overrightarrow{AB} = \mathbf{b} - \mathbf{a}$ (b) $\overrightarrow{XY} = \frac{3}{4}(\mathbf{b} - \mathbf{a})$

(c) XY is parallel to AB and $\frac{3}{4}$ of the length.

This is a very simple question, the steps are ...
$$\overrightarrow{OX} = \tfrac{3}{4}\mathbf{a}$$
$$\overrightarrow{OY} = \tfrac{3}{4}\mathbf{b}$$
So $\overrightarrow{XY} = \tfrac{3}{4}\mathbf{b} - \tfrac{3}{4}\mathbf{a} = \tfrac{3}{4}(\mathbf{b} - \mathbf{a})$.

Take care with directions. The arrows in the diagram represent $\overrightarrow{BA}$ and $\overrightarrow{YX}$, but the question asks for $\overrightarrow{AB}$ and $\overrightarrow{XY}$.

5 ABCD is a parallelogram. P and Q are the midpoints of AB and CD. Prove that X and Y are trisection points of BD, AQ and PC.

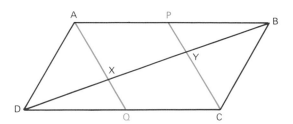

Proof

1∅ From the rotational symmetry AQ // PC; YC = AX ... etc.

2∅ Considering △DYC (i) Q is the midpoint of DC

                          (ii) QX is parallel to CY

3∅ Deduction $QX = \frac{1}{2}CY$ ... 2∅

4∅ Deduction $QX = \frac{1}{2}XA$ ... 1∅

5∅ X is a trisection point of AQ

6∅ Deduction Y is a trisection point of PC ... 1∅

7∅ Deduction X is the midpoint of DY ... 2∅

8∅ Deduction Y is the midpoint of XB ... 1∅, 2∅

9∅ Deduction DX = XY = YB ... 7∅, 8∅

1∅∅ X and Y are trisection points of DB

The problem can also be solved entirely by vectors. Treat D as the origin; $\overrightarrow{DA} = \mathbf{a}$; $\overrightarrow{DB} = \mathbf{a} + \mathbf{c}$; $\overrightarrow{DC} = \mathbf{c}$; $\overrightarrow{DQ} = \frac{1}{2}\mathbf{c}$; $\overrightarrow{QA} = \mathbf{a} - \frac{1}{2}\mathbf{c}$.

$\overrightarrow{QX} = r\,\overrightarrow{QA}$

$\overrightarrow{DX} = s\,\overrightarrow{DB}$ ... where r and s are fractions.

$\overrightarrow{DX} = \overrightarrow{DQ} + \overrightarrow{QX}$

$s(\mathbf{a} + \mathbf{c}) = \frac{1}{2}\mathbf{c} + r(\mathbf{a} - \frac{1}{2}\mathbf{c})$ we can equate the **a** parts and the **c** parts of this vector equation

$\Rightarrow$ $s = r$ ... **a** parts

and $s = \frac{1}{2} - \frac{1}{2}r$ ... **c** parts

$\Rightarrow$ $s = \frac{1}{2} - \frac{1}{2}s$

$\Rightarrow$ $2s = 1 - s$

$\Rightarrow$ $3s = 1$ $\Rightarrow s = \frac{1}{3}$

So $r = \frac{1}{3}$ and $s = \frac{1}{3}$

i.e. X is a trisection point of DB and AQ.

By symmetry Y is a trisection point of DB and PC.

Note: This problem is difficult to solve in vectors by GCSE standards but it is an interesting example of the way in which vectors can be used in geometry.

6 (a) Prove that $(\mathbf{u} + \mathbf{v}) \cdot \mathbf{w} = \mathbf{u} \cdot \mathbf{w} + \mathbf{v} \cdot \mathbf{w}$, where $\mathbf{u} = \begin{pmatrix} u_1 \\ u_2 \end{pmatrix}$;

       $\mathbf{v} = \begin{pmatrix} v_1 \\ v_2 \end{pmatrix}$; and $\mathbf{w} = \begin{pmatrix} w_1 \\ w_2 \end{pmatrix}$

   (b) Find the angle between the vectors $\begin{pmatrix} 1 \\ 1 \end{pmatrix}$ and $\begin{pmatrix} 1 \\ 3 \end{pmatrix}$. Confirm by drawing and measurement.

(a) Proof

$$1\emptyset \quad \mathbf{u} + \mathbf{v} = \begin{pmatrix} u_1 \\ u_2 \end{pmatrix} + \begin{pmatrix} v_1 \\ v_2 \end{pmatrix} = \begin{pmatrix} u_1 + v_1 \\ u_2 + v_2 \end{pmatrix}$$

$$2\emptyset \quad (\mathbf{u} + \mathbf{v}) \cdot \mathbf{w} = \begin{pmatrix} u_1 + v_1 \\ u_2 + v_2 \end{pmatrix} \cdot \begin{pmatrix} w_1 \\ w_2 \end{pmatrix}$$

$$= (u_1 + v_1)w_1 + (u_2 + v_2)w_2$$
$$= u_1 w_1 + v_1 w_1 + u_2 w_2 + v_2 w_2$$

$3\emptyset$ $\mathbf{u} \cdot \mathbf{w} = u_1 w_1 + u_2 w_2$
$4\emptyset$ $\mathbf{v} \cdot \mathbf{w} = v_1 w_1 + v_2 w_2$
$5\emptyset$ $\mathbf{u} \cdot \mathbf{w} + \mathbf{v} \cdot \mathbf{w} = u_1 w_1 + v_1 w_1 + u_2 w_2 + v_2 w_2$
$6\emptyset$ Deduction $(\mathbf{u} + \mathbf{v}) \cdot \mathbf{w} = \mathbf{u} \cdot \mathbf{w} + \mathbf{v} \cdot \mathbf{w} \ldots 2\emptyset, 5\emptyset$

(b) $26 \cdot 56°$

$1\emptyset$ The vectors are $\begin{pmatrix} 1 \\ 1 \end{pmatrix}$ and $\begin{pmatrix} 1 \\ 3 \end{pmatrix}$.

$\quad |\mathbf{r_1}| = \sqrt{1 + 1} = \sqrt{2}$
$\quad |\mathbf{r_2}| = \sqrt{1 + 9} = \sqrt{10}$

$2\emptyset$ Scalar product $x_1 x_2 + y_1 y_2 = 1 + 3 = 4$
$3\emptyset$ Scalar product $|\mathbf{r_1}||\mathbf{r_2}| \cos \theta = \sqrt{2}\sqrt{10} \cos \theta$
$4\emptyset$ $\sqrt{20} \cos \theta = 4$
$5\emptyset$ $\cos \theta = 4 \div \sqrt{20} = 0 \cdot 8944$ $4 \boxed{\div} 20 \boxed{\sqrt{\ }} \boxed{=}$
$6\emptyset$ $\theta = \text{inv} (\cos \theta) = 26 \cdot 56°$

The result can be confirmed by
measurement or by subtracting the two
outer angles from $90°$
$\theta = 90° - (\tan^{-1} 1 + \tan^{-1} \frac{1}{3})$
$\quad = 45° - 18 \cdot 435°$
$\quad = 26 \cdot 565°$.

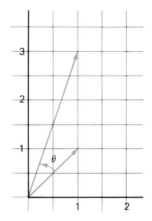

7   Unit vectors $\mathbf{i}$ and $\mathbf{j}$ are at right angles to each other.
   Given $\mathbf{p} = 3\mathbf{i} + 4\mathbf{j}$
           $\mathbf{q} = 5\mathbf{i}$
         $4\mathbf{r} = \mathbf{p} + \mathbf{q}$
         $2\mathbf{s} = \mathbf{p} - \mathbf{q}$
  show that
  (a) $|\mathbf{p}| = |\mathbf{q}|$
  (b) $|\mathbf{r}| = |\mathbf{s}|$

(c) **r ⊥ s**
(d) **|r + s| = |r − s|**
(e) **(r + s) ⊥ (r − s)**
(f) **|r + ks| = |r − ks|**   where **k** is any number.

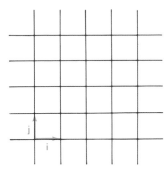

The **i, j** method of writing vectors gives each vector in terms of an x

component and y component. So $3\mathbf{i} + 4\mathbf{j}$ is the same as $\begin{pmatrix} 3 \\ 4 \end{pmatrix}$. It has the

advantage of requiring only one line of print.

i is the vector $\begin{pmatrix} 1 \\ 0 \end{pmatrix}$, length 1, parallel to the x axis.

j is the vector $\begin{pmatrix} 0 \\ 1 \end{pmatrix}$, length 1, parallel to the y axis.

You can see that $\mathbf{i} \cdot \mathbf{i} = \mathbf{j} \cdot \mathbf{j} = 1$
and $\mathbf{i} \cdot \mathbf{j} = \mathbf{j} \cdot \mathbf{i} = 0$

(a) $|\mathbf{p}| = \sqrt{3^2 + 4^2} = 5,\quad |\mathbf{q}| = 5$ so $|\mathbf{p}| = |\mathbf{q}|$

(b) $4\mathbf{r} = \mathbf{p} + \mathbf{q} = 3\mathbf{i} + 4\mathbf{j} + 5\mathbf{i} = 8\mathbf{i} + 4\mathbf{j}$
  $\Rightarrow \mathbf{r} = 2\mathbf{i} + \mathbf{j}$ $\Rightarrow |\mathbf{r}| = \sqrt{5}$
   $2\mathbf{s} = \mathbf{p} - \mathbf{q} = 3\mathbf{i} + 4\mathbf{j} - 5\mathbf{i} = {}^-2\mathbf{i} + 4\mathbf{j}$
  $\Rightarrow \mathbf{s} = {}^-\mathbf{i} + 2\mathbf{j}$ $\Rightarrow |\mathbf{s}| = \sqrt{5}$ so $|\mathbf{r}| = |\mathbf{s}|$

(c) $\mathbf{r} \cdot \mathbf{s} = \begin{pmatrix} 2 \\ 1 \end{pmatrix} \cdot \begin{pmatrix} -1 \\ 2 \end{pmatrix} = 0$ $\Rightarrow \mathbf{r} \perp \mathbf{s}$

(d) $\mathbf{r} + \mathbf{s} = (2\mathbf{i} + \mathbf{j}) + ({}^-\mathbf{i} + 2\mathbf{j}) = \mathbf{i} + 3\mathbf{j} \Rightarrow |\mathbf{r} + \mathbf{s}| = \sqrt{10}$
  $\mathbf{r} - \mathbf{s} = (2\mathbf{i} + \mathbf{j}) - ({}^-\mathbf{i} + 2\mathbf{j}) = 3\mathbf{i} - \mathbf{j} \Rightarrow |\mathbf{r} - \mathbf{s}| = \sqrt{10}$
  So $|\mathbf{r} + \mathbf{s}| = |\mathbf{r} - \mathbf{s}|$

(e) $(\mathbf{r} + \mathbf{s}) \cdot (\mathbf{r} - \mathbf{s}) = \begin{pmatrix} 1 \\ 3 \end{pmatrix} \cdot \begin{pmatrix} 3 \\ -1 \end{pmatrix} = 0$ $\Rightarrow (\mathbf{r} + \mathbf{s}) \perp (\mathbf{r} - \mathbf{s})$

(f) $\mathbf{r} + k\mathbf{s} = 2\mathbf{i} + \mathbf{j} + k({}^-\mathbf{i} + 2\mathbf{j}) = (2 - k)\mathbf{i} + (1 + 2k)\mathbf{j}$
  $\Rightarrow$ $|\mathbf{r} + k\mathbf{s}| = \sqrt{(2 - k)^2 + (1 + 2k)^2}$
       $= \sqrt{4 - 4k + k^2 + 1 + 4k + 4k^2}$
       $= \sqrt{5 + 5k^2}$

  $\mathbf{r} - k\mathbf{s} = 2\mathbf{i} + \mathbf{j} - k({}^-\mathbf{i} + 2\mathbf{j}) = (2 + k)\mathbf{i} + (1 - 2k)\mathbf{j}$
  $\Rightarrow$ $|\mathbf{r} - k\mathbf{s}| = \sqrt{(2 + k)^2 + (1 - 2k)^2}$
       $= \sqrt{4 + 4k + k^2 + 1 - 4k + 4k^2}$
       $= \sqrt{5 + 5k^2}$

  So $|\mathbf{r} + k\mathbf{s}| = |\mathbf{r} - k\mathbf{s}|$ Whatever the value of k.

• This is a long question by GCSE standards.

8 (a) ABCD is a parallelogram. A is (1, 2), B is (6, ⁻2), and D is (3, 5). Calculate the coordinates of C.

(b) OXYZ is a parallelogram with T as the midpoint of YZ. OT meets ZX at U, and YU meets OZ at V. If $\overrightarrow{OX} = \mathbf{x}$ and $\overrightarrow{OZ} = \mathbf{z}$ show that

   (i) $\overrightarrow{XZ} = \mathbf{z} - \mathbf{x}$

   (ii) $\overrightarrow{OU} = \frac{2}{3}(\mathbf{z} + \frac{1}{2}\mathbf{x})$

   (iii) $\overrightarrow{YU} = {}^{-}\frac{2}{3}\mathbf{x} - \frac{1}{3}\mathbf{z}$

C is (8, 1)

The vector $\overrightarrow{BC}$ must be equivalent to $\overrightarrow{AD}$ if ABCD is a parallelogram.

$\overrightarrow{AD} = \begin{pmatrix} 2 \\ 3 \end{pmatrix}$; adding this to $\begin{pmatrix} 6 \\ -2 \end{pmatrix}$ gives $\begin{pmatrix} 8 \\ 1 \end{pmatrix}$ as the position vector of C.

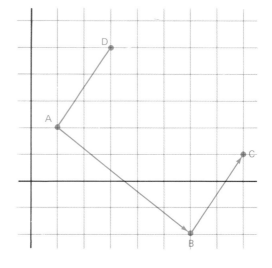

   (i) $\overrightarrow{XZ} = \mathbf{z} - \mathbf{x}$
     since $\overrightarrow{OX} + \overrightarrow{XZ} = \overrightarrow{OZ}$

  (ii) $\overrightarrow{OT} = \overrightarrow{OZ} + \overrightarrow{ZT}$
     But $\overrightarrow{ZT} = \frac{1}{2}\mathbf{x}$
     so $\overrightarrow{OT} = \mathbf{z} + \frac{1}{2}\mathbf{x}$
     and $\overrightarrow{OU} = \frac{2}{3}(\mathbf{z} + \frac{1}{2}\mathbf{x})$
     See Q·5 of these answers.

 (iii) $\overrightarrow{UT} = \frac{1}{3}(\mathbf{z} + \frac{1}{2}\mathbf{x})$ and $\overrightarrow{TY} = \frac{1}{2}\mathbf{x}$
    $\Rightarrow \overrightarrow{UY} = \frac{1}{2}\mathbf{x} + \frac{1}{3}(\mathbf{z} + \frac{1}{2}\mathbf{x})$
          $= \frac{2}{3}\mathbf{x} + \frac{1}{3}\mathbf{z}$
    $\Rightarrow \overrightarrow{YU} = {}^{-}\overrightarrow{UY} = {}^{-}\frac{2}{3}\mathbf{x} - \frac{1}{3}\mathbf{z}$

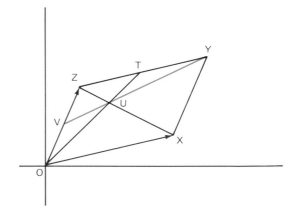

9 $\mathbf{A} = \begin{pmatrix} 1 & 1 \\ 1 & 2 \end{pmatrix}$; $\mathbf{B} = \begin{pmatrix} 2 & 1 \\ 1 & 0 \end{pmatrix}$; $\mathbf{C} = \begin{pmatrix} 2 & {}^{-}1 \\ {}^{-}1 & 1 \end{pmatrix}$.

(a) Calculate $\mathbf{A} + \mathbf{B} + \mathbf{C}$.

(b) Calculate $\mathbf{AC}$ and $\mathbf{BC}$.

(c) Find the inverse of $\mathbf{A}$ and the inverse of $\mathbf{B}$.

(d) Is it true that $(\mathbf{AB})^{-1} = \mathbf{B}^{-1} \cdot \mathbf{A}^{-1}$?

(a) $\begin{pmatrix} 5 & 1 \\ 1 & 3 \end{pmatrix}$; (b) $\begin{pmatrix} 1 & 0 \\ 0 & 1 \end{pmatrix}$; $\begin{pmatrix} 3 & ^-1 \\ 2 & ^-1 \end{pmatrix}$

(c) $\mathbf{A}^{-1} = \begin{pmatrix} 2 & ^-1 \\ ^-1 & 1 \end{pmatrix}$; $\mathbf{B}^{-1} = \begin{pmatrix} 0 & 1 \\ 1 & ^-2 \end{pmatrix}$ (d) Yes

(a) Simply add the elements in the same position in each matrix:

$$\begin{pmatrix} 1 & 1 \\ 1 & 2 \end{pmatrix} + \begin{pmatrix} 2 & 1 \\ 1 & 0 \end{pmatrix} + \begin{pmatrix} 2 & ^-1 \\ ^-1 & 1 \end{pmatrix} = \begin{pmatrix} 1+2+2 & 1+1-1 \\ 1+1-1 & 2+0+1 \end{pmatrix} = \begin{pmatrix} 5 & 1 \\ 1 & 3 \end{pmatrix}$$

(b) $\mathbf{AB} = \begin{pmatrix} 3 & 1 \\ 4 & 1 \end{pmatrix}$; $\mathbf{AC} = \begin{pmatrix} 1 & 0 \\ 0 & 1 \end{pmatrix}$; $\mathbf{BC} = \begin{pmatrix} 3 & ^-1 \\ 2 & ^-1 \end{pmatrix}$

(c) $\mathbf{A}^{-1} = \begin{pmatrix} 2 & ^-1 \\ ^-1 & 1 \end{pmatrix}$; $\mathbf{B}^{-1} = \begin{pmatrix} 0 & 1 \\ 1 & ^-2 \end{pmatrix}$

Using the rule that inverse of $\begin{pmatrix} a & b \\ c & d \end{pmatrix}$ equals $\dfrac{1}{ad-bc}\begin{pmatrix} d & ^-b \\ ^-c & a \end{pmatrix}$

(d) $\mathbf{B}^{-1} \cdot \mathbf{A}^{-1} = \begin{pmatrix} 0 & 1 \\ 1 & ^-2 \end{pmatrix}\begin{pmatrix} 2 & ^-1 \\ ^-1 & 1 \end{pmatrix} = \begin{pmatrix} ^-1 & 1 \\ 4 & ^-3 \end{pmatrix}$

$(\mathbf{AB})^{-1} = -\begin{pmatrix} 1 & ^-1 \\ ^-4 & 3 \end{pmatrix} = \begin{pmatrix} ^-1 & 1 \\ 4 & ^-3 \end{pmatrix}$

Thus $(\mathbf{AB})^{-1} = \mathbf{B}^{-1}\mathbf{A}^{-1}$.

10 **T** is the transformation with matrix $\begin{pmatrix} 0 & 1 \\ ^-1 & 0 \end{pmatrix}$. What transformations on $\begin{pmatrix} x \\ y \end{pmatrix}$ are caused by $\mathbf{T}^2$, $\mathbf{T}^3$ and $\mathbf{T}^4$.

T   is a clockwise rotation of 90°
$\mathbf{T}^2$ is a half turn
$\mathbf{T}^3$ is an anticlockwise rotation of 90°
$\mathbf{T}^4$ is the complete turn through 360°.

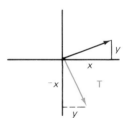

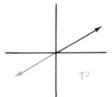

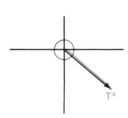

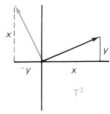

These transformations can be found by simple matrix multiplication.

$$\mathbf{T} = \begin{pmatrix} 0 & 1 \\ ^-1 & 0 \end{pmatrix}\begin{pmatrix} x \\ y \end{pmatrix} = \begin{pmatrix} y \\ ^-x \end{pmatrix}$$

$$\mathbf{T}^2 = \begin{pmatrix} 0 & 1 \\ ^-1 & 0 \end{pmatrix}\begin{pmatrix} 0 & 1 \\ ^-1 & 0 \end{pmatrix}\begin{pmatrix} x \\ y \end{pmatrix}$$

$$= \begin{pmatrix} ^-1 & 0 \\ 0 & ^-1 \end{pmatrix}\begin{pmatrix} x \\ y \end{pmatrix} = \begin{pmatrix} ^-x \\ ^-y \end{pmatrix}$$

$$\mathbf{T}^3 = \mathbf{T}\mathbf{T}^2 = \begin{pmatrix} 0 & 1 \\ ^-1 & 0 \end{pmatrix}\begin{pmatrix} ^-1 & 0 \\ 0 & ^-1 \end{pmatrix}\begin{pmatrix} x \\ y \end{pmatrix}$$

$$= \begin{pmatrix} 0 & ^-1 \\ 1 & 0 \end{pmatrix}\begin{pmatrix} x \\ y \end{pmatrix} = \begin{pmatrix} ^-y \\ x \end{pmatrix}$$

$$\mathbf{T}^4 = \mathbf{T}^2 \cdot \mathbf{T}^2 = \begin{pmatrix} ^-1 & 0 \\ 0 & ^-1 \end{pmatrix}\begin{pmatrix} ^-1 & 0 \\ 0 & ^-1 \end{pmatrix}\begin{pmatrix} x \\ y \end{pmatrix}$$

$$= \begin{pmatrix} 1 & 0 \\ 0 & 1 \end{pmatrix}\begin{pmatrix} x \\ y \end{pmatrix} = \begin{pmatrix} x \\ y \end{pmatrix}$$

11 Under a transformation whose matrix is $\begin{pmatrix} p & q \\ r & s \end{pmatrix}$, the images of (1, 1)

and (1, 0) are ($^-$1, 0) and (2, 3). Find the values of p, q, r and s.

$p = 2$, $q = {}^-3$, $r = 3$, $s = {}^-3$

The question data give equations from which p, q, r and s can be found.

$1\emptyset$ $\begin{pmatrix} p & q \\ r & s \end{pmatrix}\begin{pmatrix} 1 \\ 1 \end{pmatrix} = \begin{pmatrix} ^-1 \\ 0 \end{pmatrix} \Rightarrow \begin{cases} p + q = {}^-1 \\ r + s = 0 \end{cases}$

$2\emptyset$ $\begin{pmatrix} p & q \\ r & s \end{pmatrix}\begin{pmatrix} 1 \\ 0 \end{pmatrix} = \begin{pmatrix} 2 \\ 3 \end{pmatrix} \Rightarrow \begin{cases} p = 2 & \ldots p + 0.q = 2 \\ r = 3 & \ldots r + 0.s = 3 \end{cases}$

$3\emptyset$ $\left.\begin{matrix} p + q = {}^-1 \\ p = 2 \end{matrix}\right\} \Rightarrow q = {}^-3$

$4\emptyset$ $\left.\begin{matrix} r + s = 0 \\ r = 3 \end{matrix}\right\} \Rightarrow s = {}^-3$

12 For the network shown in the diagram
    matrix **A** gives the number of routes between nodes,
    matrix **B** is a 3 × 6 incidence matrix showing which arcs
             end at which nodes,
    matrix **C** is the incidence matrix showing which nodes are
             at the ends of which arcs.
    (a) Calculate **BC**
    (b) Calculate **BC** − **A**. What information does this give?

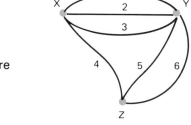

Matrix A   X   Y   Z
            X $\begin{bmatrix} 0 & 3 & 1 \\ 3 & 0 & 2 \\ 1 & 2 & 0 \end{bmatrix}$
            Y
            Z

Matrix B   1 2 3 4 5 6
            X $\begin{bmatrix} 1 & 1 & 1 & 1 & 0 & 0 \\ 1 & 1 & 1 & 0 & 1 & 1 \\ 0 & 0 & 0 & 1 & 1 & 1 \end{bmatrix}$
            Y
            Z
        arcs 1,2,3 and 4 end at X.

Matrix C

	X	Y	Z
1	1	1	0
2	1	1	0
3	1	1	0
4	1	0	1
5	0	1	1
6	0	1	1

X and Y are at the end of arc 1.

$$\text{BC} \begin{bmatrix} 4 & 3 & 1 \\ 3 & 5 & 2 \\ 1 & 2 & 3 \end{bmatrix} \qquad \text{BC} - \text{A} \begin{bmatrix} 4 & 0 & 0 \\ 0 & 5 & 0 \\ 0 & 0 & 3 \end{bmatrix}$$

BC − A presents the numbers of arcs at each node.
This is obvious from the diagram but if there were millions of nodes and arcs (as in neurology), the information could not be obtained by simple counting.

13 $\mathbf{A} = \begin{pmatrix} 1 & 2 \\ 0 & 3 \end{pmatrix}; \quad \mathbf{B} = \begin{pmatrix} 1 & -\frac{2}{3} \\ 0 & \frac{1}{3} \end{pmatrix}; \quad \mathbf{C} = \begin{pmatrix} 2 & 0 \\ 4 & 1 \end{pmatrix}; \quad \mathbf{D} = \begin{pmatrix} \frac{1}{2} & 0 \\ p & 1 \end{pmatrix}$

(a) Evaluate **AB**.
(b) Find the value of p which makes **CD** the unit matrix.
(c) Simplify **CABD** with the value of p found in (b). What does this show about the inverse of **CA**?

(a) $\mathbf{AB} = \begin{pmatrix} 1 & 0 \\ 0 & 1 \end{pmatrix}$ (b) $p = {}^-2$ (c) **CABD** = **CD** = **I**; $(\mathbf{CA})^{-1} = \mathbf{BD}$

The answers follow from simple matrix multiplication and algebra.

(a) $\mathbf{AB} = \begin{pmatrix} 1 & 2 \\ 0 & 3 \end{pmatrix}\begin{pmatrix} 1 & -\frac{2}{3} \\ 0 & \frac{1}{3} \end{pmatrix} = \begin{pmatrix} 1+0 & -\frac{2}{3}+\frac{2}{3} \\ 0+0 & 0+1 \end{pmatrix} = \begin{pmatrix} 1 & 0 \\ 0 & 1 \end{pmatrix}$

(b) $\mathbf{CD} = \begin{pmatrix} 1 & 0 \\ 2+p & 1 \end{pmatrix}$. If **CD** = **I**, p must be $^-2$.

(c) $\mathbf{CABD} = \mathbf{C(AB)D}$
$\qquad\qquad = \mathbf{CID}$
$\qquad\qquad = \mathbf{CD}$ where **I** is the unit matrix.
But **CABD** = (**CA**)(**BD**) = **I**   when $p = {}^-2$.
Thus, if $p = {}^-2$, **BD** is the inverse of **CA**.

14 The matrix represents a network of main roads joining four towns. All roads are dual carriageway.

	P	Q	R	S
P	0	2	1	2
Q	2	0	1	1
R	1	1	0	2
S	2	1	2	0

(a) Calculate the total number of roads involved.
(b) Make a diagram of the network.
(c) How many different ways can a motorist travel P → Q → R → S?

(a) 9 roads, 18 carriageways.

(b)

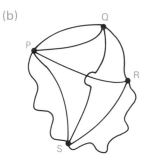

(c) 4 different routes.

(a) The number of roads will be half the total sum of the elements in the matrix.
(b) The network must be constructed from the matrix. Of course, the network does not give any information about the distances or positions of the towns. Can you construct a network which does not need a bridge?
(c) P → Q   two choices
     Q → R   only one choice
     R → S   two choices
     There will therefore be 2 × 1 × 2 different routes.
     [If you want to make the answer even clearer you can number the arcs.]

15 (a) The simultaneous equations
$$2x + 3y = 3$$
$$3x - 4y = 13$$
are solved by writing the pair of equations in matrix form
$$\begin{pmatrix} 2 & 3 \\ 3 & -4 \end{pmatrix} \begin{pmatrix} x \\ y \end{pmatrix} = \begin{pmatrix} 3 \\ 13 \end{pmatrix}$$ Complete the solution.

(b) Explain why the inverse of a matrix $\begin{pmatrix} a & b \\ ka & kb \end{pmatrix}$ cannot be found.

Hence or otherwise show that the equations
$$2x + 3y = 14$$
$$4x + 6y = 21$$
cannot be solved.
[Illustrate your answer with a diagram.]

(a) $x = 3, \quad y = {}^-1$
$$\begin{pmatrix} 2 & 3 \\ 3 & -4 \end{pmatrix} \begin{pmatrix} x \\ y \end{pmatrix} = \begin{pmatrix} 3 \\ 13 \end{pmatrix}$$

$$A = \begin{pmatrix} 2 & 3 \\ 3 & {}^-4 \end{pmatrix} \Rightarrow |A| = {}^-17 \quad \text{and} \quad A^{-1} = \frac{{}^-1}{17} \begin{pmatrix} {}^-4 & {}^-3 \\ {}^-3 & 2 \end{pmatrix}$$

$$= \frac{1}{17} \begin{pmatrix} 4 & 3 \\ 3 & {}^-2 \end{pmatrix}$$

$$\frac{1}{17} \begin{pmatrix} 4 & 3 \\ 3 & {}^-2 \end{pmatrix} \begin{pmatrix} 3 \\ 13 \end{pmatrix} = \frac{1}{17} \begin{pmatrix} 51 \\ {}^-17 \end{pmatrix} = \begin{pmatrix} 3 \\ {}^-1 \end{pmatrix}$$

Thus $\begin{pmatrix} x \\ y \end{pmatrix} = \begin{pmatrix} 3 \\ {}^-1 \end{pmatrix} \qquad \Rightarrow x = 3, \quad y = {}^-1$

Check: $\left. \begin{array}{l} 2x + 3y = 6 - 3 = 3 \\ 3x - 4y = 9 + 4 = 13 \end{array} \right\}$

(b) $\begin{pmatrix} a & b \\ ka & kb \end{pmatrix}$ does not have an inverse

because $|A| = kab - kab = 0$.

$\left. \begin{array}{l} 2x + 3y = 14 \\ 4x + 6y = 21 \end{array} \right\} \Rightarrow \begin{array}{l} 2x + 3y = 14 \\ 2x + 3y = 10\frac{1}{2} \end{array}$

Obviously, $2x + 3y$ cannot be 14 and $10\frac{1}{2}$ simultaneously

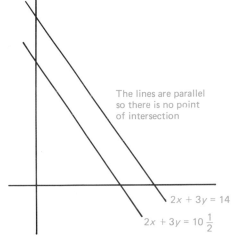

The lines are parallel so there is no point of intersection

$2x + 3y = 14$

$2x + 3y = 10\frac{1}{2}$

16 The matrix $\begin{pmatrix} \dfrac{1}{\sqrt{2}} & \dfrac{{}^-1}{\sqrt{2}} \\ \dfrac{1}{\sqrt{2}} & \dfrac{1}{\sqrt{2}} \end{pmatrix}$ produces a rotation of $\begin{pmatrix} x \\ y \end{pmatrix}$.

(a) Calculate the determinant of the matrix.

(b) Find the angle of rotation.

(c) Construct a matrix that would rotate $\begin{pmatrix} x \\ y \end{pmatrix}$ clockwise through 50°.

Comment on any difficulties that might arise in using this rotation.

(a) $\begin{vmatrix} \dfrac{1}{\sqrt{2}} & \dfrac{{}^-1}{\sqrt{2}} \\ \dfrac{1}{\sqrt{2}} & \dfrac{1}{\sqrt{2}} \end{vmatrix} = 1$ \qquad (b) 45° anticlockwise

(c) $\begin{pmatrix} \cos 50° & \sin 50° \\ {}^-\sin 50° & \cos 50° \end{pmatrix}$

[Since cos 50° and sin 50° are not exact numbers the x' and y' values would be approximations only.]

(a) $\begin{vmatrix} \dfrac{1}{\sqrt{2}} & \dfrac{^-1}{\sqrt{2}} \\[2mm] \dfrac{1}{\sqrt{2}} & \dfrac{1}{\sqrt{2}} \end{vmatrix} = \dfrac{1}{\sqrt{2}} \cdot \dfrac{1}{\sqrt{2}} - \dfrac{^-1}{\sqrt{2}} \cdot \dfrac{1}{\sqrt{2}} = \dfrac{1}{2} + \dfrac{1}{2} = 1$

(b) Putting $\dfrac{1}{\sqrt{2}} = \cos \theta$, θ is found to be 45°.

(c) The general matrix for a clockwise rotation through angle θ is
$\begin{pmatrix} \cos \theta & \sin \theta \\ ^-\sin \theta & \cos \theta \end{pmatrix}$.

So $\begin{pmatrix} \cos 50° & \sin 50° \\ ^-\sin 50° & \cos 50° \end{pmatrix}$ will produce the required rotation.

Examination technique

Answering questions

Always remember that someone will be looking at your work and marking it. You can put the examiner in a good mood by neat writing, good-looking pages and careful underlining. If you make a mistake and have to cross something out, cross out clearly and neatly

$2x + 3 = 17$ $2x - 3 = 17$,

so that there is no doubt about which piece of writing is the one to be marked.

The use of a correction pen or 'snow paint' is a good idea but check first with your teacher that it will be allowed in your examination.

[Remember, always let the snow paint dry hard before you write over it. And don't leave the   blanked out to dry and then forget to come back to fill in the correction!]

The following suggestions will help you to make your work easy to read for the examiner. Of course, it is no real use if you keep tidy work for the examination and use untidy layout in your everyday work. It is far better to develop a careful style in every piece of work you do and then you will have no problems working neatly in the examination.

1 Writing

Write carefully and neatly. If you write 1 [one] like 7 [seven] then cross your seven: 1 [one] 7 [seven].
Put decimal points in clearly: 1·3 not 1˙3
Take care that your symbols such as £, π, etc. are clear. Remember that the index of a power should be written small: 2^3 not 2^3. Fractions should also be written carefully: 1½ looks like $\frac{11}{2}$ as well as $1\frac{1}{2}$.

2 Drawings

Diagrams should be clearly labelled. It is well worth buying a 'see through' ruler and learning how to use it.
Geometrical figures should have letters at important vertices and intersections. Colour makes a diagram look more interesting.

Colour can liven up diagrams.

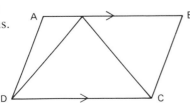
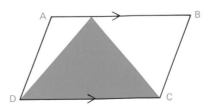

Where possible, diagrams should be drawn to scale so that you have an independent check of your answer.

Graphs should always be carefully labelled. The x and y axes and the scales should all be clearly marked. Use squared paper (or the paper provided in the exam). Give your graph plenty of space—room to breathe, you might say. Here again, colour adds quality to a diagram.

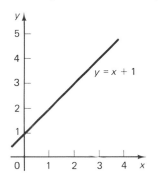
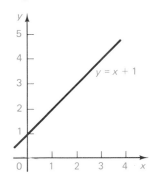

3 Use of = and ⇒

An = sign should never be used to connect two mathematical sentences.

wrong!

6 eggs = 72p = 1 egg = 12p.

This is wrong because it says that 6 eggs = 1 egg and 72p = 12p.
The correct way to set out this work is like this:

　6 eggs = 72p
⇒ 1 egg　= 12p.

The ⇒ sign means 'it follows that'.

Each mathematical sentence is given a line of its own. The examiner will be able to see where any mistakes have occurred and will give marks for the part of the answer that is correct.

4 Layout

The way your answer is 'laid out' on the page can affect your examiner's feelings. Try not to cramp things up but avoid spreading your work all over the place.

The worked answers to 'examination' questions in this book are intended to act as broad models. When you correct your work, rewrite your answers so that they include all the workings in my answers. [Don't copy them exactly, but make sure you understand them and then write your answers in your own way.] You should get into the habit of laying out your work in a pleasing way. Of course, good layout will not make wrong answers right, but it will give your examiner the chance to award marks for partly correct answers.

Checking

The first rule in any examination is always to read the question carefully! Most mistakes come from not answering the question asked or mixing up the information which is given, so the first check is to read the question twice. Note how the answer is to be given and how many parts there are in the question.

1 When you are working on a question check your calculations and measurements at least once. Check calculations by using a different calculator sequence and compare the result with a simple estimate, especially if decimals are involved. Check that your units are the right ones, and most of all check that your answer makes sense.

Example

A cylinder has radius 7 cm and length 11 cm.

Taking π as $\frac{22}{7}$ calculate
(a) the area of one end of the cylinder,
(b) the volume of the cylinder.

Area of circle $= \pi r^2$ Volume of cylinder $= \pi r^2 h$

Checks: (i) Note that: two answers are required, and
                         π is to be taken as $\frac{22}{7}$.
            (ii) The area formula gives A as $(22 \div 7) \times 7^2$
                  22 $\boxed{\div}$ 7 $\boxed{=}$ $\boxed{\times}$ 7 $\boxed{(\ )^2}$ $\boxed{=}$ ... 154 cm^2
                  Check with 7 $\boxed{\times}$ $\boxed{=}$ $\boxed{\times}$ 22 $\boxed{\div}$ 7 $\boxed{=}$ ... i.e. start from the other end.
            (iii) Estimating, $\frac{22}{7} \times 7^2 \rightarrow 3 \times 50 = 150$.
            (iv) Take care not to leave off the 'cm^2' from the answer.

Similar checks could be made for part (b) of the question.

---

2 It is always worth looking through each answer before going on to the next question. Remember—if you do not finish the paper you will not have time to come back for a final look at the end. A quick check before you leave each question could save you lost marks.

Draw a record table on a separate piece of paper and mark in your checks as you do them. [You may be allowed to take a ready prepared chart with you into the examination, but confirm this with your teacher.]

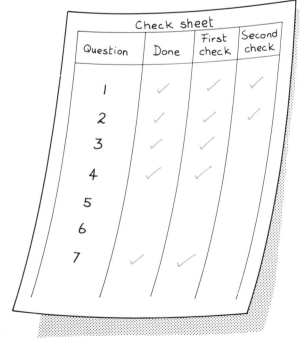

Questions 5 and 6 were missed out first time round but the other questions were looked over before the next question was started.

When looking through, you don't want to waste much time so just check that
- (i) your answers are clearly shown,
- (ii) your working is clearly laid out,
- (iii) you have not missed out any parts of the question by accident,
- (iv) you have clearly crossed out any parts of the answer that you do not want the examiner to mark,
- (v) your diagrams and graphs are properly labelled.
  [Most diagrams will be drawn for you on your examination paper.]

3 You should always go back over your work if you have got to the end of the paper before the end of the time. Do not leave unless you are quite sure there is nothing more you can do. I suggest the order of going back over your answers should be as follows.
- (i) Go back to the questions you missed out and try a second time. But don't spend too long on any question.
- (ii) Make sure you have not missed out any sections of the questions you have answered. If there are any questions where you have answered the first part but not the second, work on the second part. A fully completed question is often awarded a 'bonus' mark.
- (iii) Check again in the same way as when you 'looked through' (point **2** above), but beware of making changes out of nerves!

Finally, look over your check sheet. Ideally every question will be answered and checked twice and you can go home knowing you have given a fair account of yourself. Even if you have not managed to produce a perfect result you will know that you have not thrown away your chances by pure carelessness.

Multiple choice questions

1 Why multiple choice questions?

Multiple choice questions which give the answer, together with three or four wrong answers, are used for two main reasons. First, they are easy to mark and therefore cheaper. Secondly, because the questions are short, a multiple choice examination can ask a lot of questions and cover a wide syllabus in a short time.

2 Tackling a multiple choice question

Direct method

If you can answer the question directly, do so. Then compare your answer with the choices.

Example 1

Given that $2p - 3 = 8$, then $p = \ldots$

A $2\frac{1}{2}$ B $4\frac{1}{2}$ C $5\frac{1}{2}$ D 5   E 11

Direct: $2p - 3 = 8$

$\Rightarrow \quad 2p = 11$

$\Rightarrow \quad p = 5\frac{1}{2}$ Correct answer $5\frac{1}{2}$, choice C.

In Example 1, the choices A, B, C, D, E are used to check your work. If none of the answers agrees with yours then you are wrong.

Indirect methods

It is possible to try all the given answers, one at a time, to see which one fits the question. This is usually slower than the direct method but can be used if you are not able to find the answer directly.

In Example 1 above,
A $p = 2\frac{1}{2} \Rightarrow 2p - 3 = 5 - 3 = 2$ does not agree with the equation
B $p = 4\frac{1}{2} \Rightarrow 2p - 3 = 9 - 3 = 6$ does not agree with the equation
C $p = 5\frac{1}{2} \Rightarrow 2p - 3 = 11 - 3 = 8$ ✓

As you can see, it has only taken three steps to find the answer.
Sometimes you can use common sense to work your way to the answer.

Example 2

What is c?
A 3   B $\sqrt{20}$ C $\sqrt{41}$ D 9   E 20
Think like this:
$c = 3$ is obviously too small   A̶
$c = 9$, $c = 20$ are obviously much too large   D̶, E̶
The choice is between $\sqrt{20}$ and $\sqrt{41}$.
$\sqrt{20} = 4\cdot47$ cm but c must be the longest side in the triangle
(it's the hypotenuse)   B̶
So the correct answer **must be** $\sqrt{41}$.

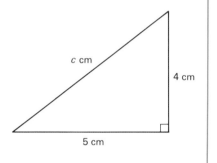

The direct answer comes from applying Pythagoras' theorem to the triangle.
$c^2 = 4^2 + 5^2 = 16 + 25 = 41$
$\Rightarrow c = \sqrt{41}$.
But you can get the correct answer from the knowledge that
(i) the sum of any two sides of the triangle must be greater than the third side (so 9 and 20 are too large);
(ii) the side opposite the right angle is the longest side in any right-angled triangle.

3 Avoiding the traps

Only one of the four or five choices can be right so the others must be wrong. But the examiner will not want the wrong answers to look too obvious. The wrong answers will be made to look attractive to someone who is guessing. If an answer 'looks right', but you don't know why, be very careful. It may be a trap.

4 Guessing

Sometimes you will try a question and find that you cannot decide which is the right answer. If you are working on an examination leave that question and continue with the next one. When you have completed the rest of the paper, come back to the question again for a second try.

First of all eliminate the answers that seem obviously wrong. This will possibly reduce your choice to two answers. Pick your final answer by some random method. [For example, toss a coin or use your calculator to generate a random number: e.g. choose any number between 1 and 100 then press $\boxed{\sin}$; the last digit will be odd or even.]

'It's the multiple choice section . . .'

5 Working through a paper

Multiple choice papers demand rather fast work so it is important not to get stuck on any question. First of all divide the total time for the exam by the number of questions. (For example, 40 questions in one hour will mean $1\frac{1}{2}$ minutes per question. Try not to spend more than this amount of time on any question.) Work steadily through the paper and leave any questions which you cannot solve in the proper time. Make a clear mark against those questions so that you do not forget to go back to them. If you have time left at the end use it to check. Use the opposite method to the one you used to solve the problem. If you solved it by direct working, check it by indirect working if you can. Do not alter your first answer unless you are absolutely sure you were wrong the first time.

Answers [to self assessments, exercises and puzzles]

Topic A Number

Self assessment (pp. 1–3)

Count 1 mark for each question or part. If you score 43+ in section 2 go on to next self assessment.

Section 1

1 25 **2** 119
3 8·3; the first calculator added 1·3 to 5 before multiplying by 1·4, whereas the second calculator multiplied 5 by 1·4 before adding 1·3. The second was correct.
4 0 **5** 8 **6** $^-1 \times {}^-3 = 3$
7 $^-13°C$ **8** E
9 There is no equivalent fraction.
10 $\frac{36}{99} = \frac{4}{11}$ **11** 67 **12** 60

Section 2

1 (i) 215, 342, 511 (ii) $\frac{11}{18}, \frac{18}{29}, \frac{29}{47}$
(iii) 161051, 1771561, 19487171. You might like to look for the connection between these numbers and the number sequences generated by Pascal's triangle.

$$
\begin{array}{ccccccc}
 & & & 1 & & & \\
 & & 1 & & 1 & & \\
 & 1 & & 2 & & 1 & \\
1 & & 3 & & 3 & & 1 \dots \text{etc}
\end{array}
$$

2 $2^1, 3^2, 3^4$; $n^{n+1} > (n+1)^n$ for $n > 2$.
3

+	o	e		×	o	e
o	e	o		o	o	e
e	o	e		e	e	e

Difficulties: with subtraction you have to consider negative numbers. With division, the table cannot be constructed as the numbers may not divide exactly.
4 (i) You can't divide by zero.
(ii) Line 5Ø, since $a - b = 0$ and therefore you can't divide by $a - b$.
5 (i) satisfactory (ii) could give you infinity
(iii) is a poor definition.
6 $a + \infty = \infty$ $a \div \infty = 0$ $a \times \infty = \infty$
$a - \infty = {}^-\infty$

7 (i) 7
(ii) $n < 0$, $m^2 < {}^-n$, eg . . .
$n = {}^-3$, $m^2 < 3 \Rightarrow m = 1$
$n = {}^-4$, $m^2 < 4 \Rightarrow m = 1$
$n = {}^-5$, $m^2 < 5 \Rightarrow m = 1, 2$
$n = {}^-6$, $m^2 < 6 \Rightarrow m = 1, 2$
etc.
8 6Ø $^-12 + ({}^-3 \times {}^-4) = 0 \dots$ from 4Ø, 5Ø
7Ø $^-3 \times {}^-4 = 12 \dots$ from 6Ø
9 Yes; note that
$(n - 1)^2 + (n - 1) + 1 = ({}^-n)^2 + {}^-n + 1$,
i.e. $n^2 + n + 41$ has the same value for 9 and $^-10$, 8 and $^-9$, etc (or use differences!)
10 (i) $2 \times 2 \times 2 \times 3 \times 3 \times 5 = 2^3 \times 3^2 \times 5$;
$3 \times 3 \times 3 \times 3 \times 5 = 3^4 \times 5$
(ii) $3 \times 3 \times 5 = 45$
11 (i) 0·6525 (ii) 0·5825, 0·585, 0·5875
(iii) 0·3 m is correct to the nearest 10 cm; 0·30 m is correct to nearest cm; 0·300 m is correct to the nearest mm.
12 The result should be approximately $55 \div 5 = 11$. $25·92 = 54 \times 0·48$ or $5·4 \times 4·8$ so Tina put the decimal point in the wrong place and multiplied.
13 (a) 5·1 (b) 1·9 (c) 5·6 (d) 2·1875; (d)
14 (a) $\frac{2}{9}$ (b) $\frac{5}{16}$ (c) $\frac{54}{99} = \frac{6}{11}$
15 (i) $2\frac{11}{12} = 2·92$ (ii) 40 **16** (v)
17 (iii) ; $a = 2, b = 6, c = 30$; $a = 3, b = 6, c = 30$
18 B **19** C **20** C
21 (i) 2·7495
(ii) C; make sure you check on your calculator!
22 Two examples are . . .
(i) $16^{\frac{1}{2}} \times 16^{\frac{1}{4}} = 4 \times 2 = 8 = 2^3 = (16^{\frac{1}{4}})^3$
$= 16^{\frac{3}{4}} = 16^{\frac{1}{2} + \frac{1}{4}}$
(ii) $3^{-2} \times 3^{-3} = \frac{1}{3^2} \times \frac{1}{3^3} = \frac{1}{9} \times \frac{1}{27} = \frac{1}{243} = \frac{1}{3^5}$
$= 3^{-5} = 3^{-2 + {}^-3}$
Your own will probably be something like mine.
23 (i) A
(ii) If $a \leq x \leq b$ x can be equal to a, or to b, which is not allowed if $a < x < b$.
24 D and E

Exercise A.1 (pp. 5–6)

1 36 **2** (a) 13 (b) 30 (c) 0·6
3 (a) 9 (b) 144 (c) 1369
4 0, 3, 8, 15, 24; 2499

5 $1101101_2 = 1 \times 2^0 + 0 \times 2^1 + 1 \times 2^2 + 1 \times 2^3$
$\qquad\qquad + 0 \times 2^4 + 1 \times 2^5 + 1 \times 2^6$
$\qquad = 1 + 4 + 8 + 32 + 64$
$\qquad = 109$

6 Base 8

Exercise A.2 (p. 7)

1 0

2 4·3 m is measured correct to 10 cm; 4·30 m is correct to the nearest cm.

3 1432000　　**4** $m = {}^-1$ or $n = 2$

5 1∅ Suppose there is an i such that $a \times i = a$
　　　 for all a
　　 2∅ $1 \times i = 1$ ... from 1∅
　　 3∅ $1 \times i = i$ ... from rule I for 1
　　 4∅ $i = 1$ ... from 2∅, 3∅

6 1·618 or ${}^-0·618$. You probably arrived at this result by trial and error (if you didn't forget the negatives). The numbers can also be obtained
from solving $n = 1 + \dfrac{1}{n}$.

Exercise A.3 (p. 9)

1 (i) ${}^-2$　(ii) 12　**2** (i) 12　(ii) ${}^-3$

3 (i) max $= 19°C$, min $= {}^-15°C$　(ii) $2°$

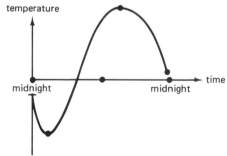

4 (i) 18　(ii) ${}^-2$

5

$\times$	$+$	$-$
$+$	$+$	$-$
$-$	$-$	$+$

$\div$	$+$	$-$
$+$	$+$	$-$
$-$	$-$	$+$

Explanation: The result of adding and subtracting $+$ and $-$ numbers depends on the size of the numbers, so there is no rule such as
$(+) + (-) = -$.

6 (i) 1∅ $({}^-8 \times 5) + (8 \times 5) = ({}^-8 + 8) \times 5$
　　 2∅ $({}^-8 \times 5) + (8 \times 5) = 0 \times 5 = 0$
　　 3∅ Thus ${}^-8 \times 5 = {}^-40$
　　 4∅ $({}^-8 \times {}^-5) + ({}^-8 \times 5) = {}^-8({}^-5 + 5)$
　　　　 $= {}^-8 \times 0 = 0$
　　 5∅ Thus $({}^-8 \times {}^-5) = {}^-({}^-40) = 40$

(ii) ${}^-a.b = a.{}^-b = {}^-(ab)$ ... see para A.3.3
$\Rightarrow \dfrac{{}^-a}{{}^-b} = \dfrac{a}{b}$　since for any four numbers $p, q,$
r, s　$\dfrac{p}{q} = \dfrac{r}{s} \Leftrightarrow ps = qr.$

Exercise A.4 (p. 13)

1 $1\frac{1}{2} \times 2\frac{3}{4} = 1·5 \times 2·75 = 4·125 = 4\frac{1}{8}$　**2** 9

3 $\dfrac{p}{q} + \dfrac{r}{s} = \dfrac{ps + qr}{qs}$　(i) $\frac{67}{72}$　(ii) $\frac{29}{16} = 1\frac{13}{16}$

(i) $\frac{3}{8} + \frac{5}{9} = 0·375 + 0·555\ldots = 0·930555\ldots$
$\qquad = \frac{67}{72}$ (by division)

(ii) $\frac{9}{16} + 1\frac{1}{4} = 0·5625 + 1·25 = 1·8125$
$\qquad = \frac{29}{16}$ (by division)

4 $\dfrac{a}{b} \div \dfrac{c}{d} = \dfrac{a}{b} \times \dfrac{d}{c}$　This treats *division* as *multiplication by inverse.*

(i) $\frac{2}{3} \div \frac{3}{4} = \frac{2}{3} \times \frac{4}{3} = \frac{8}{9}$

(ii) $\frac{4}{5} \div \frac{3}{15} = \frac{4}{5} \times \frac{15}{3} = \frac{60}{15} = 4$

5 The percentage fractions are changed into equivalent fractions base 360. This gives the angle of each sector of the pie chart;
e.g. $25\% \rightarrow \frac{25}{100} \rightarrow \frac{90}{360} \rightarrow 90°$.

6 $\dfrac{p}{q} = \dfrac{r}{s} \Rightarrow ps = rq \Rightarrow ps + qs = rq + qs \ldots$
$\qquad\qquad\qquad\qquad$ adding qs to both sides
$\qquad\qquad\qquad \Rightarrow (p + q)s = (r + s)q \ldots$
$\qquad\qquad\qquad\qquad$ distributive law
$\qquad\qquad\qquad \Rightarrow \dfrac{p + q}{q} = \dfrac{r + s}{s} \ldots$
$\qquad\qquad\qquad\qquad$ dividing by qs

Exercise A.5 (p. 16)

1 (i) 65536　(ii) 5·2338355　(iii) 1·5241579

2 $5\frac{1}{2}$　**3** 10

4 (i) $(x^m)^n = x^{m \times n} = x^{n \times m} = (x^n)^m$. Check by giving values to x, m and n.
　　 (ii) 3

5 $2·142 \times 10^{-6}$ mm². $21·42 \times 10^{-7}$ is correct but not in standard form.

6 $1·25 \times 10^9$

Exercise A.6 (pp. 18–19)

1 (i) 7　(ii) $\frac{1}{5}$　(iii) $2·4495 = \sqrt{6}$

2

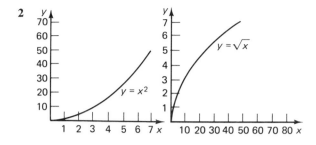

One graph can be obtained from the other just by changing the axes round, i.e. $y \to x$ and $x \to y$.

3 (i) $1{\cdot}0779$ (ii) $0{\cdot}6463$

4 $\sqrt{50} = \sqrt{2 \times 25} = \sqrt{2} \times \sqrt{25} = \sqrt{2} \times 5$
$= 1{\cdot}414 \times 5 = 7{\cdot}07$
$\sqrt{98} = \sqrt{2 \times 49} = \sqrt{2} \times \sqrt{49} = \sqrt{2} \times 7$
$= 1{\cdot}414 \times 7 = 9{\cdot}898$

5 $3{\cdot}8730$; 3 steps if $a_1 = 4$

6 (i) $\dfrac{a}{b}$ (ii) $xy^2z^3\sqrt{x}$

7 $1\emptyset$ suppose $\sqrt{10} = \dfrac{p}{q}$ where all common factors of p, q have been cancelled

$2\emptyset$ $10 = \dfrac{p^2}{q^2}$ (squaring both sides)

$3\emptyset$ $p^2 = 10q^2 \Rightarrow p^2$ ends in 0
$\qquad\qquad\qquad \Rightarrow p$ ends in 0
$\qquad\qquad\qquad \Rightarrow p = 10\,r$

$4\emptyset$ $100\,r^2 = 10\,q^2$

$5\emptyset$ $10\,r^2 = q^2 \Rightarrow q^2$ ends in 0 $\Rightarrow q$ ends in 0

$6\emptyset$ Thus both p and q end in 0. So ten can be cancelled and line $1\emptyset$ is false.

8 No pattern will appear. If a pattern did appear then $\sqrt{2}$ could be made into a fraction.

9 $\text{GM} < \text{AM} \Leftrightarrow \sqrt{mn} < \dfrac{m + n}{2}$

$\Leftrightarrow 4\,mn < (m + n)^2 \Leftrightarrow 4\,mn < m^2 + 2\,mn + n^2$
$\Leftrightarrow m^2 - 2\,mn + n^2 > 0 \Leftrightarrow (m - n)^2 > 0$.
Since the last statement is always true it must be the case that GM < AM is always true. Confirm with random values of m, n, including $+$, $-$ and fractional values.

Exercise A.7 (p. 20)

1 Primes other than 2 are odd. The sum of two odds is an even and therefore cannot be prime.

2 840

3 (b) 799 is not a prime number, because it has 17 as a factor.

4 (a) $a = mc, b = lc$
  (b) a is a factor of $b \Rightarrow b = na$; a is a factor of $c \Rightarrow c = ma$. Therefore, $b + c = (n + m)a \Rightarrow a$ is a factor of $b + c$.

5 (a), (b); (c) is false, e.g. 3 is a factor of 27, 3 is a factor of 15, but 27 is *not* a factor of 15.

6 (a) $2^m(m^2) - 1$ is not prime for $m = 2$
  (b) OK up to 5! $- 1$

Exercise A.8 (p. 22)

1 (a) $<$ (b) $<$ (c) $>$ (d) $<$

2 $x \geqslant 2$ or $x \leqslant {}^-2$

3 (a)   **4** $x \geqslant \dfrac{3{\cdot}6}{4} (= 0{\cdot}9)$ i.e. $x \geqslant 0{\cdot}9$

5 (a) $\dfrac{5}{7}$ (b) $\dfrac{100}{150}$ (easily checked by division)

6

Activities and investigations A

Competition quiz A (p. 25)

'A's questions for B'

1 36   **2** 26   **3** £25·84   **4** 400   **5** 41
6 3   **7** 18   **8** 6
9 A number less than $^-10$ and more than $^-100$, e.g. $^-11, {}^-12, \ldots, {}^-98, {}^-99$, i.e. a negative number whose value is between 10 and 100.
10 0·043   **11** 0·0028   **12** 0·004   **13** 19·1
14 0·056
15 A fraction equivalent to $\dfrac{24}{30}$ such as $\dfrac{4}{5}, \dfrac{8}{10}, \dfrac{12}{15}$, $\dfrac{16}{20}, \dfrac{240}{300}$, etc., i.e. a fraction with the value 0·8.
16 $\dfrac{9}{8}$ **17** 45   **18** 2; $128 = 2^7$
19 83, 89, 97
20 1, 2, 4, 5, 8, 10, 20, or 40
21 True
22 $2 + 3 + 17$ or $2 + 7 + 13$ **23** 27, 823543
24 1 or $^-1$ **25** 12   **26** $8^{-2} = 0{\cdot}015625$
27 $1{\cdot}805 \times 10^{-2}$ **28** 40×4 **29** 4·35   **30** $\dfrac{1}{5}$

'B's questions for A'

1 17   **2** 45   **3** 6993
4 12 (use $37 \times 3 = 111$)
5 5556   **6** $^-26$ **7** 15   **8** 45

9 A number between 12·075 and 12·076 such as 12·0751, 12·0752, etc. You can check like this: 12·076 minus your number should be positive; your number minus 12·075 should be positive.

10 45   **11** 0·024   **12** 4·28   **13** 0·405

14 A fraction equivalent to $\frac{30}{36}$ such as $\frac{5}{6}, \frac{10}{12}, \frac{15}{18}, \frac{300}{360}$, ie, a fraction with the value 0·8333 . . . .

15 $1\frac{7}{8}$ **16** $\frac{9}{16}$

17 A fraction whose value is between 0·2 and 0·25, e.g. $\frac{2}{9}, \frac{21}{100}, \frac{11}{50}, \frac{6}{25}$.

Note: $\frac{2}{9}$ may be found by adding tops and bases.

18 3

19 *Possible answers*: $5 = 1 + 4$; $13 = 4 + 9$; $17 = 1 + 6$; $29 = 4 + 25$; $37 = 1 + 36$; $41 = 16 + 25$; $53 = 49 + 4$; $61 = 25 + 36$; $73 = 9 + 64$; $89 = 25 + 64$; $97 = 16 + 81$.

20 False

21 The digits add up to a multiple of 3 and therefore the number is a multiple of 3.

22 2^9 **23** 2   **24** 45   **25** 17·32   **26** 0·0743

27 12

28 An approx. answer to 495×62 is $500 \times 60 = 30000$. Also if you multiply the last digit of each number together (here $2 \times 5 = 10$), this indicates that the answer should end in 0.

29 110   **30** $\frac{5}{8}$.

Treasure hunt (pp. 25–27)

Treasure number T_1: $p = 7, q = 11, r = 13, s = 1001$
so $T_1 = 1\,002\,001$
Treasure number T_2: $w = 111, x = 73, y = 137$,
$z = 10\,001$
so $T_2 = 11\,102\,220\,111$ *or* $1·1102 \times 10^{10}$

Puzzles for two (pp. 27–29)

1 The family of numbers which cannot be written as sums of consecutive numbers are the powers of 2, i.e. 1, 2, 4, 8, 16, 32, etc.

2 5, 12, 13   9, 40, 41   6, 8, 10
10, 24, 26   18, 80, 82   etc.

3 (a) $5! = 120$, $6! = 720$, $7! = 5040$
(b) Varies from calculator to calculator; approx. 69!
(c) Answers are not unique; here are a few suggestions:

$$2 = \frac{4}{4} + \frac{4}{4} \qquad 3 = \frac{4}{4} + \frac{4}{\sqrt{4}}$$

$$4 = \frac{4 \times 4}{\sqrt{4} \times \sqrt{4}} \qquad 5 = \frac{4 \times 4 + 4}{4}$$

$$6 = 4 + \sqrt{\frac{4 \times 4}{4}} \qquad 7 = 4 + \sqrt{4} + \frac{4}{4}$$

$$8 = \frac{4 \times 4 \times \sqrt{4}}{4} \qquad 9 = 4 + 4 + \frac{4}{4} \qquad \text{and so on}$$

4 (a) $\frac{1}{4}$ (b) $\frac{3}{4}$ (c) $\frac{1}{8}$ (d) $\frac{3}{8}$ (e) $\frac{1}{3}$
(f) $\frac{2}{3}$ (g) $\frac{8}{9}$ (h) $\frac{1}{7}$ (i) $\frac{1}{11}$ (j) $\frac{4}{11}$

5 If you divide any term by the previous one the answer is close to 1·618 033 988 . . . . The answers get closer as you choose bigger numbers. In mathematical language

$$\frac{a_{n+1}}{a_n} \to 1·618\,033\,988\ldots \text{ as } n \text{ increases.}$$

6 It is worth looking at the thirteenths, seventeenths, nineteenths and twenty firsts.

7 $\frac{355}{113}$

9 (a) $\frac{1}{17} = 0·\dot{0}58\,823\,529\,411\,764\,\dot{7}$
(c) $\frac{1}{19} = 0·\dot{0}52\,631\,578\,947\,368\,42\dot{1}$
$\frac{1}{23} = 0·\dot{0}43\,478\,260\,869\,565\,217\,391\,\dot{3}$
$\frac{1}{31} = 0·\dot{0}32\,258\,064\,516\,12\dot{9}$

Topic B   Measurement

Self assessment (pp. 39–42)

Count 1 mark for each question or part of question. If you score 32+ in part B go on to next self assessment.

Part A

1 B, D   **2** C   **3** C   **4** C   **5** C
6 2·54   **7** 1   **8** 8   **9** $2\frac{1}{4}$ [or 2·2]   **10** 2

Part B

11 $27\frac{1}{2}$ mm, $37\frac{1}{2}$ mm

12 Diameter 47 mm, circumference 148 mm (approx); $C : D = 3·1 : 1$

13 (i) 52·5 cm^2 (ii) 52·5 cm^2
(iii) The areas are equal

14 (i) 2 squares [$= 200$ mm^2]
(ii) hexagon $= 8·79$ cm; octagon $= 10·25$ cm

15 496 sq units   **16** 8352 m^3

17 336000 cm^3 [or 0·336 m^3]

18 (a) $<$ (b) $=$ (c) $=$

19 (a) $2\pi r$ (b) πr^2 (c) $\pi r^2 h$ (d) $2\pi rh$
(e) $\frac{1}{3}\pi r^2 h$ (f) $4\pi r^2$

20 452·4 in^3 **21** 2827·4 g [$= 2·83$ kg]

22 175·9 cm^3 **23** 237·5% more

24 Perimeter 18·85 cm, area 75·4 cm^2

25   (i) 18·85 cm   (ii) 28·3 cm²   (iii) 7·42 cm
       (iv) 69·9 cm³

26   16·18 cm   **27**   70·36 cm²

28   136·14 cm³

29   The volume stays the same, but surface area would increase if the pile was pushed out of the vertical.

30   Volume of wood = 8·108 m³
       Volume of lead = 0·377 m³
       Weight = 6·2 tonnes

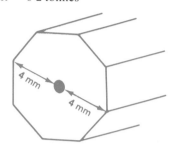

Exercise B.1 (pp 44–45)

1   (a) metres   (b) 20   (c) 142   (d) 150
     (e) 16·55   (f) 11   (g) 11   (h) 23571
     (i) 5 lb 1·144 oz

2   Not exactly: they differ by about 1p per gallon.   £8800

3   2340 kg

4   (a)   (i) 50·8 mm × 25·4 mm
         (ii) 50·8 mm × 38·1 mm
         (iii) 76·2 mm × 50·8 mm
         (iv) 101·6 mm × 50·8 mm
         (v) 63·5 mm × 63·5 mm
     (b)   (i) 7·5 metres of 60 mm × 100 mm
         (ii) 18 metres of 64 mm × 64 mm

5   (i) $1·07 × 10^9$ km/hr
     (ii) $9·4 × 10^{12}$ km or $5·87 × 10^{12}$ miles
     (iii) $4·23 × 10^{13}$ km
     (iv) $4·23 × 10^8$ hrs = 48287 years!!

Exercise B.2 (pp 49–50)

1   7 cm²

2   (a) AB = 4·47 cm, BC = 5·1 cm, AC = 3·16 cm
     (c)   ⊥ from A = 2·75 cm;
         ⊥ from B = 4·43 cm;
         ⊥ from C = 3·13 cm

4

     (b) A triangle is treated as a trapezium with one parallel side zero in length. A parallelogram is a trapezium with equal parallel sides

5   £2·2 million

6   (a) 2900 mm²
     (b) Methods which do not involve the measurement of angles.
     (c) Because you need to know the size of at least one of the angles. The quadrilateral is not rigid so the area can vary.

Exercise B.3 (pp. 52–53)

1   1400 cm³ [or 0·0014 m³]   **2**   5·25 cm

3   415·7 m³   **4** $23906\frac{1}{4}$ gallons

5   329 m³; 69·27 m³   **6**   2478

Exercise B.4 (pp 55–56)

1   Volume 9048 cm³, curved surface 2262 cm³

2   Height 7·64 cm, area 397·08 cm

3   (i) 85·44 cm   (ii) 126·4°

4   14782·3 cm² [= 1·48 m²]   **5**   197·4 mm³

6   (a) 8 m   (b) 10104 m³

Exercise B.5 (p. 57)

1   (a) 30 cm; 32 cm   (b) 408 cm²

2   (a) Width 7.4 m, height 4 m

3   Area = 74·82 cm²; n = 5·15

4 $2 × 10^6$ g [= 2000 kg]

5   (a) 18·52 cm
     (b) Base is 7·56 cm × 11·34 cm, height is 23·36 cm.

6   (a) 12·73 cm
     (b) height 15·488 cm, radius 6·08 cm

Activities and investigations B

Competition quiz B (pp. 63–64)

'*A's questions for B*'

1   The distance around the edge, or $2l + 2w$, where l is the length and w the width.

2 $a × b$ cm² [or ab cm²]

3 $b × h ÷ 2$ cm² $\left[\text{or } \dfrac{bh}{2} \text{ cm}^2\right]$

4   The area of a parallelogram is the base × the perpendicular height.

5 $\dfrac{a + b}{2}$ × perpendicular height.

6   A square with side 11 cm.

7   equilateral   **8**   1000   **9**   10000

10   36   **11**   144   **12**   1000   **13**   2·2

14 April, June, November and September
15 3600   16 $365\frac{1}{4}$ 17 10 000
18 $l \times w \times h$ cm^3 [or lwh cm^3]
19 $l \times A$ cm^3 [or lA cm^3]
20 $\pi\left(\dfrac{d}{2}\right)^2$ cm^2
21 πr^2 (the area)   22 $2\pi r^3$
23 $4\pi r^2$ (*Note*: this is also the surface area of a sphere!)
24 $\frac{1}{2}$ tonne

'B's questions for A'

1 20 cm   2 $\sqrt{A}$ cm
3 $\dfrac{x^2}{2}$ cm^2 4 $b \times h$ [or bh] cm^2
5 trapezium   6 $2ab$ cm^2
7 12 cm^2 8 1000
9 100 000   10 39·37 (39 approx.)
11 1000   12 453·6 (450 approx.)
13 112   14 366
15 1440   16 28 days
17 4840   18 3 m
19 $\dfrac{V}{A}$ cm   20 50·9 cm
21 $14\cdot4\pi$ cm^3 22 $\dfrac{A}{2\pi r}$ 23 $\dfrac{500}{\pi}$ ft^3
24 23·625 cwt

Puzzles and investigations (pp. 65–69)

Numerical answers only—and a few clues!

1 The fly on the cuboid: Shortest route is 8·6 cm. Longest route along edges is 30 cm.
2 The missing square: Check the angles of each piece.
3 Pin board: Trapezium 1 = 16 sq. units; rhombus 2 = 12 sq. units; triangle 3 = 15 sq. units; triangle 4 = 18 sq. units.
7

8 Volume investigations: 74 cm^3 is the maximum volume.
9 The largest volume?: 76·8 cm^3 is the maximum volume.

Topic C   The world of money

Self assessment (pp. 91–93)

Score 1 mark for each question or part you get right. If you score 44+ go on to the next self assessment.

1 Abdul earns the most, by £340 per year. [George's annual salary is £10 660.]
2 £315·90
3 (a) German   (b) Spanish
   [France £169·64, Germany £290, Spain £148·15, Italy £170, UK £180]
4 £572   5 £1575   6 £490
7 Ali £18·69;   Gill £23·02;   Dave £31·04
8 (a) Total earnings: £22 950
   (b) Total allowances: £4800
   (c) Taxable income: £18 150
   (d) Tax payable is: £5445
9 £86·25   10 £120·75   11 £135
12 £28 more
13 The frozen 5 lb pack is 80p less. [5 lb fresh mince cost £4·75.]
14 581, £45·27   15 £30·30
16 [Score a maximum of 3 points for each part.]
   Expenses which can be shared: rent, heating, lighting, furnishings, telephone rental, rates, house insurance, etc.
   Expenses which cannot be shared: clothes, food, travel, entertainment, holidays, personal insurance, etc.
17 £5·45
18 The dispenser costs £1·05 per 150 ml so the tube is better value. [They can be compared like this: The tube is 0·57p per ml or 1·76 ml per p. The dispenser is 0·7p per ml or 1·43 ml per p.]
19 Metric box costs 70p per kg or 32p per lb. Imperial box costs 79p per kg or 36p per lb. The Christmas box is better value.
20 The medium size is best value for money.
   [Small: £1 per kg   or 45p per lb
   Medium: 80p per kg   or 36p per lb
   Large: 97p per kg   or 44p per lb]
21 £11·50   22 £5·39
23 [Score 1 point for each sensible answer!]
   The *car* would probably be old and have many things wrong with it. The *shoes* would probably be made of poor material and of a design that no-one likes. The *record* may be old, scratched or not a very popular group. The *suit* may be a bargain, but you would need to check the quality of material and of manufacture, and the style.

24 (a) £32 (b) £65 (c) £68
[Choice and reasons may vary; no score for this part.]

25 £143·26 **26** £41·60, £546·09 **27** 18 weeks

28

	1 Jan	*Interest*	*31 Dec*
1987	£2800	£224	£3024
1988	£3024	£241·92	£3265·92
1989	£3265·92	£261·27	£3527·19
1990	£3527·19	£282·18	£3809·37
1991	£3809·37	£304·75	£4114·12

[Score 1 point for each correct amount.]

Exercise C.1 (p. 94)

1 £161·50
2 (a) £46·90 (b) £100·80 (c) £70·40 (d) £15
   (e) £189 (f) £50·40 (g) £193·20
3 120 **4** £102·90 **5** £80·77 **6** £2·50
7 £198 **8** £218·50 **9** £306·67
10 (a) £7640 (b) £146·92.

Exercise C.2 (pp. 97–98)

1 (a) £3·30 (b) £24 (c) £5·70
2 (a) £1885 (b) £37·70 (c) £243·60 (d) £1·38
3 £4800 **4** £75·90 **5** £640
6 Transport, education, social services, unemployment benefit, housing, aid to developing countries, defence etc.
7 Income tax, VAT, rates, water rates, national insurance, corporation tax.
8 (a) **9** £8·70 **10** £355.

Exercise C.3 (p. 99)

1 £64·80 **2** £82 **3** £106·67 **4** £9·50
5 Rent, rates, lighting, heating, telephone, food, possibly furniture and kitchen utensils, TV, hi-fi, etc.
6 15·8% **7** pie chart

Exercise C.4 (pp. 100–101)

1 £3640 **2** £450 **3** £1690
4 The monthly rent is £184·17, each girl pays £61·39.
5 £58·33 each
6 Approximately £20, depending on how economically they can live.
7 Mike £60 000; Jim £50 000 **8** £4000
9 £835 **10** £1927·50 or £1931 if it is a leap year.
11 £47 610
12 Cost, responsibility of ownership such as repairs, long-term investment, additional insurance etc.

Exercise C.5 (pp. 102–103)

Part 1

1 1 lb **2** 150 g **3** 1 km
4 5 litres **5** 75 mph **6** 500 ft
7 35 000 ft **8** (c) **9** 110·25 lb
10 81p for 5 litres, or 16p per litre.
11 64p per kg, much cheaper than 80p per lb.
12 53p (to nearest penny) **13** 5 kg
14 5400 tonnes **15** weight × 1000 cubic cm

Part 2

1 63p (to nearest penny) **2** 15p **3** 5p per lb
4 Large bottle: £1·23 per kg (to nearest penny)
   Small bottle: £1·09 per kg
   So the small bottle is better value.
5 The small packet is 81p per kg (to nearest penny).
   The large packet is 96p per kg (to nearest penny).
   The smaller is better value.
6 The $\frac{1}{2}$ litre size costs £2·50 per litre.
   The 1 litre size costs £2·25.
   The 5 litre size costs £1·05 per litre.
   It would be foolish to buy the 'better value' size unless you needed most of it. [Estimate how much you need from the information about 'coverage' which is usually given on the can.]
7 £7·50. You would expect a reduction for bulk buying.
8 Possible answers: TV, calculator, clothes, shoes.
9 1·18 kg **10** £2·77
11 Frozen cod is £2·49 per lb which is dearer than fresh. Or: fresh cod is £4·30 per kg and frozen is £5·50 per kg.

Exercise C.6 (p. 105)

1 £48 **2** £70 **3** Simple interest → £7072
4 S.I. → £196·44 per month
5 After 1 year: £1·08
   after 2 years: £1·17
   after 3 years: £1·26
   after 4 years: £1·36
   after 5 years: £1·47
6 £430·90 **7** C.I. → £835·44
8

After	Amount owing	Interest	Repayment	Total owing
	£450		£45	£405
1 month	£405	£8·10	£45	£351·90
2 months	£351·90	£7·04	£45	£299·86
3 months	£299·86	£6·00	£45	£248·86

Notice that no interest is paid on 1st repayment.

Exercise C.7 (p. 106)

Variety of answers.

Activities and investigations C

Competition quiz C (pp. 109-110)

'A's questions for B'

1	Both the same	**2**	£138	**3**	£283·33
4	£1632	**5**	£88·46	**6**	£514
7	£59	**8**	£660	**9**	£36
10	£90	**11**	26·8%		
12	Credit card, usually.				

'B's questions for A'

1	£98·46 per week	**2**	£4620	**3**	£6900
4	£1386·67	**5**	£148	**6**	£346·67
7	£322	**8**	£2160	**9**	Yes
10	£910	**11**	£266·67		
12	Generally the lowest APR is best.				

Team games

Hurdle race (p. 89)

A

1	£3·86	**2**	£13·16	**3**	$50 - 10 = 40$
4	£102	**5**	£4446	**6**	£8·48
7	£19·50	**8**	£28	**9**	£96
10	1 kg packet	**11**	16		
12	£40 or 40p or any multiple of 40.				

B

1	£4·65	**2**	£11·56	**3**	$53 - 28 = 25$
4	£81	**5**	£3978	**6**	£9·39
7	£13·50	**8**	£64	**9**	£72
10	1 kg	**11**	7		
12	£30 or 30p or any multiple of 30.				

C

1	£6·18	**2**	£12·28	**3**	$28·5 - 4 = 24·5$
4	£111	**5**	£4326·40	**6**	£18·26
7	£66	**8**	£72	**9**	£60
10	200 g	**11**	15		
12	£105 or 105p or any multiple of 105.				

D

1	£2·78	**2**	£11·04	**3**	$21 - 9 = 12$
4	£90	**5**	£4815·20	**6**	12·52
7	£26·25	**8**	£40	**9**	£84
10	1 kg	**11**	6		
12	£120 or £1·20 or any multiple of 120.				

Topic D   Geometry

Self assessment (pp. 127–136)

If you score a total of 91+ for parts I, II and III together, go on to the next self assessment.

Part I [maximum score 42]

1	B	**2**	C	**3**	B	**4**	B
5	B	**6**	C	**7**	C	**8**	C

9 Square, rectangle, rhombus, parallelogram, trapezium, isosceles trapezium, kite, arrow, cyclic quadrilateral. [Score maximum of 6.]

10 D **11** (i) $\hat{ABD}$, $\hat{CBD}$, $\hat{BDC}$
(ii) 62°   (iii) 124°

12 D **13** 108° **14** (i) 5   (ii) 9

15 (i) 7   (ii) 1260°   (iii) 900°

16 (i) 16 cm   (ii) diameter

17 [Four points for this diagram.]

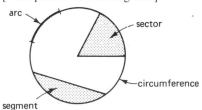

18 X = circumference, Y = diameter

19 (i) An infinite number.
(ii) They all go through the centre of the circle.

20 [Maximum 7 points.]
OP = OQ, $\hat{OPQ}$ = $\hat{OQP}$, $\hat{POX}$ = $\hat{XOQ}$,
PX = XQ, $\hat{PXO}$ = $\hat{QXO}$ = 90°, $\triangle$ OPQ is isosceles.

Part II [Maximum score 31]

1 (i) $\hat{C}$ = 90°   (ii) $\hat{B}$ = 70°

2 (a) ABCE, ABDE   (b) $\hat{C}$ = $\hat{D}$ = 70°
(c) $\hat{DEC}$ = $\hat{DBC}$

3 All statements are true; because opposite angles add up to 180°. Therefore, $180 - \hat{F} = \hat{C} = \hat{D} = \hat{E}$

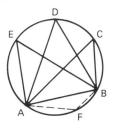

4 (i) AP and DP
(ii) They are equal. The diameter which passes through P is an axis of symmetry.

5

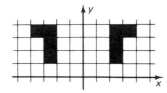

6 C and D

7 (a) 25° (b) 65° (c) 65°

8 (i) (1, 4) (3, 4) (1, 6) (4, 6) (ii) (2, 5)

9

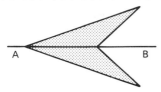

10 (i)

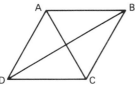

   (ii) Triangles ABC and ACD are reflections of each other. Triangles ABD and CBD are reflections of each other.

   (iii) Missing word is 'perpendicular'.

11 C **12** P′($^-$3, $^-$3), Q′($^-$6, $^-$3), R′($^-$4, $^-$6)

13 30. Each of the six triangles can be moved to one of the other 5 positions.

14 (iii) **15** D

16 $10\sqrt{5} = 22·36$ cm

17 (a) tetrahedron (b) pyramid with square base (c) prism with triangular cross-section

18 The diagonals of the faces of the van are approx. 150 cm, 190 cm and 180 cm. Hence the chest will fit (provided the van door is big enough!)

Part III [Maximum score 40]

1 (a) 1∅ Data: $B\hat{A}C + C\hat{B}A + A\hat{C}B = 180°$
   2∅ Data: $A\hat{C}D + A\hat{C}B = 180°$
   3∅ $B\hat{A}C + C\hat{B}A = A\hat{C}D$ ... from 1∅, 2∅
   Other proofs are possible.

   (b) 1∅ Data. POQ, POR, QOR are isosceles triangles

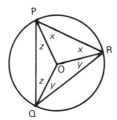

2∅ $Q\hat{P}O = P\hat{Q}O$, $R\hat{P}O = P\hat{R}O$; $O\hat{R}Q = O\hat{Q}R$
   ... from 1∅
3∅ Label the diagram as shown
4∅ $Q\hat{O}R = 180 - 2y = 2(90 - y)$
5∅ $2x + 2y + 2z = 180$ ... angles in a △
6∅ $x + y + z = 90$ ... from 5∅
7∅ $90 - y = x + z$ ... from 6∅
8∅ $Q\hat{O}R = 2(x + z) = 2 Q\hat{P}R$ ... from diagram
Other proofs are possible.

2 (a) Complete proof.

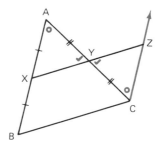

3∅ △AXY, △XZC are congruent (AAS)
4∅ ZC = AX = XB
5∅ XZCB is a parallelogram (ZC is a translation of XB)
6∅ XZ//BC

   (b)

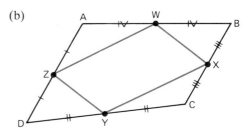

1∅ WX and YZ are both parallel to AC (from (a) above)
2∅ WZ and XY are both parallel to BD
3∅ WXYZ is a parallelogram
   (i) The inner parallelogram has sides which are half the diagonals of the original ... etc.
   Repeating the process reproduces a half size copy of the original.

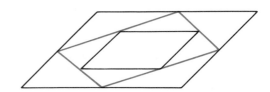

(ii) A rectangle is formed.
(iii) A rhombus is formed.
(iv) Another square is formed.

This question is really an investigation.

3 (a) 9. The external angle is $180° - 140° = 40°$. This is equal to $360°/n$, where n is the number of sides. So $n = 360/40 = 9$.
(b) 396 cm^2

4 (a) $\dfrac{360}{2\pi} = 57\cdot3°$
(b) The area of the sector is
$$\dfrac{360/2\pi}{360} \times \pi r^2$$
$$= \dfrac{360 \times \pi r^2}{2 \times \pi \times 360} = \tfrac{1}{2}r^2$$

5 (a) Suppose it does not, then an angle equal to B will be created where the circle cuts DA. But this angle will be larger (or smaller) than A.
(b) The angles in their new position will form a cyclic quadrilateral (opposite angles add to 180°).

6 (a) There are four sides and four vertices; the internal angles add to 360°.
(b) If PQRS is a parallelogram, X and/or Y do not exist.

7 (a) 22 faces, 30 vertices, 50 edges. So Eulers formula is satisfied.

8 (a) (i) Squares   (ii) Equilateral triangles.
(b) Any plane parallel to a diagonal of a face but skew to the cube (amongst others)

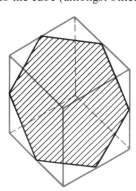

(c) An octahedron; 12 edges, 6 vertices, 8 equilateral triangles
9 (a) △ YBQ and △ AQR are congruent. The area of the square AXYQ is equal to the area of the rectangle PQRS.
(b) If U is the point of intersection of PR and QS, then the congruent triangles are PTS and PSU; PQU and SUR; PTS and PQR; PQS and PSR; SRQ and PTS; PSU and SRQ.

10 (a) *Possible answers*: AXD and BXC; AYD and BYC; ABY and CYD; BCD and ABC; ACD and ABD; DBX and ACX.
(b) Triangles ACX and DBX are congruent, with XA corresponding to XD; AC corresponding to BD; and XC corresponding to XB. So
$$\dfrac{XA}{XC} = \dfrac{XD}{XB} \Rightarrow XA \cdot XB = XC \cdot XD$$
(c) (i) PA · PB is constant
(ii) PA · PB = PT^2
(d) PA · PB is still constant but it is (obviously) not possible to draw a tangent.

Exercise D.1 (p. 138)

1 25°   2 b, e, g, j, l, m, o   3 76°
4 $x + y + x + y = 360°$ (angles of quadilateral), i.e. $2(x + y) = 360°$ so that $x + y = 180°$. But x and y are the internal angles where AB crosses the lines AD and BC, so AD and BC are parallel. Similarly, AB is parallel to DC.

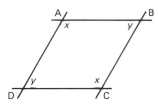

[N.B. there are other proofs]

Exercise D.2 (p. 143–144)

1 $X\hat{B}C = 58°$, $C\hat{A}B = 58°$, $A\hat{B}X = 32°$
2 BEID is a parallelogram, CHGF is a trapezium, FGJI is a parallelogram, ACKI is a square, DBCI is a trapezium, CHJI is a trapezium.
3 $B\hat{A}D = D\hat{C}E = 80°$. The opposite angles at the centre are equal.
4 156°

Exercise D.3 (p. 150)

1

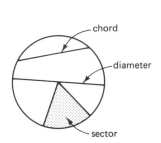

2 Both are 40°

3 Draw any chord and bisect it at right angles—this line will be another diameter. Where the two diameters intersect is the centre of the circle.

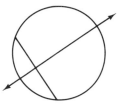

4 (a)

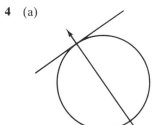

(b)

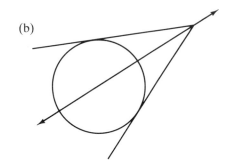

(c)

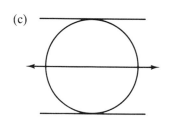

Exercise D.4 (p. 156)

1

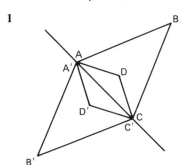

2 $(-3, 4)$

3

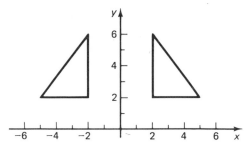

4 (a) rotation   (b) reflection   (c) rotation

Exercise D.5 (p. 158)

1 (a) 12 edges, 8 vertices, 6 faces
    (b) 12 edges, 8 vertices, 6 faces
    (c) 6 edges, 4 vertices, 4 faces
    (d) 8 edges, 5 vertices, 5 faces
2 Several possibilities. Check by cutting out and folding.
3 They will all be identical isosceles triangles. The longer the sides, the higher the pyramid.
4 They are all prisms:
    volume = area of cross section × length.

Activities and investigations D

Quiz: 'Are you in good shape?' (p. 165)

1 cuboid   **2** polygon
3 quadrilateral   **4** rhombus
5 square   **6** rectangle
7 segment   **8** kite   **9** pentagon
10 tetrahedron   **11** sector
12 trapezium   **13** octagon   **14** prism
15 parallelogram   **16** cylinder
17 triangle   **18** isosceles
19 equilateral triangle   **20** cone

Topic E Sets, statistics and probability

Self assessment (pp. 201–206)

Total score 84. Score 68+ to go on to next self assessment.

Sets

1 (i) {E, R}   (ii) {P, E, T, R, K, A, N}

(iii) {A, B, C, D, F, G, H, I, J, K, L, M, N, O, Q, S, U, V, W, X, Y, Z}

(iv) {B, C, D, F, G, H, I, J, L, M, O, P, Q, S, T, U, V, W, X, Y, Z}

(v) {B, C, D, F, G, H, I, J, L, M, O, Q, S, U, V, W, X, Y, Z}

2 (iv), (v)　　**3** (i) 13　　(ii) 4　　(iii) 7　　(iv) 25

4 {Football teams}　　**5** {5, 10, 13, 14, 17}

6

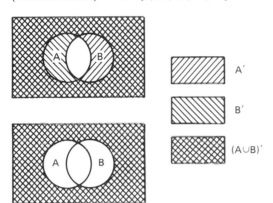

(b) Both state that every member of A is also a member of B.

7 (a) The first diagram represents A ∩ B, the second represents B, and the third represents A.

(b)

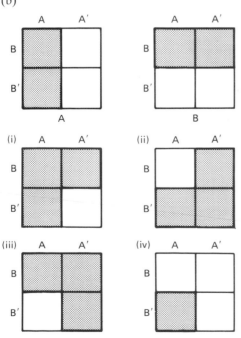

8 (a) 2

(b) There is not enough information to solve this question. 20 speak English but not Urdu, but we do not know how many of these speak Hindi.

Statistics

1 Roughly 870 motorists had no accidents, 80 motorists had 1 accident, 40 motorists had 2 accidents, 10 motorists had 3 accidents.

2 Over the period of the graph, unemployment rose from about 3 million to 3·2 million, yet it looks as though unemployment had more than doubled. This is because the vertical axis starts at 2·9 million, not zero. Although unemployment fell over the last 3 months, the fall was negligible compared to the amount it had risen in the previous year.

3

Height (cm)	Tally	Frequency
164·0–165·9	ЖЖ ||||	9
166·0–167·9	ЖЖ ЖЖ |||	13
168·0–169·9	ЖЖ ЖЖ ЖЖ ЖЖ |||	23
170·0–171·9	ЖЖ ЖЖ ЖЖ |||	18
172·0–173·9	ЖЖ ЖЖ |||	13
174·0–175·9	ЖЖ |||	8
176·0–177·9	ЖЖ ЖЖ	10
178·0–180	ЖЖ |	6

4 agriculture $4\frac{1}{2}$ km², forestry 4 km², recreation 2 km², housing 3 km², industry 2 km². 'Comments' will vary: no points for this part.

5 (i) 29　　(ii) 28　　(iii) 258

(iv) Reasons may vary, but the girls did slightly better than the boys because there were fewer girls with 0, 1 or 2 passes.
Slightly more boys than girls obtained 6, 7 or 8 passes, but more boys were entered.

6 (i) If they were picked from a telephone directory, they would all have a phone.

(ii) Most employed people would be working then.

(iii) Only a small proportion of people use the reading room in a public library and would not represent a cross-section of all people.

7 Matthew's average position is approximately 9th. Matthew's average mark is approx. 62. Joanna's average position is approx. 10th. Joanna's average mark is approx. 64. Matthew's average position is higher than Joanna's, but his average mark is lower. [The averages are distorted by biology and history, where Joanna's position was slightly better than Matthew's, but her mark was considerably better.]

8 Mean 322·17 sec, mode 321 sec, median 322 sec, range 5 sec.

9 'Financial' and 'shops' are labelled the wrong way round.

10 7 coaches, 22 lorries, 33 cars, 17 motorcycles, 15 bicycles

11 (a)

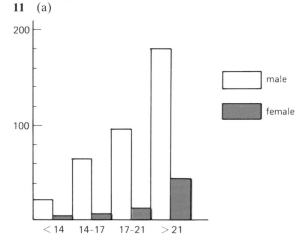

(b) We do not know what ages to use to represent the under 14, and 21 and over categories. For this we need extra information. The median ages for males and females are both above 20.

(c) Crime increased in every category except females aged 21 and over.
The largest increase was for males aged 14–17, where crime increased by about 60%.

12 (a)

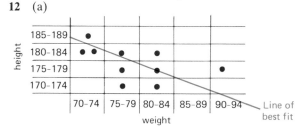

There is a strong negative association between height and weight. [This could be because police recruits are either tall or short and strongly built.]

(b) Mean 178·812 cm;   median 178·21 cm;   interquartile range 7·85 cm

Probability

1 Two aces is more likely. (i) $\frac{1}{216}$ [or 0·004 63]
(ii) $\frac{1}{169}$ [or 0·005 92]

2 $\frac{40}{365}$ [or $\frac{8}{73}$, or 0·110]

3 For every 100 parachute jumps, 1 will be fatal. This is not a good risk [so I wouldn't jump!]

4 $\frac{6}{10}$ [or $\frac{3}{5}$ or 0·6]; $(\frac{6}{10})^5 = 0.07776$

5

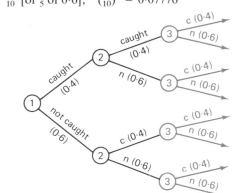

(1) $(0.6)^3 = 0.216$ (2) $(0.6)^2 \times 0.4 = 0.144$

6 $\frac{43}{500} = 0.086$

7 (a) $\frac{10}{48}$ (b) $\frac{11}{48}$ (c) $\frac{27}{48}$
The total should be 1 since all possibilities are covered.

8 (a) $\frac{4}{52}$ or $\frac{1}{13}$
(b) (i) $\frac{4}{52} \times \frac{3}{51} = \frac{1}{221}$ (ii) $\frac{48}{52} \times \frac{4}{51} = \frac{16}{221}$

Exercise E.1 (p. 208)

1 Any nine from 10, 20, 30, 40, 50, 60, 70, 80, 90

2 (i) {10, 20, 30, 40, 50, 60, 70, 80, 90, 100}
(ii) All evens under 100, together with {5, 15, 25, 35, 45, 55, 65, 75, 85, 95, 100}
(iii) {5, 15, 25, 35, 45, 55, 65, 75, 85, 95}
(iv) All evens under 100 except {10, 20, 30, 40, 50, 60, 70, 80, 90}

3 (i) {2}   (ii) ∅   (iii) {2}   (iv) ∅   **4** Yes

5 10 read T only; 12 read S only; 7 read YL only.

6 (a) {a}, {b}, {c}, {a, b}, {a, c}, {b, c}, {a, b, c}
(b) {p}, {q}, {r}, {s}, {p, q}, {p, r}, {p, s}, {q, r}, {q, s}, {r, s}, {p, q, r}, {p, q, s}, {p, r, s}, {q, r, s}, {p, q, r, s}.
(c) 1024

7

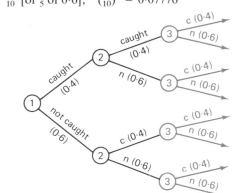

(ii) 1

8

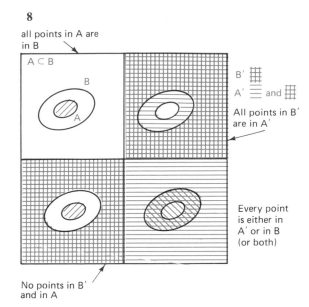

all points in A are in B

A ⊂ B

B

A

B′ ▦

A′ ≣ and ▦

All points in B′ are in A′

Every point is either in A′ or in B (or both)

No points in B′ and in A

Exercise E.2 (pp. 221–223)

1 A small amount of blood for testing.

2 *Matches*

over 50	*Tally*	*Frequency*
0	⩊⩊ ⩊⩊ ⩊⩊	15
1	⩊⩊ ⩊⩊ ⩊⩊ |	16
2	⩊⩊ ⩊⩊ ⩊⩊ ⩊⩊ |	21
3	⩊⩊ ‖‖	8

3 (i) Wednesday and Saturday; the busiest days.
(ii) Sunday   (iii) Approximately 380.

4 British 650 000, Japanese 330 000, Italian 195 000, French 218 000, German 213 000

5

	mean	*median*	*mode*
1a	1·78	1	1
1b	1·70	2	1
1c	1·74	2	0
2a	1·53	1	1
2b	1·79	2	0
2c	1·62	1	1
3a	1·72	2	1
3b	2	1	1
Total	1·73	1	1

6 England: mean 59 weeks, mode 104^+, median 38 weeks
Scotland: mean 62 weeks, mode 104^+, median 39 weeks
People are, on average, unemployed for a longer period in Scotland.
Here I have assumed that the representative weeks are 1, 6, 11, 20, 40, 78, 156.

7

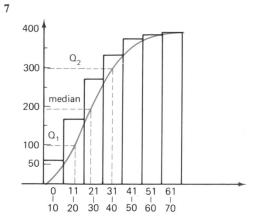

Median 23 days
Interquartile range $34·1 - 13·5 = 20·6 \simeq 21$ days

8

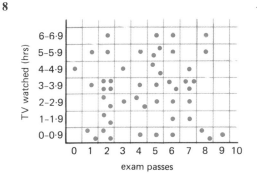

No association

Exercise E.3 (p. 228)

1 $\frac{250}{2501} = 0·09996 \simeq \frac{1}{10}$

2

Score	*Probability of throwing this score*
2	$\frac{1}{36}$
3	$\frac{2}{36}$
4	$\frac{3}{36}$
5	$\frac{4}{36}$
6	$\frac{5}{36}$
7	$\frac{6}{36}$
8	$\frac{5}{36}$
9	$\frac{4}{36}$
10	$\frac{3}{36}$
11	$\frac{2}{36}$
12	$\frac{1}{36}$

3 (a) $(0·4)^3 = 0·064$
(b) $3 \times 0·4^2 \times 0·6 = 0·288$

4

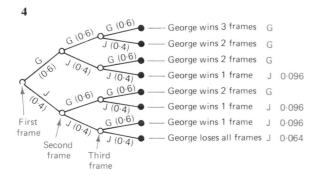

George wins 3 frames — G
George wins 2 frames — G
George wins 2 frames — G
George wins 1 frame — J   0·096
George wins 2 frames — G
George wins 1 frame — J   0·096
George wins 1 frame — J   0·096
George loses all frames — J   0·064

G: George wins
J: Jake wins

The probability that Jake wins the match is 0·352
$[= 0·6 × 0·4^2 × 3 + 0·4^3]$

5 $\frac{2}{33} = 0·0606\ldots$ **6** $\frac{40}{87}$

7 (a) $\frac{1}{3}$ (b) $\frac{13}{33}$ (c) $\frac{1}{11}$
(d) The odds are in the bank's favour because of the zero.

8 (a) $\frac{32}{135} = 0·24$ (b) $\frac{113}{270} = 0·42$ (c) $\frac{17}{75} = 0·23$
(d) $\left(\frac{32}{135}\right)^3 = 0·013$

In the 0–5 mins interval, I have divided the 6 possible times (measured in mins) equally between the 16 buses that arrived early, and then between the 34 buses that arrived late.

In the 5^+–10 mins interval, I divided the 5 possible times between the 29 buses that arrived late.

Activities and investigations E

Competition quiz E (pp. 233–239)

'A's questions for B'

1 $\frac{1}{6}$ [or 0·167]   **2** $\frac{1}{2}$ [or 0·5]
3 Approximately 0·25
4 $\frac{16}{20}$ [or 0·8]   **5** 0·09   **6** 150
7 6 or 7   **8** 36   **9** 11   **10** 6
11 8: HHH, HHT, HTH, THH, TTH, THT, HTT, TTT
12 A small group taken to represent a larger group.
13 A *random number* picked from (0, 1, 2, . . . 999) is any number, all numbers being equally likely. An *odd number* between 0 and 999 is any number not divisible by 2.
14 A means of collecting information whereby people are asked their opinions etc.
15 26—the die must have been thrown an extra time!
16 A graph showing the frequency of data by means of bars.
17 They were probably friends who came to school together.

18 4   **19** median = D, mode = E
20 Distorting axes, misleading use of 3 dimensional drawings, leaving out relevant information; etc.

'B's questions for A'

1 $\frac{1}{13}$ [or 0·077]   **2** $\frac{2}{6}$ [or $\frac{1}{3}$ or 0·333]
3 0·6   **4** 12   **5** 0·24
6 90% [or 0·9]; 0·81
7 8   **8** $\frac{8}{512}$ [or 0·0156]
9 1, 2, 3, 4, 5, 6, 8, 9, 10, 12, 15, 16, 18, 20, 24, 25, 30, 36
10 (2, 6); (3, 5); (4, 4); (5, 3); (6, 2); i.e. 5 ways
11 $\frac{1}{12}$ [or 0·0833]
12 A number selected in such a way that no number is more likely than another.
13 Estimating statistical information about a large population, in an economical way.
14 A list of questions used in a survey.
15 A sample which has not been collected randomly and gives a false picture of the population.
16 A circular graph showing the proportional, relation between data.
17 A sample of the whole batch has been tested and 90% grew.
18 7   **19** 7
20 Possible answers [score 1]:
To show something is good for you, or at least not harmful, as in certain food products or toothpaste, to prove efficiency, for domestic appliances, cars etc; to compare cost.
Statistics used in advertising may not be reliable.

Experiments with dice: comments (p. 237)

1 There are more ways of getting some scores than others.
2 The most likely scores are 10 and 11, the next most likely are 9 and 12 etc.
3 5 of the same → 0·0007716
4 of the same → 0·0192901
high straight → 0·015432
low straight → 0·015432
full house → 0·0385802
3 of the same → 0·1543209
Two pairs → 0·2314814
One pair → 0·4629629
Very rough approximations to these are acceptable.

4

No. of sixes	0	1	2	3
Expected frequency	579	347	69	5

The actual frequency may vary.

5 (a) The pattern should be the same.
(b) It should be the same for any number.

Topic F   Algebra and graphs

Self assessment (pp. 257–259)

If you score 24+ go on to the next self assessment.

1	C	**2**	D	**3**	A	**4**	C	**5**	C
6	B	**7**	A	**8**	C	**9**	C	**10**	D
11	A	**12**	C	**13**	B	**14**	C	**15**	B
16	C	**17**	A	**18**	B	**19**	A	**20**	B
21	D	**22**	C	**23**	D	**24**	D	**25**	B
26	D	**27**	B	**28**	C	**29**	C	**30**	C

Exercise F.1 (pp. 260–261)

3 (i) $m = 1$ (ii) $n = 0$
5 line 2∅ $a = b \Rightarrow a + c = b + c$ and rule (ix)
line 3∅ $a(b + c) = ab + ac \ldots$ twice!
line 4∅ $ab = 0 \Rightarrow a = 0$ or $b = 0$
line 5∅ as for line 2∅
6 (ii) is the correct answer.
7 All the rules still apply.
8 The result of adding n and m is the remainder when $m + n$ is divided by 4. $[0 \leqslant m, n \leqslant 3]$
$a + (b \cdot c) = (a + b) \cdot (a + c)$ and others.

Exercise F.2 (p. 261)

1 $3xy - x^2 = x(3y - x)$
2 $3x^2 - 2xy^2 = x(3x - 2y^2)$
3 $^-3x^3$ **4** $2a^2b^2$
5 $\dfrac{23 - 2x}{12}$ **6** $\dfrac{^-x}{(x + 1)(x + 2)}$

Exercise F.3 (p. 262)

1 $a(a + 2b^2)$ **2** $(p - 1)(p - 3)$
3 $(x - 2y)(x + 2y)$ **4** $(2x + y)(x - y)$
5 $(3a - b)(a - b)$ **6** $\left(2x + \dfrac{1}{y}\right)\left(2x - \dfrac{1}{y}\right)$
7 $x(x + 2)(x - 7)$ **8** $(2x + 3y)(4x^2 - 6xy + 9y^2)$

Exercise F.4 (pp. 263–264)

1 1·720   **2** 33   **3** £25·80   **4** 9 m
5 10 cm^2 **6** 34·56 cm^2 **7** 1·2 kW   **8** £1620

Exercise F.5 (pp. 264–265)

1 $b = \dfrac{p}{2} - a$ **2** (i) $h = \dfrac{V}{\pi r^2}$ (ii) 0·7 cm

3 (i) $g = \dfrac{2s}{t^2}$ (ii) $s = \dfrac{gt^2}{2}$
4 (i) $c = \sqrt{\dfrac{e}{m}}$; $m = \dfrac{e}{c^2}$ (ii) 3×10^5 units.
5 $v = 28$ mph
6 (i) $\dfrac{64 - 24}{2} = 20$
(ii) $\dfrac{n^2 - 3n}{2} = 128 \Rightarrow n(n - 3) = 256 = 2^8$. Thus the product of two numbers whose difference is 3 will equal a power of 2. This is not possible because one of $n, n - 3$ must be odd.

Exercise F.6 (p. 266)

1 $x = 8$ **2** $x = 3$ **3** $x = 5$ **4** $x = 3$
5 $x = 5$ **6** $m = ^-2$ **7** $x = 10$ **8** $y = 20$

Exercise F.7 (pp. 267–268)

1 $x = 13, y = 4$ **2** $y = 3x, x + y = 5$
3 $p = 2, q = 3$
4

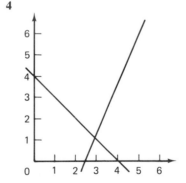

5 $x = 7, y = ^-3$. The graph involves $(0, ^-24)$ and so would be awkward to draw.
6 $x = 6, y = ^-4$

Exercise F.8 (p. 269)

1 $x = ^-4$ or 6   **2** $x = 1$ or 2
3 $x = ^-1·61$ or 3·11
4 $x = 1$ or 2   **5** $x = ^-1·62$ or 0·62
6 $6x^2 + x - 2 = 0$
$\Rightarrow x = \dfrac{^-1 \pm \sqrt{1 + 48}}{12} = \dfrac{^-1 \pm 7}{12} = ^-\tfrac{2}{3}$ or $\tfrac{1}{2}$
$6x^2 + x - 2 = 0 \Rightarrow (3x + 2)(2x - 1) = 0$
$\Rightarrow x = ^-\tfrac{2}{3}$ or $\tfrac{1}{2}$
7 $b^2 - 4ac = ^-7 < 0$ so the equation has no real roots.

8 The equation can be rewritten as
$x^2 + \frac{5}{3}x + \frac{2}{3} = 0$.
So the sum of the solutions is $-\frac{5}{3}$, and the product of the solutions is $\frac{2}{3}$. [If p and q are the solutions to $x^2 + ax + b = 0$, then
$(x - p)(x - q) = x^2 + ax + b \Rightarrow p + q = {}^-a$
and $pq = b$.]

Exercise F.9 (pp. 273–274)

1

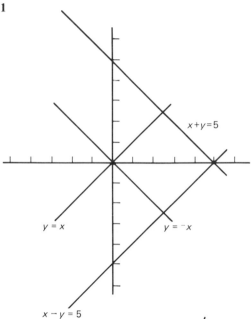

2

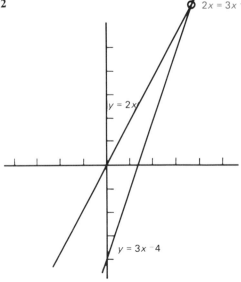

$2x = 3x\ {}^-4 \Rightarrow x = 4$

$y = 2x$

$y = 3x\ {}^-4$

3

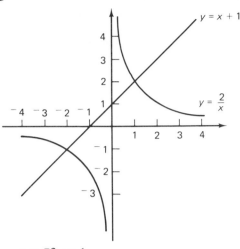

$x = {}^-2 \text{ or } 1$

4

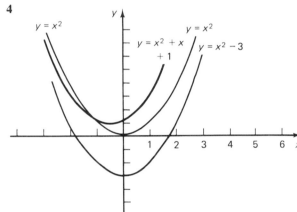

They all have the same shape. (Both $y = x^2 - 3$ and $y = x^2 + x + 1$ are translations of $y = x^2$)

5

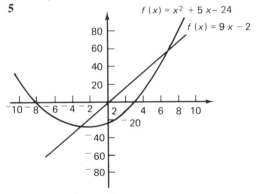

$f(x) = x^2 + 5x - 24$
$f(x) = 9x - 2$

(i) $x = 3 \text{ or } {}^-8$
(ii) $x^2 + 5x - 24 = 9x - 2 \Rightarrow x^2 - 4x - 22 = 0$
$\Rightarrow x \simeq {}^-3 \text{ or } 7$

6 $x^2 + y^2 = 3$ is a circle with centre $(0, 0)$, radius $\sqrt{3} = 1.73$. It meets $y = x^2$ at $(1.14, 1.3)$ and ɹd $(^-1.14, 1.3)$.

Exercise F.10 (pp. 275–276)

1 Graph; £31·25 **2** Graph; 2000 g
3 Graph; 3·54 **4** Graph
5 Graph **6** Graph; 82 secs

Exercise F.11 (pp. 279–280)

1 (i) $\frac{2}{3} = 0.666$ (iv) (b), (c)

(ii)

(iii)

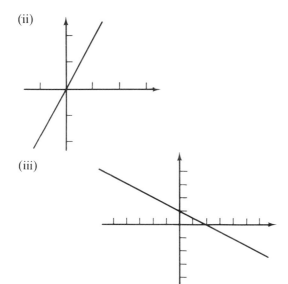

2 R $^-\frac{1}{4}$; P $^-\frac{5}{4}$; Q $^-\frac{7}{2}$ (roughly)
4 (i) maximum 1; minimum $^-1$
  (ii) $x = 27°$ or $93°$
5

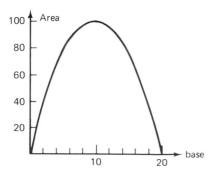

Maximum area is 100 cm^2
6 (i) 176 m (ii) 34, $^-4$
  (iii) The gradients in (ii) give the velocities of the rocket after 2·5 seconds and 6·5 seconds.

Exercise F.12 (p. 282)

1

x	0	1	2	3	4	5
y	$^-5$	$^-3$	$^-1$	1	3	5

2

x	$^-2$	$^-1$	0	1	2	3
y	2	$\frac{1}{2}$	0	$\frac{1}{2}$	2	$4\frac{1}{2}$

3 C **4** 4

Exercise F.13 (p. 283)

1 14 **2** 10 **3** $f : x \to \frac{1}{2}x$
4 $f : x \to x - 4$
5 (a) $f(^-2) = ^-30$; $f(^-3) = ^-30$
  (b) $x = ^-8$ or 3; $x = ^-9.87$ or 4·87
6 You can only choose values of x such that
  $^-1 \leqslant x \leqslant 1$ because $^-1 \leqslant \sin y \leqslant 1$ for all values
  of y.

Exercise F.14 (p. 285)

1 $\frac{1}{64} = 0.015625$ **2** 10 **3** 8
4 6·708; $\sqrt{45} = \sqrt{9 \times 5} = \sqrt{9} \times \sqrt{5} = 3\sqrt{5}$
5 $\sqrt{90} = \sqrt{9 \times 10} = 3\sqrt{10}$. Also $3^2 = 9$ and
  $4^2 = 16$ so $\sqrt{10}$ is slightly larger than 3. Take
  $\sqrt{10} \approx 3.1$, i.e. $\sqrt{90} \approx 9.3$. Now divide and
  average: $\frac{1}{2}[(90 \div 9.3) + 9.3]$ gives $\sqrt{90}$ as 9.49.
6 1∅ $\dfrac{a + b}{2} > \sqrt{ab} \Leftrightarrow a + b > 2\sqrt{ab}$

  2∅ $\Leftrightarrow (a + b)^2 > 4ab$
  3∅ $\Leftrightarrow a^2 + 2ab + b^2 > 4ab$
  4∅ $\Leftrightarrow a^2 - 2ab + b^2 > 0$
  5∅ $\Leftrightarrow (a - b)^2 > 0$
  6∅ Since the last statement is true for all values of
    a and b, it follows that the first statement is true
    for all values of a and b.

Exercise F.15 (p. 288)

1 (i) $>$ (ii) $<$ (iii) $>$ (iv) $>$
2 Diagram
3

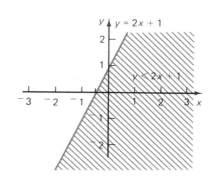

4

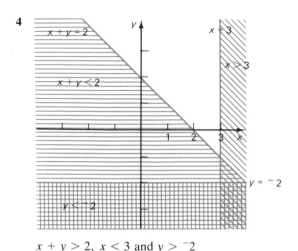

$x + y > 2$, $x < 3$ and $y > {}^-2$

5

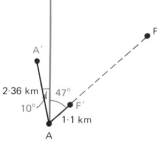

$(x + 4)(x - 2)$ must be positive or zero,
i.e. $x = {}^-4$ or 2, or $x > 2$ or $x < {}^-4$.

Topic G   Trigonometry

Self assessment (pp. 315–317)
Score 1 point per question or part. If you score 30+ go
on to the next self assessment.

1 D   **2** (i) AB   (ii) AC
    (iii) BC is 'adjacent'
3 B   **4** D
5   (i) Where the common tangents intersect.
    (ii) 5·7 cm from A, 9·85 cm from B.
6 A   **7** B is sin 63°; C is cos 36°; D is tan 36°
8 B
9 (i) 5·64 cm   (ii) 4·10 cm   (iii) 11·57 cm²
10 12·5°   **11** B   **12** 10·57 cm
13 (i) 9·17 cm   (ii) 66·4°
14 Many possibilities. Score 1 point for each pair of
    triangles. Use your judgement.
15 115·9 miles
16 The direction of your school as the crow flies;
    where north lies.
17 △A′B′C′ has coordinates $({}^-2, {}^-2)$, $({}^-4, {}^-2)$,
    $({}^-4, {}^-6)$
18 $\frac{3}{2}\sqrt{2} = 2\cdot12$ cm
19 (i) 0·3   (ii) ¯1   (iii) 0·5   (iv) 0·5
20 3·42 cm

Exercise G.1 (p. 319)

1 (a) X → Y, SF 2·3   (b) A → B, SF 3·6
2 1451·25 mm²   **3** $\frac{1}{4}$[or 0·25] ton
4 47·6 cm   **5** Diagram

Exercise G.2 (pp. 326–327)

1 4·69 cm   **2** 27·3°   **3** Drawing   **4** 18 m
5 (a) 36·90°, 143·13°   (b) 116·74°, 243·26°
    (c) 98·88°, 278·88°
6 Not possible. But this question is worth
    investigating further. [For example, rectangles on
    squares must have their sides parallel to the
    diagonal of the square and their perimeters will be
    twice the diagonal in length.]
7 $x\tan\theta + 2y\cos\theta$ **8** 40·30°

Exercise G.3 (pp. 330–331)

1 8·49 cm   **2** $4^2 + 5^2 \neq 6^2$ **3** Drawing
4 AB = sin 60° = 0·866
    AC = 0·866 × 2 = 1·73 = $\sqrt{3}$

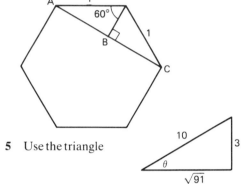

5 Use the triangle

$\cos\theta = \dfrac{\sqrt{91}}{10} = 0\cdot954$; $\tan\theta = \dfrac{3}{\sqrt{91}} = 0\cdot314$

6 XY = $\sqrt{2^2 + 6^2} = \sqrt{40} = 6\cdot32$ units
    XZ = $\sqrt{4^2 + 6^2} = \sqrt{52} = 7\cdot2$ units
    YZ = $\sqrt{6^2 + 0^2} = \sqrt{36} = 6$ units
7 EB = $\sqrt{45}$ cm, BH = $\sqrt{61}$ cm;
    EB̂H = 30·8° (approx. 30°)
8 (i) 25·25 m   (ii) 251·25 m²

Exercise G.4 (pp. 333–334)

1 505 km   **2** 313°   **3** Diagram
4 By making a scale drawing.
5 (i) 64·5°, 101°, 226°, 338°
    (ii) 230°, 273°
    (iii) 50°, 93°
6 227°
    After 10 seconds the
    aircraft is at A′ and
    the fighter is at F′.
    They are then 2 km
    apart.

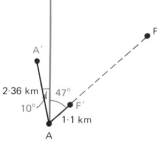

Exercise G.5 (p. 336)

1 34°, 102°, 44°

2 One number is bigger than the other two added together.

3 3·9 cm   **4** Drawing

Topic H   Vectors and matrices

Self assessment (pp. 365–366)

Score 1 point per question or part. If you score 28+ go back and revise any other topic you are unsure about.

1

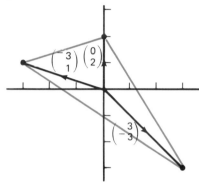

2

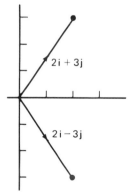

All vectors $u\mathbf{i} + v\mathbf{j}$, $u\mathbf{i} - v\mathbf{j}$ are symmetrical about the x-axis.

3 (d), because it is not the only vector with length $\sqrt{5}$, eg. $\binom{2}{1}$ also has length $\sqrt{5}$.

4

(a)   (b)

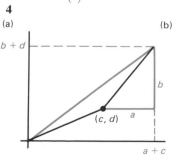   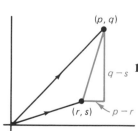

(c)

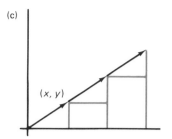

5 (a) $\sqrt{13}$ (b) $\sqrt{10}$ (c) $\sqrt{5}$

6 $\overrightarrow{CX} = \frac{1}{2}\mathbf{r}$ $\overrightarrow{BX} = \mathbf{q} + \frac{1}{2}\mathbf{r}$

7 1∅ $\overrightarrow{AC} = \mathbf{p} + \mathbf{q}$

2∅ $\overrightarrow{AX} = \frac{1}{2}(\mathbf{p} + \mathbf{q})\ldots$ from 1∅

3∅ $\overrightarrow{BX} = \overrightarrow{BA} + \overrightarrow{AX} = {}^-\mathbf{p} + \frac{1}{2}(\mathbf{p} + \mathbf{q})$

4∅ $\overrightarrow{BX} = \frac{1}{2}(\mathbf{q} - \mathbf{p})$

5∅ $\overrightarrow{BD} = \mathbf{q} - \mathbf{p}$

6∅ X is the midpoint of $\overrightarrow{BD}\ldots$ from 4∅ , 5∅.

8 Let P, Q, R, S be the midpoints of the sides of ABCD.

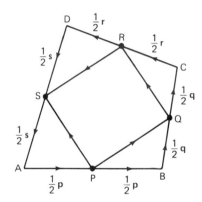

1∅ $\mathbf{p} + \mathbf{q} + \mathbf{r} + \mathbf{s} = 0 \ldots$ since both ends are the same

2∅ $\overrightarrow{PQ} = \frac{1}{2}(\mathbf{p} + \mathbf{q})$

3∅ $\overrightarrow{PQ} = {}^-\frac{1}{2}(\mathbf{r} + \mathbf{s}) \ldots$ from 1∅, 2∅

4∅ $\overrightarrow{SR} = {}^-\frac{1}{2}(\mathbf{r} + \mathbf{s})$

5∅ PQ and SR are parallel

6∅ $\overrightarrow{QR} = \frac{1}{2}(\mathbf{q} + \mathbf{r})$

7∅ $\overrightarrow{PS} = {}^-\frac{1}{2}(\mathbf{p} + \mathbf{s}) = \frac{1}{2}(\mathbf{q} + \mathbf{r}) \ldots$ from 1∅

8∅ PS, QR are parallel

9

	M	T
B	7	14
DB	0	12
SB	10	15

10 $\mathbf{AB} = \begin{pmatrix} 14 & 9 \\ 12 & 7 \end{pmatrix}$ $\mathbf{BA} = \begin{pmatrix} 11 & 24 \\ 5 & 10 \end{pmatrix}$

12 $\begin{pmatrix} 2 & ^-1 \\ ^-5 & 3 \end{pmatrix}\begin{pmatrix} 3 & 1 \\ 5 & 2 \end{pmatrix} = \begin{pmatrix} 1 & 0 \\ 0 & 1 \end{pmatrix} = \begin{pmatrix} 3 & 1 \\ 5 & 2 \end{pmatrix}\begin{pmatrix} 2 & ^-1 \\ ^-5 & 3 \end{pmatrix}$

$x = ^-16,\ y = 55$

13 $\begin{pmatrix} 0 & 1 \\ 1 & 0 \end{pmatrix}$ is a reflection in the line $y = x$

$\begin{pmatrix} 0 & ^-1 \\ 1 & 0 \end{pmatrix}$ is a rotation of 90° anticlockwise

$\begin{pmatrix} 0 & 1 \\ 1 & 1 \end{pmatrix}$ is a stretch parallel to the y-axis

14

	P	Q	R	S
P	0	1	0	2
Q	1	0	1	1
R	0	1	0	2
S	2	1	2	0

15 (a) $^-7$ (b) 14 (c) $^-17$ (d) $xy - 1$ (e) 1
(f) 1 (because $\cos^2\theta + \sin^2\theta = 1$ for all angles)

16 The matrix has no inverse.

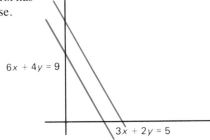

$6x + 4y = 9$

$3x + 2y = 5$

Exercise H.1 (pp. 372)

1

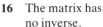

$\begin{pmatrix} 0 \\ 4 \end{pmatrix}$ $\begin{pmatrix} 2 \\ 3 \end{pmatrix}$ $\begin{pmatrix} ^-4 \\ ^-1 \end{pmatrix}$ $\begin{pmatrix} 4 \\ 0 \end{pmatrix}$ $\begin{pmatrix} 3 \\ ^-2 \end{pmatrix}$

2 $\overrightarrow{TU}; \overrightarrow{RS}; \overrightarrow{ST}; \overrightarrow{QR}; \overrightarrow{UP}.$ All six vectors add to zero.

3 (a) $\mathbf{p} + \mathbf{q}, \mathbf{q} - \mathbf{p}$ (b) $2\mathbf{q} = 2\overrightarrow{DA}$
(c)

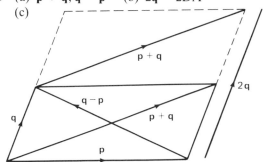

$\mathbf{p} + \mathbf{q}$

$2\mathbf{q}$

$\mathbf{q} - \mathbf{p}$

$\mathbf{p} + \mathbf{q}$

$\mathbf{q}$

$\mathbf{p}$

4 (c)
5 (a) $\sqrt{34}$ (b) $\sqrt{34}$ (c) 5 (d) $\sqrt{113}$ (e) $\sqrt{5}$
6 $|\mathbf{p}|, |\mathbf{q}|, |\mathbf{p} + \mathbf{q}|$ are three sides of a triangle, and the sum of any two sides must be longer than the third side.

Exercise H.2 (p. 374)

1 10 **2** 6·34°
3 (a), (b) are both true for all vectors $\mathbf{p}$ and $\mathbf{q}$.
4 $\sqrt{5}; \sqrt{5}; \sqrt{10}$; yes

Exercise H.3 (pp. 376–377)

1 (a) $\mathbf{a} + \mathbf{c} = \mathbf{b}$
(b) (i) $\mathbf{x} + \mathbf{y}$ (ii) $^-(\mathbf{y} + \mathbf{z})$ (iii) $\mathbf{x} + \mathbf{y} + \mathbf{z}$
(iv) $^-(\mathbf{y} + \mathbf{z} + \mathbf{w})$ (v) $\mathbf{x} + \mathbf{y} + \mathbf{z} + \mathbf{w}$
(vi) $\frac{1}{2}(\mathbf{x} - \mathbf{y} - \mathbf{z} - \mathbf{w})$ (vii) $\frac{1}{2}(\mathbf{z} + \mathbf{w} - \mathbf{x} - \mathbf{y})$
(viii) $\frac{1}{2}(\mathbf{x} + \mathbf{y} + \mathbf{z} - \mathbf{w})$

2 (i) $\frac{2}{3}\mathbf{y}$ (ii) $\mathbf{x} + \frac{2}{3}\mathbf{y}$ (iii) $^-\mathbf{x} + \frac{1}{3}\mathbf{y}$

3 (a) $\overrightarrow{AD} = \mathbf{b} - \frac{1}{2}\mathbf{a} = \mathbf{c} + \frac{1}{2}\mathbf{a} = \frac{1}{2}(\mathbf{b} + \mathbf{c})$,
$\overrightarrow{BD} = \frac{1}{2}\mathbf{a} = \frac{1}{2}(\mathbf{b} - \mathbf{c})$, $\overrightarrow{DC} = \frac{1}{2}\mathbf{a}$
(b) $\overrightarrow{AX} = \mathbf{b} + \mathbf{c}$
D is the midpoint of BC
$\Rightarrow$ D is the midpoint of AX
$\Rightarrow \overrightarrow{AD} = \frac{1}{2}\overrightarrow{AX}$

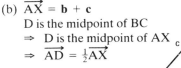

4 63·43
5 $\overrightarrow{CX} = \begin{pmatrix} 5 \\ ^-12·5 \end{pmatrix}$, OX $= \begin{pmatrix} 5 \\ 2 \end{pmatrix}$;
CX $\cdot$ OX $=$ O $\Rightarrow$ CX $\perp$ OX.
6 (a) $|\mathbf{p}| = 5, |\mathbf{q}| = \sqrt{a^2 + b^2}, |\mathbf{r}| = \sqrt{c^2 + d^2}$,
$|\mathbf{q} + \mathbf{r}| = \sqrt{(a + c)^2 + (b + d)^2}$
(b) $3a + 4b = 0$
(c) This is Pythagoras' theorem yet again!

7 1∅ $\overrightarrow{AC} = \mathbf{p} + \mathbf{q}; \overrightarrow{BD} = \mathbf{q} - \mathbf{p}$
2∅ $\overrightarrow{AC} \cdot \overrightarrow{AC} = (\mathbf{p} + \mathbf{q}) \cdot (\mathbf{p} + \mathbf{q})$
$= \mathbf{p} \cdot \mathbf{p} + \mathbf{q} \cdot \mathbf{q} + 2\mathbf{p} \cdot \mathbf{q}$
3∅ $\overrightarrow{BD} \cdot \overrightarrow{BD} = (\mathbf{q} - \mathbf{p}) \cdot (\mathbf{q} - \mathbf{p})$
$= \mathbf{p} \cdot \mathbf{p} + \mathbf{q} \cdot \mathbf{q} - 2\mathbf{p} \cdot \mathbf{q}$
4∅ $\mathbf{p} \cdot \mathbf{q} = 0$ (rectangle)
5∅ $|\overrightarrow{AC}| = |\overrightarrow{BD}|$

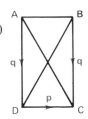

8 Take the vertex where the two equal sides meet as the origin. Then take as the x-axis the line which passes through the origin and bisects the third line. $a^2 - b^2$

Exercise H.4 (p. 381)

1
pots.	app.	str.	cost

$$(7 \quad 4 \quad 1)\begin{pmatrix} 20 \\ 35 \\ 45 \end{pmatrix} = 325$$

The scaler product gives the amount spent by Mrs Green, i.e. £3·25.

2 £2·75

3 (a) $\begin{pmatrix} 2 \\ 1 \end{pmatrix}$ (b) $\begin{pmatrix} ^-1 \\ ^-1 \end{pmatrix}$ (c) not possible

(d) $\begin{pmatrix} 5a + 6b \\ 5c + 6d \end{pmatrix}$

4 (b) $\begin{pmatrix} 4 & 0 \\ 0 & 4 \end{pmatrix}$

5 (a) $^-\frac{1}{3}\begin{pmatrix} 1 & ^-2 \\ ^-2 & 1 \end{pmatrix}$ (b) $\frac{1}{13}\begin{pmatrix} 5 & 3 \\ ^-1 & 2 \end{pmatrix}$

(c) $\frac{1}{3}\begin{pmatrix} 3 & 0 \\ 0 & 1 \end{pmatrix}$ (d) $\frac{1}{10}\begin{pmatrix} 2 & 1 \\ ^-4 & 3 \end{pmatrix}$

8 (a) $\begin{pmatrix} 0 & 0 \\ 0 & 0 \end{pmatrix}, \begin{pmatrix} 1 & 0 \\ 0 & 1 \end{pmatrix}$

(b) $\begin{pmatrix} 0 & 0 \\ 0 & 0 \end{pmatrix}, \begin{pmatrix} ^-1 & 0 \\ 0 & ^-1 \end{pmatrix}$ and also any matrix

$$\begin{bmatrix} a & ^-k(1 + a) \\ \dfrac{a}{k} & ^-(1 + a) \end{bmatrix} \text{ or } \begin{bmatrix} a & k(1 + a) \\ \dfrac{^-a}{k} & ^-(1 + a) \end{bmatrix}$$

Exercise H.5 (pp. 384–385)

1 (a) $\begin{pmatrix} ^-1 & 0 \\ 0 & 1 \end{pmatrix}$ (b) $\begin{pmatrix} ^-1 & 0 \\ 0 & ^-1 \end{pmatrix}$ (c) $\begin{pmatrix} 0 & ^-1 \\ 1 & 0 \end{pmatrix}$

(d) $\begin{pmatrix} \cos 30 & \sin 30 \\ ^-\sin 30 & \cos 30 \end{pmatrix} = \begin{pmatrix} \frac{1}{2}\sqrt{3} & \frac{1}{2} \\ ^-\frac{1}{2} & \frac{1}{2}\sqrt{3} \end{pmatrix}$

2 If $E_1 = \begin{pmatrix} a & 0 \\ 0 & a \end{pmatrix}$ and $E_2 = \begin{pmatrix} b & 0 \\ 0 & b \end{pmatrix}$ then $a = \dfrac{1}{b}$.

3

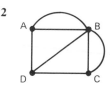

T_1T_2 produces reflection in the line $y = x$.
T_2T_1 produces reflection in the line $y = ^-x$.

4 30°. **R** produces an anticlockwise rotation of 30°. Therefore, $\mathbf{R}^3$ produces an anticlockwise rotation of $3 \times 30°$, i.e. 90°.

5 $\mathbf{T} = \begin{pmatrix} 3 & 0 \\ 0 & ^-3 \end{pmatrix}; \begin{pmatrix} 3 \\ ^-3 \end{pmatrix}, \begin{pmatrix} 3 \\ 3 \end{pmatrix}, \begin{pmatrix} 6 \\ ^-9 \end{pmatrix}.$

6 (a) (i) $\begin{pmatrix} 0 & ^-1 \\ 1 & 0 \end{pmatrix}$ (ii) $\begin{pmatrix} 0 & 1 \\ ^-1 & 0 \end{pmatrix}$ (iii) $\begin{pmatrix} ^-1 & 0 \\ 0 & ^-1 \end{pmatrix}$

(iv) $\begin{pmatrix} 1 & 0 \\ 0 & ^-1 \end{pmatrix}$ (v) $\begin{pmatrix} ^-1 & 0 \\ 0 & 1 \end{pmatrix}$ (vi) $\begin{pmatrix} 1 & 0 \\ 0 & 1 \end{pmatrix}$

(b)

	↺	↻	H	↕	↔	I
↺	H	I	↻	↗	↘	↺
↻	I	H	↺	↘	↗	↻
H	↻	↺	I	↔	↕	H
↕	↘	↗	↔	I	H	↕
↔	↗	↘	↕	H	I	↔
I	↺	↻	H	↕	↔	I

(c) H ↕ ↔ ↘ ↗ I satisfy $\mathbf{A}^2 = \mathbf{I}$; all satisfy $\mathbf{A}^4 = \mathbf{I}$; only **I** satisfies $(\mathbf{A}^{-1})^2 = \mathbf{A}$.

Exercise H.6 (p. 387)

1 (a)
	P	Q	R	S	O
P	0	1	0	2	1
Q	1	0	1	0	1
R	0	1	0	1	1
S	2	0	1	0	0
O	1	1	1	0	0

(b) $\begin{pmatrix} 6 & 1 & 4 & 0 & 1 \\ 1 & 3 & 1 & 3 & 2 \\ 4 & 1 & 3 & 0 & 1 \\ 0 & 3 & 0 & 5 & 3 \\ 1 & 2 & 1 & 3 & 3 \end{pmatrix}$, 4

2

3 (a) $x = 3, y = ^-3$ (b) $x = 1, y = \frac{3}{2}$

4 The determinant of the matrix $\begin{pmatrix} 2 & 4 \\ 3 & 6 \end{pmatrix}$ is zero so the equations cannot be solved.